Test Bank

for

Rathus, Nevid, and Fichner-Rathus

Human Sexuality in a World of Diversity

Fifth Edition

Prepared by

David Libhart
University of Phoenix, Hawaii Campus

Allyn and Bacon
Boston London Toronto Sydney Tokyo Singapore

Table of Contents

PREFACE

One of the challenges of effective teaching is effective testing. Ideally, every instructor would have plenty of time to tailor an exam precisely to the requirements of the course. Since that ideal is rarely achievable, my hope is that this testbank may become a helpful friend in your teaching of *Human Sexuality in a World of Diversity*.

The following is a list of features of this testbank:

1. Copious multiple choice, matching, true/false, and essay questions.
2. Each multiple choice question has helpful information in the left margin:
   a. The page on which the answer to the question can be found. Occasionally, the answer is found on several pages. I have listed the first page.
   b. The basic type of question: factual, conceptual, or applied.
   c. The correct answer.
   d. The level of difficulty—though this is clearly somewhat subjective.

This testbank is actually the revision of a previous edition of the testbank. In order to give professors the best of two worlds, I retained most questions from the previous edition of the testbank—as long as the answers were still available in the new edition.

I sincerely appreciate the understanding and encouragement of my son, Justin, a budding psychologist, while preparing the testbank.

If you have modifications of the testbank you would like to see or suggestions for improvement, please email me at the address below.

David L. Libhart, MA
University of Phoenix
Hawaii Campus
dlibhart@email.uophx.edu

Chapter 1: What Is Human Sexuality?

MULTIPLE CHOICE

1. The best and most accurate information that many young people receive today about human sexuality comes from
   (a) parents.
   (b) sex education classes in schools.
   (c) personal experience with a variety of partners.
   (d) police officers.

   Answer: B Difficulty: 1 Page: 4

2. Today's focus on the importance of sex education stems largely from concerns about
   (a) increasing numbers of sexual dysfunctions.
   (b) AIDS and unwanted teenage pregnancies.
   (c) a decline in moral values.
   (d) the high rate of premarital sex.

   Answer: B Difficulty: 2 Page: 4

3. A definition for the term sex is
   (a) coitus.
   (b) anatomic structures.
   (c) gender.
   (d) all of the above.

   Answer: D Difficulty: 1 Page: 5

4. Gender in this text refers to
   (a) the state of being male or female.
   (b) matching sex organs with appropriate desires and behavior.
   (c) identity assigned to individuals by parents.
   (d) identity assigned to individuals by society.

   Answer: A Difficulty: 2 Page: 5

5. Which is not a form of sexual behavior?
   (a) fantasy
   (b) kissing
   (c) masturbation
   (d) none of the above

   Answer: D Difficulty: 1 Page: 5

6. Because our society embraces a wide range of sexual attitudes and values, it is characterized as
   (a) liberal.
   (b) sexually repressive.
   (c) sexually permissive.
   (d) pluralistic.

   Answer: D Difficulty: 2 Page: 6

7. The study of human sexuality is really
   (a) the study of human sexualities.
   (b) about our common beliefs rather than our differences.
   (c) acknowledging cultural differences but teaching right and wrong.
   (d) only about the physiological mechanisms of sexual arousal and response.

   Answer: A Difficulty: 1 Page: 7

8. Efforts to understand sexuality throughout the world have occurred primarily because of
   (a) an increased interest in anthropology.
   (b) efforts to create a global economy.
   (c) the AIDS epidemic.
   (d) concerns about declining morality.

   Answer: C Difficulty: 2 Page: 7

9. In Islamic Pakistan, the Hudood Ordinance
   (a) forbids kissing between males and females.
   (b) allows a man to offer his wife to visitors.
   (c) permits sexual experimentation between young children.
   (d) grants more credibility to the testimony of men in a court of law.

   Answer: D Difficulty: 3 Page: 7

10. When people think critically, they
    (a) remain skeptical of any behavior differing from their own.
    (b) maintain an open mind.
    (c) criticize abnormal behavior.
    (d) are narrow minded.

    Answer: B Difficulty: 1 Page: 8

11. In terms of critical thinking, the statement, "Homosexuality is inborn," is an example of
    (a) oversimplification.
    (b) skepticism.
    (c) overgeneralization.
    (d) an assumption.

    Answer: A Difficulty: 1 Page: 9

12. Important research on human sexuality from the historical perspective starts
    (a) with the ancient Greeks.
    (b) before written records were kept.
    (c) with Alfred Kinsey.
    (d) with the age of enlightenment.

    Answer: B Difficulty: 2 Page: 10

13. In the Stone Age, emphasis on the female reproductive role may have signified
    (a) male superiority within the culture.
    (b) ignorance of the male's contribution to reproduction.
    (c) an agrarian society.
    (d) a prehistoric division of labor.

    Answer: B Difficulty: 2 Page: 10

14. Knowledge of paternity is believed to have developed around
    (a) 2000 B.C.
    (b) 5000 B.C.
    (c) 7000 B.C.
    (d) 9000 B.C.

    Answer: D Difficulty: 3 Page: 10

15. Phallic worship may have come into being as
    (a) women's roles became more subservient.
    (b) people grew aware of the male role in reproduction.
    (c) religious ceremonies gained precedence.
    (d) men hunted wild animals.

    Answer: B Difficulty: 2 Page: 10

16. Phallic symbols figured in religious ceremonies in ancient Egypt glorified
    (a) paternity.
    (b) masculinity.
    (c) the penis.
    (d) certain gods.

    Answer: C Difficulty: 1 Page: 10

17. Knowledge of paternity may have developed as a result of
    (a) hunting wild animals.
    (b) gathering roots.
    (c) farming.
    (d) herding livestock.

    Answer: D Difficulty: 1 Page: 10

18. The first sexual taboo involved
    (a) male-male sexual behavior.
    (b) premarital sex.
    (c) incestuous sexual relations.
    (d) female-female sexual behavior.

    Answer: C Difficulty: 2 Page: 11

19. Which of the following statements is true regarding incestuous sexual relations?
    (a) In ancient Egypt, brother-sister marriages were outlawed.
    (b) Father-daughter marriages were permitted among the aristocracy of Egypt.
    (c) Among the Incas, brother-sister relationships were permitted for commoners.
    (d) In most early civilizations, incest was acceptable among the lower classes.

    Answer: B Difficulty: 3 Page: 11

20. The Hebrew bible permitted
    (a) polygamy.
    (b) incest.
    (c) homosexual relations.
    (d) adultery.

    Answer: A Difficulty: 2 Page: 11

21. Hebrew wives who committed adultery were punished by
    (a) imprisonment.
    (b) a penance.
    (c) a stiff fine.
    (d) death.

    Answer: D Difficulty: 1 Page: 11

22. The ancient Hebrews and Greeks were alike in that both
    (a) valued family life.
    (b) permitted sexual relations only within marriage.
    (c) condemned homosexual relations.
    (d) had a great admiration for the human body.

    Answer: A Difficulty: 1 Page: 12

23. The ancient Greeks viewed men and women as
    (a) heterosexual.
    (b) bisexual.
    (c) homosexual.
    (d) androgynous.

    Answer: B Difficulty: 2 Page: 12

24. In early Greek culture, gods and goddesses were seen as
    (a) gatekeepers of sexual morality.
    (b) sexually deviant.
    (c) voracious seekers of sexual variety.
    (d) asexual.

    Answer: C Difficulty: 2 Page: 12

25. In ancient Greek culture, pederasty involved
    (a) sexual activity between an adult male and a prepubescent boy.
    (b) sexual intercourse between an adult male and his daughters.
    (c) sexual activity between two adult males.
    (d) sexual activity between an adult male and an adolescent boy.

    Answer: D Difficulty: 1 Page: 12

26. In ancient Greece, male-male sexual behavior was tolerated as long as it did not
    (a) threaten the institution of the family.
    (b) involve an adult and an adolescent.
    (c) exist in the public sphere.
    (d) interfere with duties to the state.

    Answer: A Difficulty: 3 Page: 12

27. In Greek culture, courtesans were
    (a) prostitutes who lived in brothels.
    (b) the educated wives of high-ranking officials.
    (c) refined and exceptionally skilled prostitutes.
    (d) gods and goddesses who advocated love.

    Answer: C Difficulty: 1 Page: 12

28. Which of the following statements best characterizes the status of women in Greek society?
    (a) They did not have many rights, but they had more rights than slaves.
    (b) They were educated if their husbands were high-ranking officials.
    (c) They were allowed to take part in economics and could hold public office.
    (d) They were subject to the authority of male next-of-kin or their husbands.

    Answer: D Difficulty: 2 Page: 13

29. If you were in ancient Rome, as opposed to Greece, which would be true regarding male-male sexual behavior?
    (a) The behavior would be acceptable if both men were adults.
    (b) The behavior would be viewed as a threat to the Roman family and Roman women.
    (c) The behavior would be acceptable if you were a member of the lower class.
    (d) The behavior would be viewed as a threat to masculinity.

    Answer: B Difficulty: 2 Page: 13

30. Early Christian views on sexuality were largely shaped by
    (a) Julius Caesar and Homer.
    (b) Aristotle and Socrates.
    (c) Moses and Jesus.
    (d) Saint Paul and Saint Augustine.

    Answer: D Difficulty: 3 Page: 13

31. The ancient Hebrews and early Christians were similar because both
    (a) wanted to restrict sex to the marriage bed.
    (b) practiced polygamy.
    (c) believed that marriage was inferior to celibacy.
    (d) viewed sex as sinful.

    Answer: A Difficulty: 2 Page: 13

32. During the early Christian era, divorce
    (a) could be initiated by a man but not a woman.
    (b) was not encouraged but acceptable if the woman was barren.
    (c) was completely outlawed.
    (d) was granted if church officials approved the dissolution.

    Answer: C Difficulty: 2 Page: 13

33. Which of the following ideas *most* influenced early Christian views of sexuality?
    (a) Jesus' idea that love and tolerance are paramount in human relations.
    (b) Augustine's idea that sexual lust began with the original sin of Adam and Eve.
    (c) Paul's idea that it was "better to marry than to burn."
    (d) Moses' idea that sex is reserved for procreation alone.

    Answer: B Difficulty: 1 Page: 13

34. Which statement *best* characterizes the contrast between St. Augustine's views of sexuality and those of Muhammad?
    (a) Augustine viewed lustful sex as appropriate within marriage while Muhammad viewed lustful sex as appropriate between any two consenting adults.
    (b) Augustine viewed all sexual activity as sinful and depraved while Muhammad encouraged public displays of sexual expression between men and women.
    (c) Augustine saw intercourse as an abomination in the eyes of God while Muhammad advocated for sexual expression both in and outside of marriage.
    (d) Augustine viewed celibacy as the highest state of grace while Muhammad decreed that marriage was the road to virtue.

    Answer: D Difficulty: 3 Page: 14

35. According to Augustine, men and women could attain a state of grace only through
    (a) celibacy.
    (b) remaining faithful to one another.
    (c) critical thinking.
    (d) avoidance of sexual decadence.

    Answer: A Difficulty: 1 Page: 14

36. Which of the following is true regarding Islamic culture?
    (a) Both men and women must be monogamous.
    (b) The family is considered the backbone of society.
    (c) Premarital intercourse is acceptable.
    (d) Celibacy is encouraged.

    Answer: B Difficulty: 2 Page: 14

37. In Islamic cultures ____ is frowned upon.
    (a) celibacy
    (b) polygamy
    (c) dancing
    (d) marriage

    Answer: A Difficulty: 1 Page: 14

38. The first detailed sex manual was produced by the
    (a) cultures of the Near East.
    (b) Chinese.
    (c) Hindus.
    (d) Christians.

    Answer: B Difficulty: 1 Page: 14

39. To Taoist masters of China, masturbation was
    (a) acceptable for men but not for women.
    (b) shameful.
    (c) acceptable for women only.
    (d) considered a healthy sexual outlet for men.

    Answer: C Difficulty: 1 Page: 14

40. The *Kama Sutra* reflected
    (a) the Hindu belief that sex was a religious duty.
    (b) the Taoist belief in yin and yang.
    (c) the Medieval belief in courtly love.
    (d) the Islamic belief in polygamy.

    Answer: A Difficulty: 1 Page: 14

41. The rock star, Madonna, combines the name of the Virgin Mary and crucifixes with highly erotic garments and simulated sex. Madonna's image is similar to the view of women during the
    (a) Reformation.
    (b) Middle Ages.
    (c) Renaissance.
    (d) late Roman era.

    Answer: B Difficulty: 2 Page: 15

42. Which of the following helped to elevate the status of women in Europe during the Middle Ages?
    (a) the story of Eve and the Garden of Eden
    (b) the *Kama Sutra*
    (c) acceptance of sex for non-procreative purposes
    (d) the cult of the Virgin Mary

    Answer: D Difficulty: 2 Page: 15

43. Martin Luther
    (a) agreed with the Roman Catholic doctrine that sex was only for procreational purposes.
    (b) believed that sex was permissible outside of marriage.
    (c) disputed many of the Roman Catholic doctrines on sexuality.
    (d) believed that sex depleted a man's vital energy and health.

    Answer: C Difficulty: 1 Page: 15

44. Queen Victoria's name is associated with
    (a) sexual repression.
    (b) cohabitation.
    (c) sexual expressiveness.
    (d) courtly love.

    Answer: A Difficulty: 1 Page: 16

45. In the late 18th and early 19th centuries, physicians in the United States
    (a) believed that sexual activity promoted better health.
    (b) thought sexual activity drained men of fluids essential to health.
    (c) recognized that women derived great pleasure from sexual activity.
    (d) recommended frequent intercourse.

    Answer: B Difficulty: 2 Page: 16

46. The Rev. Sylvester Graham believed that a man would dangerously deplete his vital energies if he had intercourse more than
    (a) once a week.
    (b) once a month.
    (c) every fortnight.
    (d) once a day.

    Answer: B Difficulty: 1 Page: 16

47. In his studies of sexuality, Havelock-Ellis concluded that
    (a) women were "sexually anesthetized."
    (b) sexual dysfunctions and sexual problems had physical causes.
    (c) frequent intercourse was a risk to the health of men.
    (d) homosexual orientations were naturally occurring sexual variations.

    Answer: D Difficulty: 2 Page: 17

48. The first scientific study of sexual behavior in the United States was conducted by
    (a) Masters and Johnson.
    (b) Alfred Kinsey.
    (c) D. H. Lawrence.
    (d) Richard von Krafft-Ebing.

    Answer: B Difficulty: 1 Page: 17

49. Alfred Kinsey is credited with
    (a) making the first scientific attempts at a comprehensive picture of sexual behavior in the U.S.
    (b) the first statistically valid studies of human sexuality.
    (c) the idea that homosexuality is a deviant sexual behavior.
    (d) recognizing that humans throughout the world engage in very similar sexual behavior.

    Answer: A Difficulty: 2 Page: 17

50. In the 1960s, the increase in recreational or casual sex was most related to
    (a) the events of the Vietnam War.
    (b) the increasing popularity of television.
    (c) the introduction of the pill.
    (d) the Human Potential Movement.

    Answer: C Difficulty: 2 Page: 18

51. Casual sex in the United States is gradually declining, but the incidence of premarital sex is rising among
    (a) single women.
    (b) homosexual men.
    (c) teenagers.
    (d) divorced men and women.

    Answer: C Difficulty: 1 Page: 18

52. Which of the following perspectives would be most interested in the role of hormones in male and female sex drive?
    (a) sociobiological
    (b) biological
    (c) psychological
    (d) cross-cultural

    Answer: B Difficulty: 2 Page: 19

53. As we move up the evolutionary ladder
    (a) the sexual behaviors of humans are quite similar to those of other animals.
    (b) instincts become increasingly more important in determining sexual behavior.
    (c) experience and learning play increasingly more important roles in sexual behavior.
    (d) the social behavior of animals and human becomes remarkably similar.

    Answer: C Difficulty: 2 Page: 20

54. Which statement best describes the concept of natural selection?
    (a) Better-adapted species are more likely to survive to reproduce.
    (b) Plant and animal species were created independently.
    (c) The strongest offspring live to reproduce.
    (d) Exploited species will eventually become extinct.

    Answer: A Difficulty: 1 Page: 20

55. Each normal human cells contains
    (a) 46 pairs of chromosomes.
    (b) 23 pairs of chromosomes.
    (c) 23 chromosomes.
    (d) 92 chromosomes.

    Answer: B Difficulty: 1 Page: 20

56. Genes are segments of chromosomes, which are composed of
    (a) molecules.
    (b) hormones.
    (c) DNA.
    (d) proteins.

    Answer: C Difficulty: 2

57. Evolutionary psychology proposes that dispositions toward behavior patterns
    (a) are learned from are parents.
    (b) are created in response to socio-cultural pressures.
    (c) is determined by how individuals balance forces of the id and ego.
    (d) may be genetically transmitted.

    Answer: D Difficulty: 1 Page: 21

58. A female of a species eats the male after mating. According to the theory of sociobiology
    (a) this behavior will not enhance reproductive success.
    (b) the female will eventually eat her offspring as well.
    (c) this behavior has a genetic basis that will enhance reproductive success.
    (d) this trait is probably no longer adaptive but served a purpose in prehistoric times.

    Answer: C Difficulty: 1 Page: 21

59. Considerable evidence indicates that
    (a) women's reproductive success is enhanced by mating with multiple partners.
    (b) men have to be selective with respect to mating partners.
    (c) biology has very little to do with modern sexual behavior.
    (d) males are naturally more promiscuous than women.

    Answer: D Difficulty: 2 Page: 23

60. In the quote, "human beings are like marionettes on strings being tugged by invisible puppet masters," what are the "puppet masters?"
    (a) their emotions
    (b) their genes
    (c) their environment
    (d) their hormones

    Answer: B Difficulty: 2 Page: 22

61. Which of the following is a criticism of sociobiological theory?
    (a) Human behavior largely reflects learning and personal choice.
    (b) There is direct genetic evidence that human males are more promiscuous.
    (c) There is great uniformity in sexual behaviors across cultures.
    (d) Marriage, or some form of marriage, does not exist in all societies.

    Answer: A Difficulty: 2 Page: 23

62. Female promiscuity is
    (a) rare in most animal species.
    (b) fairly common in most animal species.
    (c) generally not found in the animal kingdom, although it is extreme in some species.
    (d) a myth.

    Answer: B Difficulty: 1 Page: 23

63. Margaret Meade's research laid the groundwork for research
    (a) on cross-cultural infertility problems.
    (b) on extramarital affairs.
    (c) on challenging gender-role stereotypes.
    (d) on homosexual orientation.

    Answer: C Difficulty: 2 Page: 24

64. Virtually all cultures
    (a) kiss frequently.
    (b) have an incest taboo.
    (c) accept masturbation as healthy.
    (d) are monogamous.

    Answer: B Difficulty: 3 Page: 25

65. According to Ford and Beach's findings on preliterate societies
    (a) 84% practiced polygamy.
    (b) 70% practiced monogamy.
    (c) 65% practiced polyandry.
    (d) 33% practiced polygyny.

    Answer: A Difficulty: 3 Page: 25

66. It can be said that *all* societies
    (a) believe that biology is destiny.
    (b) have similar moral codes regulating sexual behavior.
    (c) are more common than different in their sexual practices.
    (d) regulate sexual behavior in some fashion.

    Answer: D Difficulty: 2 Page: 28

67. Ethnocentrism is the tendency to
    (a) accept diversity across cultures.
    (b) judge other cultures by one's own cultural standards.
    (c) disregard the relativity of normalcy.
    (d) adopt a European standard and judge all cultures by that standard.

    Answer: B Difficulty: 1 Page: 28

68. According to Freud, the id
    (a) represents reason and good sense.
    (b) houses the biologically based drives or instincts.
    (c) seeks socially appropriate outlets for satisfying drives.
    (d) contains the moral conscience.

    Answer: B Difficulty: 1 Page: 28

69. Which is true of Frayser's study of polygyny?
    (a) Polygyny is practiced by some 30% of preliterate societies.
    (b) Polygyny is a reflection of a man's wealth and status.
    (c) The proportion of polygynus families to monogamous families is about 1:1.
    (d) Each of the cultures had several hundred thousand members.

    Answer: B Difficulty: 2 Page: 28

70. What best describes Freud's superego?
    (a) It is characterized by self-awareness, planning, and delay of gratification.
    (b) It functions as a moral guardian.
    (c) It embodies physiological drives and is fully unconscious.
    (d) It is anxiety evoking.

    Answer: B Difficulty: 2 Page: 28

71. The contents of the mind that lie outside of conscious awareness is called
    (a) the unconscious mind.
    (b) the superego.
    (c) the ego.
    (d) the id.

    Answer: A Difficulty: 1 Page: 28

72. Which is not a stage of psychosexual development according to Freud?
    (a) mental
    (b) anal
    (c) oral
    (d) latency

    Answer: A Difficulty: 2 Page: 28

73. Freud's most controversial theory involved
    (a) infantile sexuality.
    (b) repression.
    (c) the interpretation of dreams.
    (d) the existence of the unconscious.

    Answer: A Difficulty: 2 Page: 30

74. According to behavioral theory, sexual dysfunctions in adulthood result from
    (a) repression of sexual feelings.
    (b) fixation in one of the psychosexual stages of development.
    (c) learned associations between sexual stimulation and feelings of anxiety.
    (d) observational learning.

    Answer: C Difficulty: 2 Page: 30

75. Social learning theorists define modeling as acquiring knowledge and skills by
    (a) molding, step by step, fantasy into reality.
    (b) relating concepts of beauty and desirability.
    (c) observing and imitating others.
    (d) behaving according to anticipated rewards.

    Answer: C Difficulty: 2 Page: 30

76. Anthropologists and sociocultural theorists differ in that anthropologists study
    (a) past cultures while socioculturalists study only modern cultures.
    (b) biology within a single society while socioculturalists compare societies.
    (c) evolutionary factors while socioculturalists study psychological factors.
    (d) cross-cultural variance while socioculturalists study variance within subgroups of a society.

    Answer: D Difficulty: 2 Page: 31

77. According to sociocultural studies in the United States, which is a liberalizing influence on sexual behavior?
    (a) a college education
    (b) being a member of the Hispanic race
    (c) belonging to a Catholic church or Orthodox Jewish synagogue
    (d) being an Asian American

    Answer: A Difficulty: 1 Page: 31

78. In studying human sexuality, which of the following statements is true?
    (a) Human sexuality is a complex interaction between biological, sociocultural, and psychological factors.
    (b) Human sexuality is largely driven by biology and secondarily driven by culture.
    (c) Cultural values and beliefs determine what is normal, natural, and moral in sexual behavior.
    (d) There are many universal patterns of sexual behavior and universal beliefs about the morality of sexual behaviors.

    Answer: A Difficulty: 2 Page: 33

Chapter 1: What Is Human Sexuality?

MATCHING

For each of the following sexual practices, match the practice to the culture where the practice originated.

(a) The Middle Ages

(b) The Puritans

(c) The Stone Age

(d) The Roman Era

(e) The Victorian Period

(f) The Islamic Tradition

(g) The Greek Era

(h) The Ancient Hindus

(i) The Early Christian Era

79. Fertility symbols depicted females with pendulous breasts, rounded hips, and prominent sex organs.

    Answer: c

80. Phalluses were worn as jewelry.

    Answer: d

81. Women had to avoid all contact with men other than their husbands.

    Answer: f

82. Pederasty was a common practice.

    Answer: g

83. Divorce was outlawed.

    Answer: i

84. A man was expected to extend intercourse as long as possible.

    Answer: h

85. The cult of the Virgin Mary flourished.

    Answer: a

86. Adulterers were flogged or branded with a scarlet letter.

    Answer: b

87. Women were described as born with a sexual anesthesia.

    Answer: e

TRUE/FALSE

88. Human sexuality is the way we experience and express ourselves as sexual beings.
    Answer: True

89. Biology overrides environmental influences and is the most important factor in sexual behavior.

Answer: False

90. According to sociobiologists, women seek the fittest males as reproductive partners.

Answer: True

91. Margaret Mead found that gender-roles are acquired through cultural expectations.

Answer: True

92. Freud believed that sexual ideas and impulses appeared as symbols in dreams.

Answer: True

93. Skinner advocated that children acquire gender roles by observing the gender-role behavior of parents.

Answer: False

94. According to sociocultural studies, fewer than 10 percent of men report having 11 or more sexual partners since age 18.

Answer: False

95. Persons with little formal education seem to have more liberal views regarding sexual behavior.

Answer: False

96. According to studies, Asian Americans appear to be the most sexually restrained ethnic group in the United States.

Answer: True

97. The term coitus refers to any form of genital stimulation for both male and females.

Answer: False

98. Gender identity is one's personal experience of being male or female.

Answer: True

99. In the society of Islamic Pakistan, women who have brought rape charges against men have been given prison sentences.

Answer: True

100. In the United States, polygamy is legal in Hawaii and Utah.

Answer: False

101. Some ancient Greek men would take a sexual interest in an adolescent boy, often with the blessing of the boy's parents.

Answer: True

102. In ancient Greece, there was no social stigma attached to visiting a courtesan.

Answer: True

103. Early Christians taught that procreation should govern sexual conduct.

Answer: True

104. While family is the backbone of Islamic society, celibacy is seen as the highest good.

Answer: False

105. Luther and Calvin both disagreed with the Roman Catholic doctrines on sexuality.

    Answer: False

106. The actual behavior of Victorians was not as repressed as advertised.

    Answer: True

ESSAY

107. Summarize the skills needed for good critical thinking and the importance of each skill.

    Answer:

108. Discuss how the history of sexuality sheds light on current sexual attitudes, morality, and gender issues.

    Answer:

109. Compare and contrast Eastern and Western religious traditions and discuss the impact of each tradition in terms of human sexuality.

    Answer:

110. Summarize the ideas of Saint Paul and Saint Augustine, the impact of their ideas within the Roman Catholic Church, and how those ideas influenced sexual attitudes and practices.

    Answer:

111. Trace the beginnings of the scientific study of human sexuality by noting the early researchers and their contributions.

    Answer:

Chapter 2: Research Methods

MULTIPLE CHOICE

1. Scientists and researchers who study human sexuality take a(n) _____ approach.
   (a) Freudian
   (b) empirical
   (c) demographic
   (d) radical

   Answer: B Difficulty: 1 Page: 38

2. An empirical approach to the study of human sexuality implies that knowledge is based on
   (a) objective evidence.
   (b) a combination of intuition and concrete evidence.
   (c) intuition.
   (d) subjective evidence.

   Answer: A Difficulty: 1 Page: 38

3. The first step in the scientific method is
   (a) establishing a hypothesis.
   (b) testing a hypothesis.
   (c) formulating a research question.
   (d) designing a method.

   Answer: C Difficulty: 2 Page: 38

4. A hypothesis is a(n)
   (a) established theory.
   (b) prediction about behavior.
   (c) question.
   (d) statement of fact.

   Answer: B Difficulty: 1 Page: 38

5. Which of the following is *not* one of the four goals of science?
   (a) explain
   (b) coerce
   (c) describe
   (d) predict

   Answer: B Difficulty: 1 Page: 39

6. Which of the following is an example of anthropomorphic inference?
   (a) watching humans kiss and assuming that animals also kiss
   (b) uncovering phallic symbols from an early civilization and assuming that modern civilizations also revere male sexuality
   (c) watching United States citizens kiss and assuming that all people kiss
   (d) watching felines in heat and assuming that human females experience a similar event

   Answer: A Difficulty: 2 Page: 39

7. In order to label a sexual behavior as deviant, it must deviate from
   (a) a universal norm.
   (b) descriptions of moral behavior.
   (c) a cultural norm.
   (d) religiously sanctioned behavior.

   Answer: C Difficulty: 2 Page: 39

8. What is an example of a demographic?
   (a) age
   (b) religious background
   (c) cultural expectations
   (d) all of the above

   Answer: D Difficulty: 1 Page: 40

9. In the goals of science, the concept of "controlling human behavior" means
   (a) limiting the variety of sexual behaviors people express.
   (b) educating people to help them make sexual decisions.
   (c) coercing people to change harmful sexual behaviors.
   (d) expanding the variety of sexual behaviors people express.

   Answer: B Difficulty: 2 Page: 40

10. A method of *objectively* measuring sexual arousal in men is to
    (a) ask men to rate their level of arousal.
    (b) interview men about their level of arousal.
    (c) measure vasocongestion with a penile strain gauge.
    (d) determine the number of times men engage in sexual activity.

    Answer: C Difficulty: 3 Page: 41

11. What could be at least a partial operational definition of sexual attraction?
    (a) arousal
    (b) sexual fantasies
    (c) heart rate
    (d) hoping for a conversation with an attractive person

    Answer: C Difficulty: 3 Page: 41

12. A vaginal photoplethysmograph works by measuring
    (a) the length of the vagina.
    (b) how much the vagina expands.
    (c) how much light is reflected from vaginal walls.
    (d) how much the clitoris expands.

    Answer: C Difficulty: 2 Page: 41

13. The fact that sometimes people are aroused according to physiological indicators, but
    not psychological measures, indicates that
    (a) the response may be purely a reflex.
    (b) the respondent may be unwilling to admit being aroused.
    (c) the respondent may be unwilling to be tested.
    (d) the respondent may not, in fact, be aroused.

    Answer: B Difficulty: 2 Page: 41

14. What is the value of an operational definition?
    (a) It measures the value of a stimulus.
    (b) It facilitates measurement among reticent subjects.
    (c) It permits measurement of observable phenomena like penile length.
    (d) It links constructs like arousal to measurable phenomena.

    Answer: D Difficulty: 3 Page: 41

15. In human sexuality research, a population is a
    (a) representative sample.
    (b) target group.
    (c) percentage of a larger group.
    (d) complete group of people.

    Answer: D Difficulty: 1 Page: 42

16. Why do researchers usually not choose to measure populations?
    (a) The data are not as reliable as data from samples.
    (b) Populations are not representative of selected samples.
    (c) Data from populations can be skewed by deviant subjects.
    (d) It is virtually impossible to measure populations.

    Answer: D Difficulty: 3 Page: 42

17. The individuals who participate in research are said to comprise a
    (a) group.
    (b) sample.
    (c) population.
    (d) conduit.

    Answer: B Difficulty: 1 Page: 43

18. A representative sample is defined as a group of subjects who
    (a) accurately reflect the population.
    (b) volunteer to be in a research study.
    (c) represent at least 75% of the population.
    (d) represent some but not all demographics.

    Answer: A Difficulty: 3 Page: 43

19. Dr. Colson wants to study the relationship between different types of sex education and
    teenage pregnancy rates. To ensure that she can generalize her results, Dr. Colson needs
    to select participants by using
    (a) teenage volunteers.
    (b) random sampling.
    (c) group sampling.
    (d) a convenience sample.

    Answer: B Difficulty: 2 Page: 43

20. Which is not a type of sample?
    (a) random
    (b) categorized
    (c) probability
    (d) stratified

    Answer: B Difficulty: 1 Page: 43

21. To study frequency of intercourse after age 65, the publishers of *65 Plus* magazine
    include a survey in their January issue. Twenty-five percent of the subscribers return
    the survey. What claims can the publishers make from this survey?
    (a) The results can be generalized to the complete readership of *65 Plus*.
    (b) The results cannot be generalized to the adult population over 65.
    (c) The response rate was high enough to represent the adult population over age 65.
    (d) The sample can be adjusted so that it represents a random sample of adults over age
        65.

    Answer: B Difficulty: 2 Page: 43

22. Which method would probably produce the most accurate results?
    (a) volunteers filling out a survey
    (b) volunteers compensated to fill out a survey
    (c) sample the population randomly and try to persuade each subject to respond
    (d) sample the population randomly and for each subject who declines to participate, find at least two willing subjects

    Answer: C Difficulty: 3 Page: 43

23. When subgroups in a sample are represented in proportion to their members in the the population, the sample is called a(n)
    (a) stratified random sample.
    (b) probability sample.
    (c) adjusted random sample.
    (d) random sample.

    Answer: A Difficulty: 1 Page: 43

24. A group of researchers uses the U.S. Census to determine that 8% of the United States population are Asian Americans. In their study of sexual practices in the United States, they make sure that 8% of their subjects are Asian Americans. The researchers utilized a(n)
    (a) target population of Asian Americans.
    (b) stratified random sample of Asian Americans.
    (c) convenience sample of Asian Americans.
    (d) adjusted random sample of Asian Americans.

    Answer: B Difficulty: 2 Page: 43

25. Convenience samples generally consist of
    (a) older people from several ethnic groups.
    (b) lower-class, urban, black people.
    (c) white, middle-class, college students.
    (d) middle-class, rural, middle-aged adults.

    Answer: C Difficulty: 2 Page: 43

26. As a research project, a group of researchers studies the interactions of three homosexual teens in a predominantly heterosexual high school by going to classes with them for the first six months of their junior year. Which method is the research team using?
    (a) experimental
    (b) interview
    (c) survey
    (d) case study

    Answer: D Difficulty: 1 Page: 44

27. In sex research, case studies have been especially helpful in
    (a) developing new varieties of sexual techniques.
    (b) identifying the social barriers encountered by homosexuals.
    (c) treating sexual dysfunctions.
    (d) recording ethnic differences in sexual responsiveness.

    Answer: C Difficulty: 2 Page: 44

28. Researchers using the case study method must be especially aware of
(a) observer bias.
(b) sample adjustment.
(c) participant bias.
(d) sample stratification.

Answer: A Difficulty: 2 Page: 44

29. Disadvantages of the case-study method include
(a) lack of thorough descriptions of the demographic variables.
(b) uncertainty about the subject's background.
(c) too little contact time between client and clinician.
(d) uncertainty about the cause of the treatment outcome.

Answer: D Difficulty: 3 Page: 45

30. An advantage to using interviews instead of questionnaires is that interviews
(a) are more objective.
(b) take less time to administer.
(c) give researchers the opportunity to probe.
(d) are less expensive.

Answer: C Difficulty: 2 Page: 45

31. Which of the following is a disadvantage of the questionnaire method?
(a) Questionnaires are expensive to develop.
(b) The return rate for questionnaires is always very low.
(c) Questionnaires are too subjective.
(d) Questionnaires cannot represent illiterate individuals.

Answer: D Difficulty: 2 Page: 45

32. Kinsey and his colleagues were interested in studying
(a) the causes of sexual behaviors.
(b) the frequency of sexual behaviors.
(c) the treatment of sexual dysfunctions.
(d) the sexual response cycle.

Answer: B Difficulty: 1 Page: 45

33. Which is true regarding the major surveys of sexual habits?
(a) They are methodologically sound and accurately represent the U.S. population.
(b) The researchers surveyed a truly representative sample of the U.S. population.
(c) They probably do not precisely reflect the U.S. population.
(d) The lack of representativeness renders them unhelpful.

Answer: C Difficulty: 3 Page: 45

34. Which of the following groups were underrepresented in Kinsey's studies?
(a) gays, lesbians, and urban populations
(b) the elderly, the upper class, and ethnic populations
(c) the upper class, ethnic minorities, and homosexuals
(d) the poor, ethnic minorities, and rural populations

Answer: D Difficulty: 2 Page: 46

35. Reliability refers to
(a) how trustworthy subjects' responses can be considered.
(b) how accurately different interviewers record subjects' responses.
(c) how accurately the questions measure what they're intended to measure.
(d) how consistently a question elicits the same answer on different occasions.

Answer: D Difficulty: 3 Page: 46

36. In what ways did Kinsey encourage honesty in his subject?
    (a) He assured subjects that their answers were confidential.
    (b) The interviewers were trained to be objective.
    (c) The subjects were assured that no judgment was being passed on their behavior.
    (d) All of the above.

    Answer: D Difficulty: 1 Page: 46

37. In reliability studies done eighteen months after his original surveys, Kinsey found
    (a) significant changes in the sexual behavior of his subjects.
    (b) consistency in the frequency of sexual behavior reported by his subjects.
    (c) consistency in the incidence of sexual behavior reported by his subjects.
    (d) inconsistencies in the incidence of sexual behavior reported by subjects.

    Answer: C Difficulty: 2 Page: 46

38. How did Kinsey attempt to validate his subjects' responses?
    (a) He compared the reports of husbands and wives.
    (b) He assured participants that their responses would be confidential.
    (c) He trained interviewers not to show emotional responses.
    (d) He re-interviewed subjects eighteen months later.

    Answer: A Difficulty: 2 Page: 46

39. The National Health and Social Life Survey (NHSLS) was intended to gain *specific* information that might be used to
    (a) predict and prevent the spread of HIV.
    (b) study the treatment of sexual dysfunctions.
    (c) understand ethnic differences in sexual practices.
    (d) stop the spread of pornographic materials.

    Answer: A Difficulty: 2 Page: 47

40. A completion rate of 80% for the National Health and Social Life Survey (NHSLS) can be credited to the fact that
    (a) most respondents were sexually curious individuals.
    (b) participants were given a financial incentive.
    (c) most participants were college-educated.
    (d) most respondents were young, liberal adults.

    Answer: B Difficulty: 3 Page: 47

41. Of studies cited in your text, the most statistically sound are the
    (a) Janus Report and the Kinsey studies.
    (b) NHSLS and the Hite Reports.
    (c) Kinsey studies and the NHSLS.
    (d) the Hite Reports and the Janus Report.

    Answer: C Difficulty: 3 Page: 47

42. The *major* flaw in the Playboy foundation survey is that
    (a) the survey was completed only by subscribers to *Playboy* magazine.
    (b) the survey was overrepresented by rural participants.
    (c) interviewers were not adequately trained.
    (d) 80% of the people contacted refused to participate.

    Answer: D Difficulty: 3 Page: 48

43. In sex research surveys, an unavoidable bias in the people who participate may be
    (a) an overrepresentation of older adults.
    (b) more permissive attitudes about sex.
    (c) a lack of education.
    (d) more conservative beliefs about premarital sex.

    Answer: B Difficulty: 2 Page: 48

44. Which is true of the surveys conducted by magazines like *Psychology Today, Redbook, and Consumer Reports*?
    (a) The large sample size compensates for volunteer bias.
    (b) The sampling techniques were scientific and unbiased.
    (c) They give accurate insights only into the attitudes of each magazine's readers.
    (d) They fail the test for randomness and cannot be generalized to a population.

    Answer: D Difficulty: 3 Page: 48

45. The Hite Reports were overrepresented by
    (a) readers of sexually explicit magazines.
    (b) gay and lesbian participants.
    (c) Catholic and Jewish participants.
    (d) readers of popular women's magazines.

    Answer: A Difficulty: 2 Page: 49

46. What is the greatest value of the Kinsey Institute's book *Homosexualities*?
    (a) It gives valuable insight on gay lifestyles nationwide.
    (b) It gives valuable insight on gay lifestyles in San Francisco.
    (c) It gives valuable insight on gay lifestyles in larger cities.
    (d) It gives valuable insight on the diversity of lifestyles among gay people.

    Answer: D Difficulty: 2 Page: 49

47. Which population was not surveyed in the Kinsey studies, the Hunt Report, and the Wyatt studies?
    (a) African Americans
    (b) Native Americans
    (c) Latinos
    (d) Asian Americans

    Answer: B Difficulty: 2 Page: 50

48. In the Billings Indian Health Service Survey, researchers found that
    (a) Native and African American women were twice as likely as White American women to have intercourse by the age of 17.
    (b) White American women bore more children than Native American women.
    (c) the incidence of female sterilization as a contraceptive method was highest among African American women.
    (d) the percentage of unplanned pregnancies was highest among White American women.

    Answer: A Difficulty: 3 Page: 50

49. According to the Wyatt Survey, when social-class differences between African American and European American women were taken into account, the age of first intercourse
    (a) is higher among European American women.
    (b) is higher among African American women.
    (c) is quite similar among both groups.
    (d) differs but is a function of sampling error.

    Answer: C Difficulty: 2 Page: 51

50. Native American women living off the reservation and African American women in the larger community tend to have intercourse at an ____ age and have a ____ use of contraceptives.
    (a) early; moderate
    (b) older; moderate
    (c) early; high
    (d) older; high

    Answer: A Difficulty: 1 Page: 51

51. In Wyatt's survey of African American and White women in Los Angeles, Wyatt noted that
    (a) women's attitudes about sex had changed little since the Kinsey studies.
    (b) 98% of the women in her study had engaged in premarital intercourse by age 20.
    (c) African American women engaged in sexual intercourse at an earlier age than White women.
    (d) about 20% of African American and White women engaged in sex before age 20.

    Answer: B Difficulty: 2 Page: 51

52. The Lui Report revealed that the Chinese are
    (a) more accepting of homosexuality than United States citizens.
    (b) more accepting of extramarital affairs than United States citizens.
    (c) largely unaccepting of premarital intercourse.
    (d) better educated in the art of sexual foreplay than United States citizens.

    Answer: B Difficulty: 3 Page: 52

53. The Kinsey studies were criticized, in part because the interviewers
    (a) miscalculated the statistical information.
    (b) were inadequately trained.
    (c) displayed observer bias.
    (d) were all male.

    Answer: D Difficulty: 1 Page: 52

54. In a sexual survey, participant X brags to the interviewer that he has had twelve different partners in the last year when, in actuality, he has had only two. Participant X is an example of a research limitation called
    (a) observer bias.
    (b) volunteer bias.
    (c) social desirability.
    (d) denial.

    Answer: C Difficulty: 1 Page: 53

55. People who desire more frequent sex tend to underestimate the frequency of marital coitus. This is an example of
    (a) faulty estimation.
    (b) denial.
    (c) volunteer bias.
    (d) the social desirability bias.

    Answer: A Difficulty: 2 Page: 53

56. In survey research, which of the following can happen when subjects attempt to give a socially desirable response?
    (a) denial
    (b) exaggeration
    (c) misinterpretation of meaning
    (d) volunteer bias

    Answer: B Difficulty: 1 Page: 53

57. In naturalistic observation, scientists
    (a) manipulate a variable and observe its effects on a second variable.
    (b) interview subjects about their attitudes and lifestyle.
    (c) learn about people's behavior by directly interacting with them.
    (d) watch the behavior of animals and humans where it happens.

    Answer: D Difficulty: 1 Page: 53

58. Anthropologist Margaret Mead reported on the customs of various peoples of New Guinea. The type of research she conducted is
    (a) ethnographic research.
    (b) experimental research.
    (c) laboratory observation.
    (d) survey research.

    Answer: A Difficulty: 2 Page: 54

59. In sex research, direct observation is limited because
    (a) people are reluctant to share their sexual histories with interviewers.
    (b) it is difficult to get people to participate in sex research.
    (c) sexual activities are commonly performed in privacy.
    (d) many people are illiterate and cannot read questions posed by researchers.

    Answer: C Difficulty: 1 Page: 54

60. In the 1970s, researchers studying mate-swapping posed as novice swingers seeking sexual relations. These researchers used a method called
    (a) ethnographic research.
    (b) participant observation.
    (c) anthropological research.
    (d) field observation.

    Answer: B Difficulty: 2 Page: 54

61. The first researchers to report direct laboratory observations of couples engaged in sexual activity were
    (a) Kinsey and his colleagues.
    (b) Masters and Johnson.
    (c) Ford and Beach.
    (d) Kinsey and Hunt.

    Answer: B Difficulty: 1 Page: 54

62. To counter observer bias, ethnographers must
    (a) be subjective in evaluating results.
    (b) use random sampling.
    (c) corroborate self-reports with additional sources.
    (d) use stratified random sampling.

    Answer: C Difficulty: 2 Page: 55

63. Dr. Dennison was sexually abused as a child. Today, she conducts studies on the effects of sexual abuse on adult sexual relationships. In order to conduct unbiased research, Dr. Dennison should be especially careful about
    (a) social desirability.
    (b) volunteer bias.
    (c) observer effects.
    (d) participant bias.

    Answer: C Difficulty: 1 Page: 55

64. Correlational research
    (a) looks for margins of error between two variables.
    (b) investigates the causal relationship between two variables.
    (c) studies the effect of change in one variable on a second variable.
    (d) describes the relationship between two variables.

    Answer: D Difficulty: 1 Page: 56

65. The strength and direction of the relationship between two variables is expressed with a statistic called the
    (a) central tendency.
    (b) correlation coefficient.
    (c) standard deviation.
    (d) selection factor.

    Answer: B Difficulty: 2 Page: 56

66. In studies investigating the relationship between alcohol use and contraception, researchers found that as the individuals consumed more alcohol, they were less likely to use contraception. These results would indicate
    (a) a negative correlation between alcohol use and contraceptive use.
    (b) a causal relationship between alcohol use and contraceptive use.
    (c) a positive correlation between alcohol use and contraceptive use.
    (d) no determination can be made from these results.

    Answer: A Difficulty: 3 Page: 56

67. The primary goal of correlational research is
    (a) explanation.
    (b) control.
    (c) prediction.
    (d) description.

    Answer: C Difficulty: 1 Page: 56

68. An experimenter makes the claim that church-going increases marital happiness. In order to make this claim, the experimenter must have done a(n)
    (a) observational study.
    (b) experimental study.
    (c) correlational study.
    (d) survey study.

    Answer: B Difficulty: 2 Page: 57

69. If a researcher can say that A causes B, then the researcher has used
    (a) the correlational method.
    (b) laboratory observation.
    (c) the case study method.
    (d) the experimental method.

    Answer: D Difficulty: 2 Page: 57

70. The variable manipulated by the researcher in an experimental study is the
    (a) control variable.
    (b) independent variable.
    (c) placebo.
    (d) dependent variable.

    Answer: B Difficulty: 1 Page: 57

71. A researcher wants to study the effect of exercise on sexual responsiveness. To test her hypothesis, she assigns individuals to two groups. One group engages in thirty minutes of structured exercise four times a week. The other group does not participate in the exercise program. Each week, individuals complete a questionnaire regarding sexual responsiveness. What is the dependent variable in this study?
    (a) no exercise
    (b) thirty minutes of exercise four times a week
    (c) subjects' answers on the questionnaires
    (d) the questionnaire

    Answer: C Difficulty: 2 Page: 57

72. After exposure to thirty minutes of sexually explicit film, or erotic but not sexually explicit film, sexual arousal is measured in female and male subjects with a penile strain gauge or a vaginal photoplethysmograph. What is the independent variable in this study?
    (a) sexually explicit films
    (b) the penile strain gauge or vaginal photoplethysmograph
    (c) gender
    (d) amount of sexual arousal

    Answer: A Difficulty: 2 Page: 58

73. In experimental research, the experimental group
    (a) is the placebo group.
    (b) is the group that receives the treatment.
    (c) is the group for which variables are not manipulated.
    (d) is the control group.

    Answer: B Difficulty: 1 Page: 58

74. What should be carefully considered before applying animal research to humans?
    (a) Comparing the physiological processes of animals to those of humans is neither valid nor appropriate.
    (b) To make inferences about psychological processes, the animal model must closely match that of humans.
    (c) We can make inferences regarding physiological processes in models similar to humans, but not psychological inferences.
    (d) We cannot make inferences about either psychological or physiological processes.

    Answer: C Difficulty: 3 Page: 58

75. Exposing children to pornographic materials in order to determine the effects of pornography on sexual attitudes is a breach of ethics because
    (a) confidentiality must be maintained.
    (b) persons must not be subjected to physical or psychological harm.
    (c) children cannot be debriefed following the experiment.
    (d) parents must sign consent forms for children.

    Answer: B Difficulty: 2 Page: 59

76. Informed consent implies that
    (a) individuals are informed about procedures, purpose, risks, and benefits involved in the research.
    (b) once individuals agree to participate, they must follow through and complete the study.
    (c) individuals are informed about purpose, risks, and benefits, but not procedures.
    (d) participants are told about the benefits of the research.

    Answer: A Difficulty: 2 Page: 60

77. When a researcher intentionally does not inform the subject of the true nature of the study because it would alter the outcomes of the study, the researcher is using
    (a) coercion.
    (b) debriefing.
    (c) deception.
    (d) control.

    Answer: C Difficulty: 1 Page: 60

78. The American Psychological Association has established a set of ethical principles for research with human subjects. As a result, experimenters are required to give subjects a complete description of the experiment prior to participation. This ethical principle is called
    (a) debriefing.
    (b) freedom from coercion.
    (c) deception.
    (d) informed consent.

    Answer: D Difficulty: 2 Page: 60

MATCHING

For each of the following descriptions, match the description of the research with the appropriate method.

(a) Naturalistic Observation

(b) Case Study

(c) Correlational Study

(d) Laboratory Observation

(e) Survey Method

(f) Participant Observation

(g) Experimental Method

79. A psychologist studies courting behavior between human males and females by watching behavior in local bars and restaurants.

    Answer: a

80. To understand the mating rituals of Trobriand Islanders, a researcher performs the rituals himself in order to experience the response of

    Answer: f

81. To study the relationship between violent pornography and sexual arousal, groups of men are exposed to either violent sexually explicit films or non-violent sexually explicit films. Sexual arousal is measured by using physiological instrumentation.

    Answer: g

82. To study the sexual response cycle, couples are invited to engage in sexual intercourse while cameras record their activity and instruments measure their physiological arousal.

    Answer: d

83. A woman is experiencing inhibited sexual desire of unknown origin. A researcher decides to extensively investigate her personal history.

Answer: b

84. To determine the frequency of intercourse in elderly individuals, researchers ask elderly subjects to indicate the number of times they engaged in intercourse over the last year.

Answer: e

85. A psychologist determines that a relationship exists between formal education and increased use of contraception.

Answer: c

TRUE/FALSE

86. Convenience samples often consist of white, lower-class college students.

Answer: False

87. Case studies can be conducted by interviewing people who have known individuals or by examining court records.

Answer: True

88. Kinsey purposefully chose not to try to obtain a random sample.

Answer: True

89. The Playboy Foundation study was flawed because 20% of participants refused to participate.

Answer: False

90. The Kinsey Institute Reports on Gay People focused only on gay people in the San Francisco area.

Answer: True

91. Masters and Johnson were interested in studying the sexual response cycle.

Answer: True

92. Volunteer bias is particularly troublesome in naturalistic observation.

Answer: False

93. Nonspecific treatment factors can seriously confuse results in experimental research.

Answer: True

94. Theories provide frameworks, within which scientists can explain what they observe and make predictions.

Answer: True

95. Physiological measurement of sexual arousal in men is most often accomplished by means of a vaginal photoplethysmograph.

Answer: False

96. Convenience samples are probably not representative of the population.

Answer: True

97. Ideally research would include every member of a population.

Answer: True

98. According to the Billings Indian Health Survey, Native American women on a reservation are less likely to use contraception than European American women.

    Answer: False

99. Because individuals may be harmed if exposed to stressful situations, many potentially informative studies have not been conducted.

    Answer: True

ESSAY

100. Discuss the strengths and weaknesses of each of the research methods used in sex research.

    Answer:

101. Discuss the strengths and weaknesses of Kinsey's research.

    Answer:

102. If you wanted to study an aspect of sexuality among your college classmates, what would you need to do to ensure that your results could be generalized?

    Answer:

103. Discuss the difference between random sampling, group sampling, and stratified random sampling in research.

    Answer:

104. If you wanted to use the interview method to determine both the frequency and incidence of sexual behaviors in a population, discuss the limitations you would need to consider in conducting your research.

    Answer:

105. If you wanted to use the interview method to determine both the frequency and incidence of sexual behaviors in a population, discuss the ethical considerations you must be aware of before, during, and after you conclude your research.

    Answer:

Chapter 3: Female Sexual Anatomy and Physiology

MULTIPLE CHOICE

1. Another word for the vulva is
   (a) pudendum.
   (b) vagina.
   (c) labia.
   (d) mons.

   Answer: A Difficulty: 2 Page: 66

2. The name for the external female genitals is derived from the Latin word
   (a) vaginus.
   (b) pudendus.
   (c) animus.
   (d) genitus.

   Answer: B Difficulty: 1 Page: 66

3. The external sexual structures of the female are termed the
   (a) mons.
   (b) clitoris.
   (c) labia majora.
   (d) vulva.

   Answer: D Difficulty: 1 Page: 66

4. The mons may serve to
   (a) provide heat to the pubic area.
   (b) cushion the pubic bone.
   (c) protect the genital area from infection.
   (d) produce secretions to lure lovers.

   Answer: B Difficulty: 2 Page: 67

5. What cushions a women's body during sexual intercourse?
   (a) vulva
   (b) mons
   (c) stomach
   (d) corpora cavernosa

   Answer: B Difficulty: 1 Page: 67

6. The labia majora
   (a) are the large fleshy folds of skin on each side of the vaginal opening.
   (b) come together to form the hood covering the clitoris.
   (c) are the thinner, inner folds of flesh just outside the vaginal opening.
   (d) have few nerve endings and are relatively insensitive to stimulation.

   Answer: A Difficulty: 2 Page: 67

7. The labia minora
   (a) are insensitive to sexual stimulation.
   (b) join to form the prepuce.
   (c) are relatively uniform in size in all women.
   (d) surround the anal opening.

   Answer: B Difficulty: 2 Page: 68

8. The clitoral shaft consists of erectile tissue that contains two spongy masses called
   (a) clitoral glans.
   (b) corpora cavernosa.
   (c) sphincters.
   (d) vestibular bulbs.

   Answer: B Difficulty: 1 Page: 68

9. In the clitoris, the corpus cavernosa
   (a) innervate the glans.
   (b) cover the tip of the glans.
   (c) engorge with blood.
   (d) resemble a button under the prepuce.

   Answer: C Difficulty: 2 Page: 68

10. The clitoris and penis
    (a) develop from different embryonic tissues.
    (b) are homologous in structure.
    (c) are both involved in reproduction.
    (d) are analogous in function.

    Answer: B Difficulty: 3 Page: 69

11. In many Islamic cultures, clitoridectomy
    (a) ensures chastity.
    (b) is a form of punishment.
    (c) is authorized by the Koran.
    (d) is a rite of initiation into womanhood.

    Answer: D Difficulty: 2 Page: 70

12. Which is not a medical complication from a clitoridectomy?
    (a) infection
    (b) headaches
    (c) obstructed labor
    (d) painful menstration

    Answer: B Difficulty: 2 Page: 70

13. The purpose of infibulation is to
    (a) prevent painful childbirth.
    (b) ensure that no intercourse occurs prior to marriage.
    (c) increase sexual pleasure for men during intercourse.
    (d) protect the vagina from harmful bacteria.

    Answer: B Difficulty: 2 Page: 70

14. A precaution women can use to help prevent cystitis is to
    (a) urinate after intercourse.
    (b) avoid the use of lubricants.
    (c) drink plenty of caffeine.
    (d) avoid cranberry and orange juice.

    Answer: A Difficulty: 2 Page: 70

15. How many women in Africa and the Middle East have undergone removal of the clitoris and the labia minora?
    (a) 12 million
    (b) 30 million
    (c) 64 million
    (d) 100 million

    Answer: D Difficulty: 3 Page: 71

16. The vaginal opening is also known as the
    (a) introitus.
    (b) hymen.
    (c) urethra.
    (d) perineum.

    Answer: A Difficulty: 2 Page: 72

17. What does the word "vestibule" mean?
    (a) dominance
    (b) entranceway
    (c) closure
    (d) swelling

    Answer: B Difficulty: 2 Page: 69

18. Urine passes from the female's body through the
    (a) fallopian tubes.
    (b) urethral opening.
    (c) pancreas.
    (d) ureter.

    Answer: B Difficulty: 1 Page: 69

19. What is not true about cystitis?
    (a) it is a bladder inflammation
    (b) its primary symptoms are burning and frequent urination
    (c) pus or a bloody discharge is common
    (d) none of the above

    Answer: D Difficulty: 2 Page: 70

20. The hymen is
    (a) a ring-shaped muscle.
    (b) a fold of tissue across the vaginal opening.
    (c) a gland that lies just inside the minor lips.
    (d) the muscle that encircles the entrance to the vagina.

    Answer: B Difficulty: 2 Page: 72

21. Occasionally a hymen is completely closed and fibrous. This type of hymen is called
    (a) an annular hymen.
    (b) a parous hymen.
    (c) an imperforate hymen.
    (d) a septate hymen.

    Answer: C Difficulty: 2 Page: 72

22. Serika has recently begun menstruating. She has heard from friends that if she uses tampons, she will break her hymen. What should you tell Serika?
    (a) The hymen will protect her vagina from disease and tampon use will increase the risk of infection.
    (b) Most hymens have openings that will easily accommodate tampons.
    (c) If she has a septate hymen, it will interfere with tampon use.
    (d) A parous hymen will not permit her to insert tampons.

    Answer: B Difficulty: 2 Page: 72

23. What consists of the skin and the underlying tissue between the vaginal opening and the anus?
    (a) vestibular bulbs
    (b) perineum
    (c) crura
    (d) mons

    Answer: B Difficulty: 2 Page: 73

24. The wing-shaped structures that attach the clitoris to the pubic bone are called
    (a) vestibular bulbs.
    (b) sphincters.
    (c) pubococcygea.
    (d) crura.

    Answer: D Difficulty: 2 Page: 73

25. In sexual arousal, the vestibular bulbs
    (a) contract the vaginal opening during orgasm.
    (b) secrete drops of fluid at the vaginal opening.
    (c) allow the pelvic floor muscles to contract.
    (d) engorge with blood.

    Answer: D Difficulty: 2 Page: 74

26. Kegel exercises are designed to strengthen
    (a) Bartholin's glands.
    (b) the PC muscle.
    (c) the vesibular bulbs.
    (d) the crura.

    Answer: B Difficulty: 1 Page: 74

27. In order to heighten awareness of vaginal sensations, women can practice
    (a) clitoral stimulation.
    (b) contracting the vestibular bulbs.
    (c) contracting the pubococcygeus muscles.
    (d) vaginal stimulation with their fingers or a vibrator.

    Answer: C Difficulty: 2 Page: 74

28. Vaginal lubrication occurs when
    (a) Bartholin's glands secrete fluid.
    (b) the vestibular bulbs engorge with blood.
    (c) the pelvic floor muscles contract.
    (d) Skene's glands release fluid.

    Answer: B Difficulty: 2 Page: 74

29. The inner two-thirds of the vagina
    (a) is highly innervated and sensitive.
    (b) narrows in width.
    (c) is smoother than the outer one-third.
    (d) is insensitive to touch.

    Answer: D Difficulty: 2 Page: 75

30. Douching and vaginal sprays
    (a) are recommended for proper hygiene.
    (b) are generally ineffective.
    (c) can restore the natural chemical balance in the vagina.
    (d) increase the risk of vaginal infection.

    Answer: D Difficulty: 2 Page: 75

31. Vaginitis
    (a) refers to any vaginal inflammation.
    (b) may stem from the use of birth-control pills.
    (c) may be recognized by an abnormal discharge.
    (d) all of the above.

    Answer: D Difficulty: 1 Page: 75

32. Which of the following is *not* a potential cause of vaginitis?
    (a) birth control pills
    (b) antibiotics
    (c) water-based lubricants
    (d) poor diet

    Answer: C Difficulty: 1 Page: 76

33. To treat vaginitis, a woman might try
    (a) douching with unpasteurized, plain yogurt.
    (b) taking an antibiotic.
    (c) switching to vasoline as a lubricant.
    (d) wearing nylon instead of cotton underwear.

    Answer: A Difficulty: 2 Page: 76

34. The lower end of the uterus is called the
    (a) vulva.
    (b) cervix.
    (c) crura.
    (d) perineum.

    Answer: B Difficulty: 1 Page: 76

35. Cervical cancer is relatively uncommon in the United States, largely due to
    (a) douching.
    (b) screening programs.
    (c) the latest in medical treatment.
    (d) episiotomies.

    Answer: B Difficulty: 2 Page: 76

36. In a PAP test, what cells are examined for abnormalities?
    (a) cells from the vaginal walls
    (b) cells from the endometrium
    (c) cells from the cervix
    (d) cells from the myometrium

    Answer: C Difficulty: 2 Page: 76

37. In screening for cervical cancer, the American Cancer Society recommends that
    (a) women have an annual PAP smear once they begin menstruating.
    (b) sexually active women have a PAP smear every six months.
    (c) all women over the age of eighteen have a PAP smear annually.
    (d) only sexually active women over the age of eighteen have a PAP smear annually.

    Answer: C Difficulty: 2 Page: 76

38. What percentage of women have a retroverted uterus?
    (a) 73%
    (b) 49%
    (c) 28%
    (d) 10%

    Answer: D Difficulty: 3 Page: 76

39. The widest portion of the uterus is called the
    (a) isthmus.
    (b) fundus.
    (c) endometrium.
    (d) myometrium.

    Answer: B Difficulty: 2 Page: 77

40. The layer of the uterus that is shed during menstruation is the
    (a) endometrium.
    (b) myometrium.
    (c) ectometrium.
    (d) perimetrium.

    Answer: A Difficulty: 2 Page: 77

41. Endometriosis is a condition where
    (a) the endometrium deteriorates.
    (b) endometrial tissue grows outside of the uterus.
    (c) the endometrium becomes infected.
    (d) the endometrium fails to engorge with blood.

    Answer: B Difficulty: 2 Page: 77

42. Estrogen replacement therapy may
    (a) increase the risk of ovarian cancer.
    (b) lower the risk of breast cancer.
    (c) increase the risk of endometrial cancer.
    (d) decrease the risk of uterine cancer.

    Answer: C Difficulty: 2 Page: 77

43. What is the second layer of the uterus called?
    (a) endometrium
    (b) myometrium
    (c) perineum
    (d) perimetrium

    Answer: B Difficulty: 2 Page: 77

44. In the United States, how many women have a hysterectomy by the age of sixty?
    (a) 20 percent
    (b) 30 percent
    (c) 50 percent
    (d) 65 percent

    Answer: B Difficulty: 2 Page: 77

45. Which is not true about hysterectomies?
    (a) Most women who obtain them do so between the ages of 35 and 45.
    (b) They are the second most commonly performed operation on women in this country.
    (c) The fallopian tubes are cut and retied at the ampulla to minimize infection.
    (d) They may be performed when women develop cancer of the uterus, ovaries or cervix.

Answer: C Difficulty: 3 Page: 78

46. Which of the following statements accurately reflects the current research on hysterectomies?
    (a) Most hysterectomies for women in any age group are medically necessary.
    (b) Among older women, hysterectomies are generally necessary.
    (c) Most physicians are reluctant to perform hysterectomies even when medically necessary.
    (d) About a third of the hysterectomies performed in younger women are inappropriate.

Answer: D Difficulty: 3 Page: 78

47. Which is not a part of the fallopian tubes?
    (a) isthmus
    (b) crura
    (c) ampulla
    (d) infundibulum

Answer: B Difficulty: 2 Page: 78

48. The finger-like projections from the fallopian tubes that extend toward the ovary are called
    (a) fimbriae.
    (b) cilia.
    (c) ampulla.
    (d) crura.

Answer: A Difficulty: 2 Page: 78

49. Ova move through the fallopian tubes at a rate of about
    (a) 1 inch every three days.
    (b) 2 inches every hour.
    (c) 1 inch every four hours.
    (d) 1 inch per day.

Answer: D Difficulty: 2 Page: 78

50. Most ectopic pregnancies occur in the
    (a) ovary.
    (b) fallopian tubes.
    (c) abdominal cavity.
    (d) uterus.

Answer: B Difficulty: 1 Page: 78

51. Which of the following statements is true regarding ova?
    (a) Women begin making ova at puberty.
    (b) The human female is born with all the ova she will ever have.
    (c) Women produce ova throughout the life span.
    (d) At menopause, women stop producing ova.

Answer: B Difficulty: 1 Page: 78

52. How many of the 2 million ova that a female is born with survive into puberty?
    (a) 100,000
    (b) 400,000
    (c) almost a million
    (d) almost all 2 million

    Answer: B Difficulty: 2 Page: 79

53. The *most* common sign of early stage ovarian cancer is
    (a) irregular bleeding.
    (b) severe pain in the abdomen.
    (c) enlargement of the abdomen.
    (d) excessive urination.

    Answer: C Difficulty: 2 Page: 79

54. What percentage of women who get ovarian cancer do not have a family history of it?
    (a) 10%
    (b) 40%
    (c) 60%
    (d) 90%

    Answer: D Difficulty: 2 Page: 79

55. Women *most* at risk for ovarian cancer are those who
    (a) have a first-degree relative who had the disease.
    (b) have never given birth.
    (c) have a history of breast cancer.
    (d) frequently take acetaminophen.

    Answer: A Difficulty: 2 Page: 79

56. The bimanual vaginal exam is a technique used to
    (a) visualize the cervix.
    (b) obtain cells for the PAP smear.
    (c) examine the shape of the uterus and ovaries.
    (d) dilate the cervix.

    Answer: C Difficulty: 2 Page: 80

57. The size of female breasts is related to
    (a) the amount of fatty tissue.
    (b) the number of milk ducts.
    (c) the amount of glandular tissue.
    (d) the number of mammary glands.

    Answer: A Difficulty: 2 Page: 80

58. The nipple, which lies in the center of the ____, contains smooth muscle fibers that make the nipple become erect when they contract.
    (a) mammary glands
    (b) areola
    (c) milk ducts
    (d) labia

    Answer: B Difficulty: 1 Page: 81

59. Of women who develop breast cancer, how many will die from the disease?
    (a) one out of twenty
    (b) one out of ten
    (c) three out of ten
    (d) six out of ten

    Answer: C Difficulty: 2 Page: 82

60. By age seventy, the risk of developing breast cancer increases to
    (a) one in fifty.
    (b) one in twenty.
    (c) one in fourteen.
    (d) one in five.

    Answer: C Difficulty: 2 Page: 82

61. A key risk factor for the development of breast cancer is
    (a) early menopause.
    (b) prolonged exposure to estrogen.
    (c) late onset of menstruation.
    (d) birthing a child prior to age twenty-five.

    Answer: B Difficulty: 2 Page: 83

62. Cysts or benign tumors in the breast are called
    (a) fibroadenomas.
    (b) menarche.
    (c) malignant lumps.
    (d) cancerous lumps.

    Answer: A Difficulty: 1 Page: 84

63. To optimize their chance of early breast cancer detection, women should
    (a) get a baseline mammogram between age forty and age fifty.
    (b) get a baseline mammogram around age thirty-five and perform monthly breast
        self-exams.
    (c) have a mammogram every three years after age fifty.
    (d) perform daily breast self-exams.

    Answer: B Difficulty: 2 Page: 84

64. The first phase of the menstrual cycle is the
    (a) proliferative phase.
    (b) ovulatory phase.
    (c) luteal or secretory phase.
    (d) menstrual phase.

    Answer: A Difficulty: 2 Page: 88

65. One of the functions of progesterone is to
    (a) promote ovulation.
    (b) mature one ovum.
    (c) thicken the endometrium.
    (d) mature the corpus luteum.

    Answer: C Difficulty: 2 Page: 88

66. Variations in the menstrual cycle tend to occur between which two phases?
    (a) ovulatory and luteal
    (b) menstrual and proliferative
    (c) luteal and menstrual
    (d) proliferative and ovulatory

    Answer: D Difficulty: 3 Page: 88

67. Which is not a phase in the menstrual cycle?
    (a) proliferative
    (b) colaborative
    (c) secretory
    (d) luteal

    Answer: B Difficulty: 2 Page: 88

68. What is the period of sexual excitement when a female dog is most receptive to the advances of a male dog?
    (a) estrus
    (b) ovulation
    (c) menarche
    (d) menses

    Answer: A Difficulty: 2 Page: 88

69. The female gonads produce
    (a) estrogen and progesterone.
    (b) follicle stimulating hormone.
    (c) gonadotropic hormone.
    (d) luteinizing hormone.

    Answer: A Difficulty: 2 Page: 89

70. Which pituitary hormone stimulates milk production during pregnancy?
    (a) luteinizing hormone
    (b) oxytocin
    (c) prolactin
    (d) gonadotropic releasing hormone

    Answer: C Difficulty: 3 Page: 90

71. The proliferative phase is also known as the
    (a) menstrual phase.
    (b) follicular phase.
    (c) ovulatory phase.
    (d) secretory phase.

    Answer: B Difficulty: 2 Page: 90

72. When the hypothalamus senses low levels of estrogen in the blood, it releases
    (a) luteinizing hormone.
    (b) progesterone.
    (c) follicle stimulating hormone.
    (d) gonadotropic releasing hormone.

    Answer: D Difficulty: 3 Page: 90

73. The synthetic hormone _____ is chemically similar to LH and has been used by women who ovulate irregularly to induce consistent ovulation.
    (a) areola
    (b) prolactin
    (c) clomiphene
    (d) oxytocin

    Answer: C Difficulty: 2 Page: 92

74. Which is the correct pattern for basal body temperature in the menstrual cycle?
    (a) Temperature rises slightly just before ovulation and remains elevated for three days.
    (b) Temperature rises at ovulation then dips a degree the day after ovulation.
    (c) Temperature dips three days before ovulation and rises the day after ovulation.
    (d) Temperature dips slightly at ovulation and rises about a degree the day after ovulation.

    Answer: D Difficulty: 2 Page: 92

75. What is it called when women have cramping or discomfort during ovulation?
    (a) PMS
    (b) mittelschmerz
    (c) estrus
    (d) clomiphene

    Answer: B Difficulty: 1 Page: 92

76. The corpus luteum
    (a) is another name for the graafian follicle.
    (b) secretes estrogen and progesterone.
    (c) secretes follicle stimulating hormone.
    (d) is a thin capsule containing an ovum.

    Answer: B Difficulty: 3 Page: 93

77. What is the ritual cleansing of orthodox Jewish women called?
    (a) mikvah
    (b) shlelava
    (c) nivolasta
    (d) menstava

    Answer: A Difficulty: 3 Page: 94

78. During menstruation, how much blood do women typically lose?
    (a) 4-6 tablespoons
    (b) 8-10 tablespoons
    (c) 10-16 tablespoons
    (d) 16-20 tablespoons

    Answer: A Difficulty: 2 Page: 93

79. Toxic Shock Syndrome is caused by
    (a) poor hygiene.
    (b) Streptococcus bacteria.
    (c) Staphylococcus bacteria.
    (d) yeast infections.

    Answer: C Difficulty: 2 Page: 94

80. In many societies, menstruation has been viewed as
    (a) honorable and sacred.
    (b) unclean and a source of contamination.
    (c) healthy and a sign of fertility.
    (d) a celebrated rite of passage into womanhood.

    Answer: B Difficulty: 2 Page: 95

81. Research evidence suggests that women might experience a peak in sexual desire
    (a) just before and during ovulation.
    (b) four days prior to ovulation.
    (c) just after ovulation.
    (d) just before menstruation.

    Answer: A Difficulty: 2 Page: 95

82. Menopause occurs most commonly between the ages of
    (a) forty and forty-five.
    (b) forty-six and fifty.
    (c) fifty-one and fifty-five.
    (d) fifty-six and sixty.

    Answer: B Difficulty: 2 Page: 95

83. Menopause is a specific event in a long-term process known as the
    (a) menarche.
    (b) mittelschmerz.
    (c) climacteric.
    (d) ovulatory lifeline.

    Answer: C Difficulty: 2 Page: 95

84. With menopause
    (a) the pituitary gland stops producing FSH.
    (b) the ovaries stop producing eggs.
    (c) the pituitary gland stops producing LH.
    (d) the ovaries become insensitive to FSH and LH.

    Answer: D Difficulty: 3 Page: 95

85. A deficit in estrogen may lead to all the following except
    (a) night sweats.
    (b) kidney infection.
    (c) hot flashes.
    (d) dizziness.

    Answer: B Difficulty: 2 Page: 95

86. Long-term estrogen deficiency has been linked to
    (a) depression.
    (b) continual hot flashes and flushes.
    (c) osteoporosis.
    (d) lack of sexual desire.

    Answer: C Difficulty: 2 Page: 96

87. Menstrual cramps appear to be related to the excess secretion of
    (a) prostaglandins.
    (b) estrogen.
    (c) progesterone.
    (d) luteinizing hormone.

    Answer: A Difficulty: 2 Page: 101

88. A woman who has never menstruated is experiencing
    (a) dysmenorrhea.
    (b) amenorrhea.
    (c) secondary dysmenorrhea.
    (d) primary amenorrhea.

    Answer: D Difficulty: 1 Page: 101

89. How many women experience some premenstrual symptoms?
    (a) twenty-five percent
    (b) forty percent
    (c) seventy-five percent
    (d) eighty-five percent

    Answer: C Difficulty: 2 Page: 102

90. Premenstrual syndrome *most* likely involves
    (a) a deficiency of certain neurotransmitters.
    (b) an excess of estrogen.
    (c) a deficiency of both estrogen and progesterone.
    (d) a complex interaction between hormones and neurotransmitters.

    Answer: D Difficulty: 2 Page: 102

MATCHING

Match the hormone with the description of its role in the menstrual cycle.

(a) Estrogen

(b) Luteinizing Hormone

(c) Follicle Stimulating Hormone

(d) Progesterone

(e) Gonadotropin Releasing Hormone

91. Hormone released by the hypothalamus when it senses low levels of estrogen.

    Answer: e

92. Hormone that ripens several follicles.

    Answer: c

93. When this hormone peaks, ovulation is set into motion.

    Answer: a

94. Hormone that causes a follicle to rupture and release on ovum.

    Answer: b

95. In response to high levels of this hormone, the hypothalamus signals the pituitary to stop producing LH and FSH.

    Answer: d

TRUE/FALSE

96. Pudendum derives from the Latin *pudendus* which means "something to be proud of."

    Answer: False

97. The clitoris has no known purpose other than sexual pleasure.

Answer: True

98. Today, clitoridectomy is performed under the supervision of physicians.

Answer: False

99. About 1 million women in Africa and the Middle East have undergone removal of the clitoris and labia minora.

Answer: False

100. The *best* way to prevent vaginal infections is to cleanse the vagina by douching.

Answer: False

101. Among women who develop cervical cancer, the mortality rate for African American women is twice that of White American women.

Answer: True

102. In hormone replacement therapy, combining progesterone with estrogen decreases the risk of endometrial cancer.

Answer: True

103. The outermost layer of the uterus is the myometrium.

Answer: True

104. Intrauterine devices (IUDs) decrease the risk of ectopic pregnancy.

Answer: False

105. The five year survival rate for women whose breast cancer has not metastasized is 93%.

Answer: True

106. Fat is connected with higher levels of estrogen production.

Answer: True

107. Fibroadenomas are malignant tumors of the breast.

Answer: False

108. A common complaint of post-menopausal women is vaginal dryness.

Answer: True

109. Estrogen deficiency can impair cognitive functioning.

Answer: True

110. The labia minora are two hairless, light-colored membranes, located between the majora lips.

Answer: True

111. Men and women have a sex organ whose only function is the experiencing of sexual pleasure.

Answer: False

112. Women with larger breasts produce more milk while nursing.

Answer: True

113. Incidence of breast cancer is on the rise in the United States.

Answer: False

ESSAY

114. Describe the procedures and purpose of each procedure in a pelvic exam.

    Answer:

115. Summarize the current knowledge about breast cancer including risk factors, detection, recommendations, and treatment.

    Answer:

116. Differentiate between amenorrhea, dysmenorrhea, and premenstrual syndrome. Discuss the causes, symptoms, and potential treatments for each disorder.

    Answer:

117. Describe the breast self-exam procedure including the techniques of breast self-examination and the logic behind the techniques.

    Answer:

118. Discuss historical and cross-cultural conceptions of menstruation and how those conceptions affect women's beliefs about their sexuality.

    Answer:

119. Describe the physiological and psychological changes associated with menopause.

    Answer:

120. Discuss the advantages and disadvantages of hormone replacement therapy. Explain why some women should receive hormone replacement therapy and some should not.

    Answer:

Chapter 4: Male Sexual Anatomy and Physiology

MULTIPLE CHOICE

1. In Latin, *testis* means
   (a) to bear the burden.
   (b) to multiply.
   (c) a witness.
   (d) to hold on to.

   Answer: C Difficulty: 2 Page: 110

2. In our society, men are *mainly* preoccupied with
   (a) the amount of ejaculate.
   (b) penis size.
   (c) body musculature.
   (d) how long they can last until ejaculation.

   Answer: B Difficulty: 1 Page: 110

3. Earlier in evolution, male and female animals each had a genital opening called the
   (a) urethral meatus.
   (b) crura.
   (c) urethral opening.
   (d) cloaca.

   Answer: D Difficulty: 2 Page: 112

4. The term "boner" comes from the fact that
   (a) many mammals, other than humans, have a penile bone to facilitate copulation.
   (b) human males have a penile bone to facilitate intercourse.
   (c) the penis of the human male contains muscle tissue to aid in erection.
   (d) both semen and urine pass out of the penis through the same opening.

   Answer: A Difficulty: 3 Page: 112

5. The spongy body that runs along the bottom or ventral surface of the penis is the
   (a) corpus spongiosum.
   (b) urethral meatus.
   (c) corpora cavernosa.
   (d) corona.

   Answer: A Difficulty: 2 Page: 112

6. The corpora cavernosa
   (a) separate the glans from the shaft of the penis.
   (b) are cylinders of spongy tissue that lie side by side in the penis.
   (c) are thin strips of tissue on the underside of the penis.
   (d) are the muscles that regulate the position of the testes.

   Answer: B Difficulty: 1 Page: 112

7. Which is true of *both* males and females?
   (a) Crura anchor both the penis and the clitoris to the pelvic bones.
   (b) The shaft of the penis and the shaft of the clitoris are free-swinging.
   (c) In both males and females, only two columns of spongy tissue engorge the penis or the clitoris.
   (d) The corona in males is analogous to the prepuce in females.

   Answer: A Difficulty: 2 Page: 112

8. Which of the following is true about the prepuce?
   (a) It is the part of the penis that remains after circumcision.
   (b) It covers at least part of the penile glans.
   (c) It is fixed to the penile shaft just behind the glans.
   (d) It is attached to the scrotum.

   Answer: B Difficulty: 2 Page: 112

9. The part of the penis *least* sensitive to stimulation is the
   (a) root.
   (b) glans.
   (c) underside of the shaft.
   (d) upper side of the shaft.

   Answer: D Difficulty: 1 Page: 112

10. Male circumcision began among the Jews as a
    (a) means to increase sexual pleasure.
    (b) way to increase health.
    (c) religious rite.
    (d) means to decrease the spread of sexually transmitted diseases.

    Answer: C Difficulty: 2 Page: 113

11. Which of the following is true regarding circumcision among European American men?
    (a) Circumcision is lower among men whose mothers didn't graduate from college.
    (b) Circumcision is higher among men whose mothers graduated from college.
    (c) Circumcision is lower among European Americans than among Latino men.
    (d) Circumcision is performed on about one-third of European American men.

    Answer: B Difficulty: 3 Page: 113

12. Why did circumcision become widespread in the United States?
    (a) because it was a popular cultural phenomenon
    (b) because it was an important religious rite
    (c) because it was thought to enhance pleasure during intercourse
    (d) because research suggested that it prevented the transmission of sexual infections

    Answer: D Difficulty: 2 Page: 113

13. Which of the following is true regarding circumcision and AIDS?
    (a) Quinn and his colleagues found that circumcised men were slightly more likely to become infected than uncircumcised men.
    (b) During male/female sexual relations, uncircumcised men are at greater risk than circumcised men of becoming infected with HIV.
    (c) During male/female sexual relations, uncircumcised men are at less risk than circumcised men of becoming infected with HIV.
    (d) Ann Buve found greater incidence of HIV infection in countries where circumcision was low.

    Answer: B Difficulty: 2 Page: 114

14. In regard to circumcision, the NHSLS study found that
    (a) uncircumcised males are more likely to have genital herpes and chlamydia infections.
    (b) circumcised males were less likely to have sexual dysfunctions.
    (c) circumcised males had a higher incidence of urinary tract infections as infants.
    (d) uncircumcised males experience a reduction in the sensitivity of the glans.

    Answer: B Difficulty: 3 Page: 114

15. When the foreskin does not retract from the glans, the condition is called
    (a) phimosis.
    (b) urethritus.
    (c) cremasteritus.
    (d) frenulitus.

    Answer: A Difficulty: 1 Page: 114

16. The average erect penis is about
    (a) 3-4 inches in length.
    (b) 4-6 inches in length.
    (c) 5-7 inches in length.
    (d) 6-8 inches in length.

    Answer: C Difficulty: 2 Page: 115

17. In the locker room at the local YMCA, John has noticed that his penis size is rather small compared to other men. He is beginning to have doubts about his ability to "sexually satisfy" a woman. What should John know?
    (a) Women prefer bigger penises because a larger penis enhances sexual pleasure.
    (b) John should probably see a urologist to make sure he is making enough testosterone.
    (c) Different sizes in penises are largely cancelled out when erect.
    (d) When erect his penis will remain smaller than those of other men but he can learn to pleasure women with other techniques.

    Answer: C Difficulty: 3 Page: 115

18. Which of the following is true regarding penis size and ability to satisfy a woman sexually?
    (a) Women rarely mention penis size as an important element in their sexual satisfaction.
    (b) There is a positive relationship between penis size and the ability to satisfy.
    (c) Penis size is less important than the ability to communicate but more important than the emotional atmosphere of the relationship.
    (d) Penis size is important to women over the age of 35.

    Answer: A Difficulty: 2 Page: 115

19. Why is the *length* of a man's penis largely unrelated to sexual satisfaction?
    (a) Women can only achieve orgasm through direct clitoral stimulation.
    (b) The majority of women do not like deep penetration.
    (c) The inner vagina is relatively insensitive to touch.
    (d) The inner vagina is so highly innervated that excessive stimulation can be painful.

    Answer: C Difficulty: 2 Page: 115

20. In the scrotum, each testis is held in place by a(n)
    (a) spermatic cord.
    (b) dartos muscle.
    (c) vas deferens.
    (d) interstitial cell.

    Answer: A Difficulty: 3 Page: 115

21. When Andre jumps into the cold swimming pool, his testicles seem to move up and closer to his body. Why?
    (a) His vas deferens muscle is contracting in response to the cold.
    (b) His cremaster and dartos muscles are contracting to keep his sperm warm.
    (c) His spermatic cord is relaxing in order to keep his sperm warm.
    (d) His dartos muscle is contracting in order to cool his sperm.

    Answer: B Difficulty: 3 Page: 115

22. Typically, how much cooler than body temperature is scrotal temperature?
    (a) 2-4 degrees
    (b) 5-6 degrees
    (c) 7-9 degrees
    (d) 9-11 degrees

    Answer: B Difficulty: 2 Page: 115

23. In hot weather, men could expect the scrotum to
    (a) be more wrinkled in appearance and closer to the body.
    (b) be smoother in appearance and closer to the body.
    (c) be more wrinkled in appearance and farther from the body.
    (d) be smoother in appearance and farther from the body.

    Answer: D Difficulty: 2 Page: 115

24. Testosterone is secreted by the
    (a) interstitial cells.
    (b) seminiferous tubules.
    (c) epididymus.
    (d) Cowpers glands.

    Answer: A Difficulty: 2 Page: 117

25. Compared to the female sex hormones, testosterone levels in males
    (a) peak just prior to ejaculation.
    (b) remain relatively stable.
    (c) also vary depending on the time of day and time of month.
    (d) are not regulated by the hypothalamus.

    Answer: B Difficulty: 1 Page: 117

26. Which stimulates the secretion of testosterone?
    (a) follicle stimulating hormone (FSH)
    (b) androgens
    (c) luteinizing hormone (LH)
    (d) germ cells

    Answer: C Difficulty: 3 Page: 117

27. When blood levels of testosterone rise
    (a) the pituitary gland secretes LH.
    (b) the hypothalamus secretes LH.
    (c) the pituitary gland stops secreting LH.
    (d) the hypothalamus stops secreting LH-RH.

    Answer: C Difficulty: 3 Page: 117

28. Which of the following is true regarding *manopause*?
    (a) It is conceptually similar to menapause.
    (b) The scientific community is undecided about the existence of manopause.
    (c) Manopause has been found only in men who have been circumcised.
    (d) It's a sudden age-related decline in sex hormones.

    Answer: B Difficulty: 2 Page: 117

29. In the male aging process, testosterone levels
    (a) stay the same.
    (b) begin to fall around age 30.
    (c) decline to about half by age 80.
    (d) decline to about one-third by age 50.

    Answer: C Difficulty: 3 Page: 118

30. In aging males, a drop in testosterone levels may be connected to
    (a) reduced testicular size.
    (b) a rise in basal metabolic rate.
    (c) a reduction in body fat.
    (d) a reduction in lean muscle mass.

    Answer: D Difficulty: 2 Page: 118

31. The age-related decline in testosterone causes all of the following except
    (a) reduced energy.
    (b) lowered fertility.
    (c) termination of potency.
    (d) reduced erectile ability.

    Answer: C Difficulty: 3 Page: 118

32. Which is not true of a man of 70 years?
    (a) The number of his sperm has declined.
    (b) The motility of his sperm has declined.
    (c) His fertility is reduced.
    (d) He is no longer able to father children.

    Answer: D Difficulty: 1 Page: 118

33. Spermatogenesis takes place in the
    (a) Leydig cells.
    (b) seminiferous tubules.
    (c) epididymus.
    (d) vas deferens.

    Answer: B Difficulty: 2 Page: 118

34. How long does it take for a testis to develop a mature sperm?
    (a) 72 hours
    (b) 2 weeks
    (c) 4 days
    (d) 72 days

    Answer: D Difficulty: 3 Page: 119

35. The head of a spermatozoon houses the
    (a) tail piece.
    (b) ova.
    (c) mitochondria.
    (d) chromosomes.

    Answer: D Difficulty: 2 Page: 119

36. What happens during fertilization?
    (a) 46 chromosomes from the sperm combine with 46 chromosomes from the egg.
    (b) 23 chromosomes from the sperm combine with 23 chromosomes from the egg.
    (c) 46 genes from the sperm combine with 46 genes from the egg.
    (d) 23 genes from the sperm combine with 23 genes from the egg.

    Answer: B Difficulty: 1 Page: 119

37. Males can manufacture about
    (a) 25 sperm per second.
    (b) 250 sperm per second.
    (c) 500 sperm per second.
    (d) 1,000 sperm per second.

    Answer: D Difficulty: 3 Page: 119

38. Sperm may find their way to the egg by specialized
    (a) touch receptors.
    (b) scent receptors.
    (c) sight receptors.
    (d) taste receptors.

    Answer: B Difficulty: 2 Page: 119

39. The main function of the epididymus is
    (a) to manufacture sperm.
    (b) to release testosterone.
    (c) to house mature sperm.
    (d) to provide passage out of the body.

    Answer: C Difficulty: 2 Page: 119

40. The epididymus empties into the
    (a) urethra.
    (b) testes.
    (c) vas deferens.
    (d) prostate gland..

    Answer: C Difficulty: 2 Page: 119

41. Surgical sterilization of males involves
    (a) cutting the seminiferous tubules.
    (b) tying off the ejaculatory ducts.
    (c) tying off the epididymus.
    (d) cutting the vas deferens.

    Answer: D Difficulty: 3 Page: 119

42. The seminal vesicles contribute
    (a) a milky alkaline fluid to sperm.
    (b) testosterone to developing spermatids.
    (c) fructose to semen.
    (d) a fluid rich in fats and proteins to semen.

    Answer: C Difficulty: 2 Page: 120

43. Prostate fluid is alkaline because
    (a) the vagina is highly acidic.
    (b) sperm are acidic.
    (c) the vagina is also alkaline.
    (d) urine is alkaline.

    Answer: A Difficulty: 2 Page: 121

44. During sexual arousal, which gland(s) secrete pre-ejaculatory fluid?
    (a) prostate
    (b) seminal vesicles
    (c) ejaculatory ducts
    (d) Cowpers glands

    Answer: D Difficulty: 1 Page: 121

45. Noah and Nina use the withdrawal method for birth control. What should Noah and Nina know?
    (a) They are safe as long as Noah has ejaculatory control.
    (b) Pre-ejaculatory fluid contains viable sperm.
    (c) They are safe as long as Noah does not ejaculate near the vaginal opening.
    (d) Pregnancy cannot occur as long as the penis is withdrawn prior to ejaculation.

    Answer: B Difficulty: 2 Page: 121

46. Which gland(s) secretes enough fluids to make up about 70% of semen volume?
    (a) Cowper's glands
    (b) prostate gland
    (c) ejaculatory ducts
    (d) seminal vesicles

    Answer: D Difficulty: 1 Page: 121

47. Which of the following is true for men with vasectomies?
    (a) They ejaculate about as much semen as before the vasectomy.
    (b) They rarely ejaculate.
    (c) They are instructed to consume extra liquids to ensure a plentiful ejaculate.
    (d) They ejaculate about half as much as before.

    Answer: A Difficulty: 1 Page: 122

48. George is experiencing a strong need to urinate and burning during urination. George may have
    (a) urethritis.
    (b) prostate cancer.
    (c) penile cancer.
    (d) cryptorchidism.

    Answer: A Difficulty: 2 Page: 122

49. A preventative measure for urethritis is to
    (a) drink less water to urinate less.
    (b) drink cranberry juice.
    (c) lower the intake of sodium.
    (d) increase caffeine to increase urination.

    Answer: B Difficulty: 3 Page: 122

50. Cancer of the testicles
    (a) is the second most common cancer among males over 40.
    (b) accounts for nearly 2/3 of all deaths from cancer in men between 20-34.
    (c) often occurs along with prostate cancer.
    (d) is relatively rare.

    Answer: D Difficulty: 2 Page: 122

51. Which is true about testicular cancer?
    (a) It's generally fatal.
    (b) The survival rate before the cancer has spread beyond the testes is about 50%.
    (c) Generally, the prognosis is quite favorable.
    (d) It's usually treated with strong steroids which arrest the spread of the cancer.

    Answer: C Difficulty: 2 Page: 122

52. Which of the following is not a sign of testicular cancer?
    (a) pain during ejaculation
    (b) dull ache in the groin
    (c) sensation of heaviness in a testicle
    (d) change in the consistency of a testicle

    Answer: A Difficulty: 3 Page: 123

53. Cryptorchidism is a condition where one or both testes
    (a) fail to descend from the abdomen into the scrotum.
    (b) is/are grossly enlarged or inflamed.
    (c) is/are immature and not fully developed.
    (d) fail to produce testosterone.

    Answer: A Difficulty: 2 Page: 122

54. Benign prostatic hyperplasia is believed to be the result of
    (a) sexually transmitted diseases.
    (b) hormonal changes associated with aging.
    (c) enlargement of the urethra.
    (d) cancer of the prostate.

    Answer: B Difficulty: 2 Page: 123

55. Which of the following symptoms may occur with enlarged prostate?
    (a) urinary frequency and urgency
    (b) pain in the urethra
    (c) a bloody discharge from the urethra
    (d) pain in a testicle

    Answer: A Difficulty: 2 Page: 123

56. The American Cancer Society estimates that
    (a) one of every ten men develops penile cancer.
    (b) one of every two men develops prostate cancer.
    (c) one of every 100 men develops testicular cancer.
    (d) one of every eight men develops prostate cancer.

    Answer: D Difficulty: 2 Page: 123

57. Which of the following is *not* true of prostate cancer?
    (a) Intake of animal fat maybe a risk factor.
    (b) The incidence increases with age.
    (c) It appears to have a genetic factor.
    (d) High levels of testosterone appear to be a natural defense.

    Answer: D Difficulty: 3 Page: 124

58. Which of the following is not a symptom of prostate cancer?
    (a) urinary frequency
    (b) blood in the stools
    (c) pain in the lower back
    (d) painful urination

    Answer: B Difficulty: 3 Page: 125

59. Which is *not* true of a rectal examination?
    (a) It's a good way to detect cancer of the testes.
    (b) It's mildly uncomfortable.
    (c) The physician inserts a finger into the rectum.
    (d) Some men resist it since they associate rectal insertion with male-male sex.

    Answer: A Difficulty: 1 Page: 125

60. PSA is a
    (a) protein that combines with testosterone to promote growth of the testes.
    (b) protein that helps produce a liquid that transports sperm when it is ejaculated.
    (c) protein that indicates a diseased prostate.
    (d) type of rectal exam that detects an enlarged prostate.

    Answer: B Difficulty: 3 Page: 125

61. What is one of the risks of surgical removal of the prostate gland?
    (a) stark reduction in semen production
    (b) loss of testosterone production
    (c) problems with erection or ejaculation
    (d) onset of irritable bowel syndrome

    Answer: C Difficulty: 3 Page: 125

62. What is the desired result of androgen suppression therapy and anticancer drugs in the treatment of prostate cancer?
    (a) They reduce PSA.
    (b) They shrink the tumor.
    (c) They halt the production of damaged sperm.
    (d) They boost T-cell count.

    Answer: B Difficulty: 3 Page: 125

63. Which of the following factors appears to be directly related to a decrease in the number of deaths from prostate cancer?
    (a) male testicular exams
    (b) rectal exams
    (c) the PSA test
    (d) an increase in urologists

    Answer: C Difficulty: 2 Page: 125

64. Arthur is 79 and has been recently diagnosed with prostate cancer. He has chosen a treatment of "watchful waiting." This means
    (a) getting a second opinion.
    (b) he cannot afford more aggressive measures.
    (c) undergoing radiation therapy and then waiting.
    (d) delaying treatment.

    Answer: D Difficulty: 1 Page: 125

65. There are at least two methods of detecting prostate cancer: blood test for PSA and physical exam. What is one of the advantages of a blood test for PSA?
    (a) A blood test can detect evidence of cancer even when the prostate feels normal.
    (b) A blood test is less expensive.
    (c) A blood test can seek changes in the GSTPI gene.
    (d) A blood test can detect high levels of iron which provides an early marker of prostate cancer.

    Answer: A Difficulty: 2 Page: 125

66. Prostatitis is usually treated with
    (a) surgery.
    (b) radiation.
    (c) antibiotics.
    (d) abstinence from intercourse.

    Answer: C Difficulty: 2 Page: 130

67. In purely mechanical terms, erection most closely resembles a(n) ____ event.
    (a) chemical
    (b) electronic
    (c) hydraulic
    (d) reactionary

    Answer: C Difficulty: 2 Page: 130

68. Which of the following accounts for the firmness of an erection?
    (a) the corpora cavernosa
    (b) the tunica albuginea
    (c) the corpus spongiosum
    (d) the cremasteric muscles

    Answer: B Difficulty: 3 Page: 130

69. Which of the following events can cause a loss of erection?
    (a) response to perceived threats
    (b) sexual stimulation ceases
    (c) orgasm
    (d) all of the above

    Answer: D Difficulty: 1 Page: 131

70. Males experience erections throughout the night. These erections occur about every
    (a) 10 minutes.
    (b) 30 minutes.
    (c) 90 minutes.
    (d) 180 minutes.

    Answer: C Difficulty: 2 Page: 131

71. Regarding nocturnal erections, it has been established that they
    (a) generally take place during non-REM sleep.
    (b) are generally associated with erotic dreams.
    (c) are physiologically based.
    (d) reflect the need to urinate.

    Answer: C Difficulty: 2 Page: 131

72. Alex awakens in the morning fully erect. Most likely, he
    (a) needs to urinate.
    (b) just had an erotic dream.
    (c) is having a nocturnal erection.
    (d) none of the above.

    Answer: C Difficulty: 2 Page: 131

73. Which of the following most accurately describes male arousal?
    (a) Erection is a reflex but ejaculation is a learned response.
    (b) Both erection and ejaculation are controlled by conscious effort.
    (c) Erection and ejaculation are processes controlled by the hypothalamus.
    (d) Erection and ejaculation are reflexes.

    Answer: D Difficulty: 2 Page: 131

74. Sexual arousal like erection or vaginal lubrication is a
    (a) voluntary response to erotic stimuli.
    (b) is a reflex.
    (c) combination of conscious and unconscious response.
    (d) is an automatic response, enhanced by conscious effort.

    Answer: B Difficulty: 3 Page: 131

75. If a man's penis is stroked, an erection
    (a) may begin before he is aware of it.
    (b) will begin immediately.
    (c) may begin after his brain becomes aware of the stroking.
    (d) may occur if the sensory neurons carry the message to the brain.

    Answer: A Difficulty: 3 Page: 132

76. Erectile responses to direct stimulation of the penis involve
    (a) an erection center in the lower back.
    (b) an erection center in the cerebral cortex.
    (c) both emotions and intelligence.
    (d) an erection center in the upper spinal cord.

    Answer: A Difficulty: 2 Page: 133

77. Men with spinal cord injuries can achieve erections if the injury is above the
    (a) cervical region.
    (b) thoracic region.
    (c) lumbar region.
    (d) sacral region.

    Answer: D Difficulty: 2 Page: 133

78. Spinal-injured men whose nerve damage prevents neural communication from their genitals to the brain
    (a) experience no sexual pleasure.
    (b) may find sex psychologically fulfilling.
    (c) experience fleeting or intermittent sensations.
    (d) cannot become erect.

    Answer: B Difficulty: 3 Page: 133

79. "Hands off" or psychogenic erections are possible with the help of the erection center in the ____ region.
    (a) lumbar
    (b) thoracic
    (c) cervical
    (d) sacral

    Answer: A Difficulty: 3 Page: 133

80. In terms of erection, as men age
    (a) the autonomic nervous system is no longer working as efficiently.
    (b) they require more direct stimulation of the penis to achieve erection.
    (c) very little changes in their ability to achieve and maintain an erection.
    (d) they rely less on tactile stimulation and more on psychogenic means to achieve an erection.

    Answer: B Difficulty: 1 Page: 134

81. The nerves that effect dilation during erection belong to the ____ whereas the nerves governing ejaculation belong to the ____.
    (a) parasympathetic branch; sympathetic branch
    (b) sympathetic branch; parasympathetic branch
    (c) autonomic nervous system; somatic nervous system
    (d) somatic nervous system; autonomic nervous system

    Answer: A Difficulty: 3 Page: 134

82. Painful erections due to excessive curvature of the penis is known as
    (a) priapism.
    (b) phimosis.
    (c) Peyronie's disease.
    (d) retrograde ejaculation.

    Answer: C Difficulty: 1 Page: 135

83. Priapism may become a medical emergency if
    (a) fibrous tissue continues to build up at the end of the penile shaft.
    (b) erection continues beyond six hours.
    (c) too much sperm enters the bladder.
    (d) the curvature of the penis prevents comfortable intercourse.

    Answer: B Difficulty: 2 Page: 135

84. In males, orgasm and ejaculation
    (a) always occur at the same time.
    (b) always occur together unless a male is experiencing retrograde ejaculation.
    (c) generally occur together but are separate physiological events.
    (d) occur together once a male reaches puberty.

    Answer: C Difficulty: 2 Page: 135

85. Dry orgasms
    (a) occur only in prepubertal boys.
    (b) can occur in young and older men.
    (c) can occur before but not after a main orgasm.
    (d) are a danger signal since they are a result of retrograde ejaculation.

    Answer: B Difficulty: 3 Page: 135

86. The two stages of ejaculation are
    (a) the ampulla and emission stages.
    (b) pre-ejaculatory and expulsion stages.
    (c) emission and refractory stages.
    (d) emission and expulsion stages.

    Answer: D Difficulty: 2 Page: 136

87. In ejaculation, seminal fluid is released from the ____ and expelled from the penis.
    (a) urethral bulb
    (b) vas deferens
    (c) epididymus
    (d) crura

    Answer: A Difficulty: 1 Page: 136

88. Possible causes of retrograde ejaculation include all but which of the following?
    (a) prostate surgery
    (b) some tranquilizers
    (c) some accidents
    (d) enlarged prostate

    Answer: D Difficulty: 3 Page: 137

89. A retrograde ejaculation is a condition in which ejaculate empties into the
    (a) epididymus.
    (b) bladder.
    (c) prostate gland.
    (d) seminal vesicles.

    Answer: B Difficulty: 2 Page: 136

Chapter 4: Male Sexual Anatomy and Physiology

MATCHING

For each of the following male hormones, match the hormone with its function.

(a) Inhibin

(b) LH-RH

(c) FSH

(d) LH

(e) Testosterone

90. Stimulates testosterone production in interstitial cells in the testes.

    Answer: d

91. Regulates sperm production by inhibiting the release of FSH.

    Answer: a

92. Stimulates the production of sperm in the testes.

    Answer: c

93. Released by the hypothalamus in response to low testosterone levels.

    Answer: b

94. Stimulates sperm production in the testes, triggers the development of secondary sex characteristics, and regulates sex drive.

    Answer: e

TRUE/FALSE

95. Men with spinal cord injuries above the sacral spine can achieve both erection and ejaculation.

    Answer: True

96. Generally, one could say that the shape of the penis serves as an efficient delivery device in reproduction.

    Answer: True

97. Priapism is a condition in which it is difficult to retract the foreskin in an uncircumsized male.

    Answer: False

98. The diameter of a penis, rather than the length, may have a greater impact on a female partner's sexual sensations.

    Answer: True

99. Spermatozoa contain 46 chromosomes and spermatids contain 23.

    Answer: True

100. Undescended testicles appear to occur more commonly in boys whose mothers used birth control pills prior to becoming pregnant.

    Answer: False

101. Over 80% of all prostate cancers are diagnosed in men over the age of 65.

    Answer: True

102. White American men are one-third more likely than African American men to develop prostate cancer.

    Answer: False

103. A positive PSA test would indicate that there is a lower than normal level of the PSA protein in the blood.

    Answer: False

104. Ultrasound studies show that males may experience erection in the womb.

    Answer: True

ESSAY

105. Discuss the arguments favoring and refuting male circumcision. Given what you have learned from the text, what is your position?

    Answer:

106. Given our society's preoccupation with penis size, explain why this fear is unfounded.

    Answer:

107. Describe the process of spermatogenesis by describing the role of each of the following hormones: LH-RH, LH, FSH, testosterone, and inhibin.

    Answer:

108. While the "scientific jury" is still out on male "manopause," discuss the physiological changes that occur in the aging male and their impact on sexual arousal and responsiveness.

    Answer:

109. Outline the production of semen by tracing the path of sperm from the epididymus to the urethra and identifying the contributions of each of the seminal glands.

    Answer:

110. Differentiate between prostatitis, benign prostatic hyperplasia, and prostate cancer in terms of symptoms and treatments.

    Answer:

Chapter 5: Sexual Arousal and Response

MULTIPLE CHOICE

1. In terms of sexual attraction, visual orientation is important for both humans and
   (a) reptiles.
   (b) fishes.
   (c) birds.
   (d) cats and dogs.

   Answer: C Difficulty: 2 Page: 142

2. Which statement is true regarding visual cues in human sexual arousal?
   (a) Both men and women can become sexually aroused by visual stimuli.
   (b) Men are much more sexually aroused by visual stimuli than women.
   (c) Women are more visually oriented than men.
   (d) Visual stimuli do not play an important role for either men or women.

   Answer: A Difficulty: 2 Page: 142

3. Which is true regarding the sense of smell?
   (a) It is the most powerful of the 5 senses in sexual arousal.
   (b) The ancient Egyptians appreciated body odors — bathing to remove odors was not
       practiced.
   (c) Ancient Romans were known to put perfume on their pets.
   (d) Most Westerners actually prefer not to mask odors by use of soaps and perfumes.

   Answer: C Difficulty: 3 Page: 143

4. Marietta has begun dating a young man from a foreign country. He has asked her not to
   wear perfume or hairsprays because they mask her feminine scent. Marietta finds this
   strange. What should you tell her?
   (a) Her boyfriend is probably a very controlling person.
   (b) Natural body odors are sexually stimulating in some cultures.
   (c) There is no evidence that smell is important in human sexual arousal.
   (d) Natural body odors are a sexual turn-off in the majority of the world's cultures.

   Answer: B Difficulty: 2 Page: 143

5. The vomeronasal organ is believed to detect
   (a) perspiration.
   (b) vaginal secretions.
   (c) semen.
   (d) pheromones.

   Answer: D Difficulty: 1 Page: 143

6. Which is true of pheromones in animals?
   (a) They become more vital as one moves upward in the animal kingdom.
   (b) Lower animals use them to mark territories — not to stimulate sexual response.
   (c) Male rodents show more sexual arousal when their sense of smell is blocked.
   (d) Some animals use them to organize food gathering and maintain pecking orders.

   Answer: D Difficulty: 2 Page: 143

7. In pheromone research with heterosexual men, which of the following has been a typical
   result?
   (a) Men masturbated more frequently.
   (b) Men had sexual intercourse more frequently.
   (c) The pheromones directly stimulated sexual behavior.
   (d) The pheromones directly affected behavior.

   Answer: B Difficulty: 3 Page: 143

8. What does research suggest about the effect of pheromones on the behavior of men and women?
   (a) Pheromones affect people's moods.
   (b) Pheromones enhance men's moods, but not women's.
   (c) Pheromones enhance women's moods, but not men's.
   (d) Pheromones affect sexual receptiveness — but not moods.

   Answer: C Difficulty: 2 Page: 143

9. Overall, which is true of pheromones?
   (a) They directly stimulate behavior in lower animals and humans.
   (b) They directly stimulate courtship behavior in humans and sexual behavior in lower animals.
   (c) They may affect sexual behavior in humans but this has not been demonstrated conclusively.
   (d) Some pheromones are directly responsible for courting behaviors in humans and indirectly cause intercourse.

   Answer: C Difficulty: 3 Page: 143

10. Research suggests that women's menstrual cycles can become synchronized when they are exposed to each other's
    (a) perspiration.
    (b) menstrual blood.
    (c) vaginal secretions.
    (d) nasal secretions.

    Answer: A Difficulty: 1 Page: 144

11. Research with bees and plants suggests that
    (a) some plants emit chemical secretions that mimic those of female bees.
    (b) plants emit pheromones in an effort to trick the bees.
    (c) male bees misperceive plant secretions and will mate with females other than the queen.
    (d) some orchids emit secretions of other plants, bringing about unusual cross-pollination.

    Answer: A Difficulty: 2 Page: 144

12. Which sense has the most direct effect on sexual arousal and responsiveness?
    (a) smell
    (b) touch
    (c) vision
    (d) taste

    Answer: B Difficulty: 1 Page: 145

13. Erogenous zones are
    (a) parts of the body that are especially sensitive to tactile sexual stimulation.
    (b) genital areas.
    (c) genital areas plus the buttocks.
    (d) non-genital areas that cause stimulation like ears, inner thighs etc.

    Answer: A Difficulty: 1 Page: 145

14. Which of the following is *not* a primary erogenous zone?
    (a) the anus
    (b) the breasts
    (c) the lower back
    (d) the inner thighs

    Answer: C Difficulty: 2 Page: 145

15. Primary erogenous zones differ from secondary because primary erogenous zones
    (a) are rich in nerve endings.
    (b) are learned through experience.
    (c) produce the same response in all humans.
    (d) are learned through association with sexual stimulation.

    Answer: A Difficulty: 2 Page: 145

16. Of all the senses, which one appears to play only a minor role in sexual arousal?
    (a) hearing
    (b) smell
    (c) taste
    (d) vision

    Answer: C Difficulty: 1 Page: 145

17. Which of the following is true regarding "Spanish fly?"
    (a) It is a common aphrodisiac that produces prolonged erection in men.
    (b) If used carefully and in small amounts, it aids in vasocongestion.
    (c) Its active ingredient, *cantharidin*, is used in the impotency drug, *Viagra*.
    (d) It is a skin irritant that inflames the urinary tract.

    Answer: D Difficulty: 3 Page: 147

18. An aphrodisiac is a
    (a) nymphomaniac.
    (b) substance that increases sexual pleasure.
    (c) rare paraphilia.
    (d) substance that reduces sexual responsiveness.

    Answer: B Difficulty: 1 Page: 147

19. Today, *cantharidin* is synthetically produced to
    (a) burn off warts.
    (b) reduce fever.
    (c) enhance blood flow to the skin.
    (d) reduce stomach acid.

    Answer: A Difficulty: 2 Page: 147

20. Decreases in elephant and rhinoceros populations can be partially attributed to myths about the aphrodisiac properties of their
    (a) testicles.
    (b) horns.
    (c) hooves.
    (d) tails.

    Answer: B Difficulty: 1 Page: 147

21. Which of the following is the safest way to increase sex drive?
    (a) viagra
    (b) yohimbine
    (c) exercise
    (d) alcohol

    Answer: C Difficulty: 2 Page: 148

22. Which is not true about alcohol?
    (a) Large amounts can increase sex drive.
    (b) It lowers sexual inhibitions.
    (c) It can reduce sexual potency.
    (d) It reduces central nervous system activity.

    Answer: A Difficulty: 2 Page: 149

23. A "popper" is
    (a) a drink made from yohimbe bark.
    (b) a raw oyster.
    (c) an ampule of amyl nitrate.
    (d) a drink made from reindeer horn.

    Answer: C Difficulty: 2 Page: 147

24. Viagra was originally developed as a treatment for
    (a) ulcers.
    (b) enlarged prostate.
    (c) angina.
    (d) depression.

    Answer: C Difficulty: 1 Page: 147

25. What is potassium nitrate?
    (a) an aphrodisiac
    (b) an anaphrodisiac
    (c) an antihypertensive
    (d) a tranquilizer

    Answer: B Difficulty: 2 Page: 147

26. Two drugs that do have aphrodisiac effects are
    (a) amyl nitrate and Viagra.
    (b) bupropion and L-dopa.
    (c) Prozac and Tofranil.
    (d) nicotine and alcohol.

    Answer: B Difficulty: 2 Page: 147

27. Drugs that have aphrodisiac effects work by directly affecting
    (a) respiration.
    (b) blood flow to the genital region.
    (c) brain receptors for dopamine.
    (d) blood flow to the heart.

    Answer: D Difficulty: 2 Page: 147

28. The *most* potent chemical aphrodisiac is
    (a) testosterone.
    (b) Viagra.
    (c) amyl nitrate.
    (d) bupropion.

    Answer: A Difficulty: 1 Page: 147

29. Trevor's physician has just prescribed the tranquilizer, *Xanax*, to help Trevor cope with an anxiety disorder. One of the side effects Trevor might experience is
    (a) inflammation of the urethra.
    (b) difficulty producing an erection.
    (c) premature ejaculation.
    (d) heightened sexual desire.

    Answer: B Difficulty: 1 Page: 149

30. Susanna takes the antidepressant, *imipramine*. Her physician is careful to explain that she may experience
    (a) numbing in the vaginal area.
    (b) hot flashes.
    (c) lack of sexual desire.
    (d) decreased sexual inhibition.

    Answer: C Difficulty: 2 Page: 149

31. Which is not an example of an anaphrodisiac?
    (a) antiandrogen
    (b) Prozac
    (c) nicotine
    (d) yohimbine

    Answer: D Difficulty: 2 Page: 149

32. Two psychoactive drugs widely believed to have aphrodisiac effects are
    (a) nicotine and alcohol.
    (b) amphetamines and antidepressants.
    (c) cocaine and alcohol.
    (d) barbituates and caffeine.

    Answer: C Difficulty: 3 Page: 149

33. John is very nervous about his first sexual experience. To loosen up, his friends suggest that he buy a six-pack of beer and drink it before his date arrives. You disagree. Which explanation should you give John?
    (a) Alcohol will only raise his sexual inhibitions.
    (b) Alcohol will simply increase his anxiety.
    (c) Alcohol will increase the incidence of premature ejaculation.
    (d) Large amounts of alcohol will curb sexual response.

    Answer: D Difficulty: 2 Page: 149

34. In the University of Virginia study of college undergraduates, how many heavy drinkers reported that under the influence of alcohol, they had sex with a person they would not ordinarily become involved with?
    (a) 60%
    (b) 50%
    (c) 40%
    (d) 30%

    Answer: B Difficulty: 3 Page: 150

35. Which statement is true regarding hallucinogens and sexual response?
    (a) Any enhancement of sexual response is dependent on dosage, expectations, and experiences.
    (b) In small amounts, hallucinogens increase sexual responsiveness by stimulating the autonomic nervous system.
    (c) Hallucinogens directly affect the sexual response centers in the brain.
    (d) Hallucinogens directly heighten sexual arousal by producing elevated mood.

    Answer: A Difficulty: 2 Page: 150

36. Which is not an example of an amphetamine?
    (a) LSD
    (b) speed
    (c) bennies
    (d) uppers

    Answer: A Difficulty: 2 Page: 151

37. Stimulants may heighten sexual arousal by
    (a) depressing the central nervous system.
    (b) dilating blood vessels throughout the body.
    (c) activating the central nervous system.
    (d) increasing testosterone levels.

    Answer: C Difficulty: 1 Page: 151

38. Which is not a part of the hindbrain?
    (a) thalamus
    (b) pons
    (c) cerebellum
    (d) medulla

    Answer: A Difficulty: 2 Page: 151

39. The brain area responsible for regulating vital functions such as heart rate and respiration is the
    (a) hypothalamus.
    (b) medulla.
    (c) pons.
    (d) reticular activating system.

    Answer: B Difficulty: 1 Page: 151

40. Which brain area is involved in balance and coordination?
    (a) cerebellum
    (b) hypothalamus
    (c) medulla
    (d) thalamus

    Answer: A Difficulty: 2 Page: 151

41. Which is not a role of the thalamus?
    (a) controlling body temperature
    (b) regulating sleep
    (c) relaying sensory information to the cerebral cortex
    (d) relaying information from the eyes to the visual areas of the brain

    Answer: A Difficulty: 2 Page: 152

42. Motivation, emotion, control of body temperature, and regulation of the menstrual cycle are just a few of the functions of the
    (a) thalamus.
    (b) pons.
    (c) cerebrum.
    (d) hypothalamus.

    Answer: D Difficulty: 1 Page: 152

43. Which is not true about the limbic system?
    (a) It is involved in memory.
    (b) It regulates the heart rate.
    (c) It consists of parts of the hypothalamus.
    (d) It contains the hippocampus and the septum.

    Answer: B Difficulty: 3 Page: 152

44. Evaluating whether sensory information is a sexual turn-off or turn-on is a function of the
    (a) hypothalamus.
    (b) cerebral cortex.
    (c) thalamus.
    (d) medulla.

    Answer: B Difficulty: 1 Page: 152

45. In experiments with rats, courting and mounting behavior increased when researchers stimulated the
    (a) hypothalamus.
    (b) cerebral cortex.
    (c) cerebellum.
    (d) reticular activating system.

    Answer: A Difficulty: 2 Page: 153

46. Heath (1972) reported orgasm-like sensations in two people when he electrically stimulated the
    (a) cerebral cortex.
    (b) lateral region of the medulla.
    (c) septal region of the limbic system.
    (d) reticular formation.

    Answer: C Difficulty: 2 Page: 153

47. Substances secreted by endocrine glands are called
    (a) neurotransmitters.
    (b) enkephalins.
    (c) hormones.
    (d) stimulants.

    Answer: C Difficulty: 1 Page: 154

48. Which is true regarding testosterone?
    (a) In males a small amount of testosterone is secreted by the testes and a large amount is secreted by the adrenal glands.
    (b) In both males and females, testosterone is produced in the pituitary gland and released by the adrenal glands.
    (c) In females estrogen and progesterone mask or cancel out the little testosterone that is produced.
    (d) Testosterone is secreted in small amounts by the adrenal glands in both genders, but in larger amounts by the testes.

    Answer: D Difficulty: 3 Page: 154

49. Estrogen and progesterone are produced by
    (a) the ovaries in females.
    (b) the testes in males and the ovaries in females.
    (c) the pituitary gland in both males and females.
    (d) the ovaries in females and the hypothalamus in males.

    Answer: B Difficulty: 2 Page: 154

50. In males and females, testosterone is produced in small amounts by the
    (a) hypothalamus.
    (b) ovaries and testes.
    (c) adrenal glands.
    (d) pituitary gland.

    Answer: C Difficulty: 1 Page: 154

51. Which of the following is not a secondary sex characteristic?
    (a) lengthening of the vocal cords in males
    (b) breast development in females
    (c) pubic hair growth in males and females
    (d) maturation of ova in the female

    Answer: D Difficulty: 2 Page: 154

52. An example of the activating effect of sex hormones is
    (a) sex drive.
    (b) masculine mating behavior.
    (c) organization of the brain in a feminine direction.
    (d) differentiation of tissues into male or female genitalia.

    Answer: A Difficulty: 2 Page: 154

53. When sex hormones influence the type of sexual behavior that is expressed, it is called
    (a) a directional effect.
    (b) an organizational effect.
    (c) an adrogenizing effect.
    (d) an activating effect.

    Answer: B Difficulty: 2 Page: 154

54. Which is true regarding sex hormones?
    (a) Sex hormones act on the body and exert little influence over the brain.
    (b) Prenatal sex hormones organize the brain in masculine or feminine directions.
    (c) Sex hormones determine the differentiation of gonads but do not play a role in sexual orientation.
    (d) Prenatal alterations in sex hormones have no impact on adult sexual behavior.

    Answer: B Difficulty: 3 Page: 155

55. Researchers speculate that transsexual individuals may have
    (a) a mismatch between brain sexual organization and the differentiation of their genitals.
    (b) been exposed to large amounts of estrogen in the womb.
    (c) been socialized to behave in ways that are opposite to their brain sexual organization.
    (d) inherited an extra X or Y chromosome.

    Answer: A Difficulty: 2 Page: 155

56. Because of testicular cancer, Donald had to have both testes removed. As a result of the surgery, he can expect
    (a) little change in sexual desire.
    (b) a sudden and dramatic decrease in his ability to achieve or maintain an erection.
    (c) a gradual decrease in sexual desire and performance.
    (d) no decrease in sexual desire but a dramatic increase in his ability to achieve an erection.

    Answer: C Difficulty: 2 Page: 156

57. Hypogonadism is a condition where the
    (a) testes produce an overabundance of testosterone.
    (b) testes or ovaries produce an overabundance of sex hormones.
    (c) ovaries do not produce enough estrogen.
    (d) testes do not produce enough testosterone.

    Answer: D Difficulty: 2 Page: 156

58. Which is true regarding female hormones?
    (a) Estrogen plays a vital role in sex drive but progesterone does not.
    (b) Adequate levels of both estrogen and progesterone are required to activate sexual interest.
    (c) Progesterone plays the more important role in a female's sex drive and response.
    (d) Neither estrogen nor progesterone plays a role in sex drive or response.

    Answer: D Difficulty: 3 Page: 156

59. Estrus occurs
    (a) in lower mammals at the time of ovulation.
    (b) in both lower mammals and human females as estrogen levels fall.
    (c) in human females just prior to menstruation.
    (d) in human females and lower mammals during the menstrual period.

    Answer: A Difficulty: 2 Page: 156

60. If a female continues to be motivated sexually but starts experiencing vaginal dryness that makes intercourse painful, she may not be producing enough
    (a) testosterone.
    (b) estradiol.
    (c) progesterone.
    (d) androgen.

    Answer: B Difficulty: 2 Page: 156

61. Some researchers have noted that a woman's sexual activity increases at points in the menstrual cycle when
    (a) estrogen levels are high.
    (b) androgen levels in the bloodstream are high.
    (c) both progesterone and estrogen levels are high.
    (d) progesterone levels in the bloodstream drop.

    Answer: B Difficulty: 3 Page: 157

62. According to Masters and Johnson which is not a phase in the sexual response cycle?
    (a) foreplay
    (b) plateau
    (c) orgasm
    (d) resolution

Answer: A Difficulty: 1 Page: 158

63. For a female, how soon does vaginal lubrication begin after stimulation?
    (a) immediately
    (b) 10 to 30 seconds
    (c) about one minute
    (d) about two minutes

Answer: B Difficulty: 2 Page: 158

64. In the sexual response cycle, myotonia refers to
    (a) increased respiration.
    (b) blood pressure spikes.
    (c) dilation of the blood vessels.
    (d) muscle tension.

Answer: D Difficulty: 3 Page: 158

65. The second phase of Masters and Johnson's sexual response cycle is the
    (a) resolution phase.
    (b) refractory phase.
    (c) plateau phase.
    (d) orgasmic phase.

Answer: C Difficulty: 1 Page: 159

66. The phase of Masters and Johnson's sexual response cycle where excitement neither increases nor decreases if stimulation continues is called the
    (a) refractory phase.
    (b) plateau phase.
    (c) excitement phase.
    (d) resolution phase.

Answer: B Difficulty: 1 Page: 159

67. In females, vasocongestion swells the clitoris, flattens the labia majora, and increases the size of the labia minora in the
    (a) excitement phase.
    (b) plateau phase.
    (c) orgasmic phase.
    (d) resolution phase.

Answer: A Difficulty: 1 Page: 159

68. The term "sex flush" refers to
    (a) a darkening of the labia to a deep wine color.
    (b) the darkening of vaginal secretions during orgasm.
    (c) dilation of the capillaries in the skin.
    (d) the flow of blood to the vaginal area during sexual stimulation.

Answer: B Difficulty: 1 Page: 160

69. Which of the following is an indication that a male is in the plateau phase?
    (a) erection occurs
    (b) the scrotal skin thickens
    (c) Cowper's glands secrete a few drops of fluid
    (d) seminal fluid collects in the urethral bulb

    Answer: C Difficulty: 2 Page: 159

70. Orgasm in the female results in contractions of the
    (a) vaginal barrel, uterus, and anal sphincter.
    (b) uterus only.
    (c) vaginal barrel and urethral bulb.
    (d) uterus and urethra.

    Answer: A Difficulty: 3 Page: 160

71. What is not true regarding the orgasmic phase?
    (a) It consists of three stages.
    (b) In males it consists of muscular contractions.
    (c) The internal sphincter of the urinary bladder contracts preventing seminal fluid
        from entering the bladder in a backward, retrograde ejaculation.
    (d) In the second stage, the external sphincter of the bladder relaxes, allowing the
        passage of semen.

    Answer: A Difficulty: 2 Page: 160

72. The period following orgasm, in which the body returns to its prearoused state is called
    the
    (a) final phase.
    (b) rest phase.
    (c) resolution phase.
    (d) relaxing phase.

    Answer: C Difficulty: 1 Page: 162

73. What propels ejaculate through the urethra and out of the body?
    (a) relaxation of the vas deferens and prostate gland
    (b) contraction of the external sphincter of the bladder
    (c) contractions of the muscles surrounding the urethral bulb and base of the penis
    (d) contractions of the vas deferens, seminal vesicles, and prostate gland

    Answer: C Difficulty: 2 Page: 162

74. The term "refractory period" refers to the
    (a) relaxation and drowsiness that follows orgasm and leads to sleep.
    (b) return of the labia and orgasmic platform to an unexcited state.
    (c) post-orgasmic period when men cannot be restimulated to erection.
    (d) period where both men's and women's bodies return to an unstimulated state.

    Answer: C Difficulty: 2 Page: 162

75. Masters and Johnson's and Kaplan's models of sexual response are similar in that
    vasocongestion takes place in the
    (a) excitement phase.
    (b) desire phase.
    (c) orgasmic phase.
    (d) resolution phase.

    Answer: A Difficulty: 1 Page: 163

76. Kaplan's model differs from Masters and Johnson's model because Kaplan emphasizes
    (a) the neurological basis of desire.
    (b) psychological factors in sexual motivation.
    (c) sexual responses during masturbation.
    (d) gender differences in sexual responsiveness.

    Answer: B Difficulty: 2 Page: 163

77. Who developed the three-stage model for sexual response?
    (a) Masters
    (b) Kaplan
    (c) Johnson
    (d) Grafenberg

    Answer: B Difficulty: 1 Page: 163

78. Nick finds the idea of sexual activity repulsive. Even when he is with men or women he
    likes, sexual thoughts never enter his mind. According to Kaplan's model, Nick might be
    diagnosed as having a problem with
    (a) excitement.
    (b) desire.
    (c) orgasm.
    (d) resolution.

    Answer: B Difficulty: 1 Page: 163

79. Who said that multiple orgasm involves the occurrence of one or more additional orgasms
    following the first, within a short period of time and before the body has returned to a
    pre-plateau level of arousal?
    (a) Kinsey
    (b) Masters and Johnson
    (c) Freud
    (d) Singer

    Answer: B Difficulty: 2 Page: 164

80. A "dry orgasm"
    (a) is an orgasm where a woman fails to ejaculate fluid from the Skene's glands.
    (b) is an orgasm produced through masturbation rather than vaginal intercourse.
    (c) is a series of uterine orgasms resulting from deep intravaginal penetration.
    (d) is a male orgasm occurring without ejaculation.

    Answer: D Difficulty: 1 Page: 164

81. According to Singer and Singer (1972), the vulval orgasm is a
    (a) clitoral orgasm.
    (b) uterine orgasm.
    (c) blended orgasm.
    (d) cervical orgasm.

    Answer: A Difficulty: 2 Page: 166

82. According to the Singers, the uterine orgasm does not involve
    (a) vulva contractions.
    (b) the G-spot.
    (c) ejaculation.
    (d) discharge.

    Answer: A Difficulty: 1 Page: 166

83. The G-spot is believed to be
    (a) deep within the vagina on the posterior wall.
    (b) about 1 to 2 inches from the vaginal entrance on the anterior wall of the vagina.
    (c) near the cervix on the posterior wall of the vagina.
    (d) about 5-6 inches from the vaginal entrance on the anterior wall of the vagina.

    Answer: B Difficulty: 1 Page: 166

84. What is not true about the G-spot?
    (a) It's about 1 to 2 inches from the vaginal entrance on the anterior wall of the vagina.
    (b) It is sometimes called the master spot.
    (c) It was named after Ernest Grafenberg.
    (d) Stimulation of the G-spot produces intense erotic sensations.

    Answer: B Difficulty: 2 Page: 166

85. Female "ejaculation" may result from the release of fluids from
    (a) Bartholin's glands.
    (b) the bladder.
    (c) Skene's glands.
    (d) the cervix.

    Answer: C Difficulty: 2 Page: 167

MATCHING

For each of the following events in the sexual response cycle, match the event with the correct phase in Master and Johnson's model. Responses can be used more than once.

(a) Excitement Phase

(b) Plateau Phase

(c) Orgasmic Phase

(d) Resolution Phase

86. Contractions occur in the pelvic muscles surrounding the vaginal barrel.

    Answer: c

87. Vasocongestion causes the penis to become erect.

    Answer: a

88. The coronal ridge swells and the glans turn a deeper reddish purple.

    Answer: b

89. The vagina lubricates.

    Answer: a

90. Clitoris retracts back under the prepuce.

    Answer: b

91. Blood from the corpora cavernosa empties into other parts of the body.

    Answer: d

92. The uterus drops back to its normal position.

    Answer: d

93. Cowper's glands release a few drops of fluid at the tip of the penis.

    Answer: b

94. The testes increase in size and are fully elevated.

    Answer: b

95. Seminal fluid collects in the urethral bulb at the base of the penis.

    Answer: c

TRUE/FALSE

96. While humans possess a vomeronasal organ, its role in sexual behavior is not well understood.

    Answer: True

97. The brain is not an erogenous zone because it is not stimulated directly by touch.

    Answer: True

98. Viagra is an aphrodisiac because it facilitates erection.

    Answer: False

99. The sagest and most effective method of increasing sex drive is exercise.

    Answer: True

100. In females, androgens can only be produced in the adrenal glands.

    Answer: False

101. The differentiation of the genitalia into male or female genitalia is an example of the activating effects of the sex hormones.

    Answer: False

102. The term "sex skin" refers to the coloration of the chest and abdomen during sexual arousal.

    Answer: False

103. In the first stage of a male orgasm, seminal fluids collect in the urethral bulb.

    Answer: True

104. Studies suggest that male and female orgasms feel very similar.

    Answer: True

105. Males can orgasm without ejaculation.

    Answer: True

106. According to Singer and Singer (1972), a vulval orgasm is different than the orgasm described by Masters and Johnson.

    Answer: False

107. Some researchers suggest that stimulation of the G-spot will produce a uterine orgasm.

    Answer: True

108. The menstrual cycles of women who live together tend to synchronize.

    Answer: True

109. The brain is a primary erogenous zone.

Answer: False

110. There is evidence that marijuana and other hallucinogenic drugs directly stimulate sexual response.

Answer: False

111. The hypothalamus and pituitary gland regulate gonadal secretion of sex hormones, specifically testosterone in males and estrogen and progesterone in females.

Answer: True

112. In terms of psychological measurement, orgasms attained through masturbation appear to be more "intense" than those attained through coitus.

Answer: True

ESSAY

113. Outline the roles that each of the five senses might play in human sexual motivation and response.

Answer:

114. Summarize information about the effects of alcohol on sexual response, performance, and decision making.

Answer:

115. Explain the separate and combined roles of the spinal reflexes and the cerebral cortex in sexual response.

Answer:

116. Differentiate between the organizing and activating effects of the sex hormones by citing examples of activating and organizing effects in animal or human studies.

Answer:

117. Discuss the similarities and differences between Masters and Johnson's sexual response cycle and Kaplan's sexual response model.

Answer:

118. Explain the physiological events in the two stages of male orgasm.

Answer:

119. Differentiate between Singer and Singer's vulval, uterine, and blended orgasm in females.

Answer:

Chapter 6: Gender Identity and Gender Roles

MULTIPLE CHOICE

1. Sexual differentiation means
   (a) the process by which males and females develop distinct reproductive anatomy.
   (b) the complex behavior patterns deemed masculine or feminine in a particular culture.
   (c) differences in the preconceptions held regarding men and women.
   (d) the process by which children distinguish between expectations of girls and of boys.

   Answer: A Difficulty: 2 Page: 172

2. A fertilized ovum is called a
   (a) formation.
   (b) zygote.
   (c) embryo.
   (d) fetus.

   Answer: B Difficulty: 2 Page: 172

3. In the fertilization process, chromosomes from each parent combine to form
   (a) 23 chromosomes.
   (b) 23 pairs of chromosomes.
   (c) 46 pairs of chromosomes.
   (d) 92 chromosomes.

   Answer: B Difficulty: 1 Page: 172

4. During the first six weeks of development, embryonic structures of both genders resemble
   (a) primitive male structures.
   (b) primitive female structures.
   (c) both male and female structures.
   (d) neither male nor female structures.

   Answer: B Difficulty: 2 Page: 173

5. Sexual differentiation of gonads, genital ducts, and external genitals begins about
   (a) seven weeks after conception.
   (b) nine weeks after conception.
   (c) twelve weeks after conception.
   (d) fifteen weeks after conception.

   Answer: A Difficulty: 2 Page: 173

6. The 23rd pair of chromosomes determines
   (a) gender.
   (b) eye color.
   (c) height.
   (d) weight.

   Answer: A Difficulty: 1 Page: 173

7. An embryo at 5 to 6 weeks is on average
   (a) 1/4 to 1/2 inch long.
   (b) 1 to 2 inches long.
   (c) 1/8 inch long.
   (d) 2 to 3 inches long.

   Answer: A Difficulty: 2 Page: 173

8. The basic blueprint of the human embryo is
   (a) male.
   (b) neither male nor female.
   (c) female.
   (d) both male and female.

   Answer: C Difficulty: 1 Page: 173

9. Which of the following statements is true?
   (a) The "natural course" of embryonic development is male.
   (b) The absence of a Y chromosome alters the developmental course from male to female.
   (c) The presence of only one X chromosome, instead of two, will result in a male fetus.
   (d) The presence of a Y chromosome alters the developmental course from female to male.

   Answer: D Difficulty: 2 Page: 173

10. Around the 7th week of development, the Y chromosome stimulates the production of
    (a) testosterone.
    (b) H-Y antigen.
    (c) dihydrotestosterone (DHT).
    (d) Mullerian inhibiting substance (MIS).

    Answer: B Difficulty: 1 Page: 174

11. Fruit fly researchers conclude that sex determination, sexual orientation, and sexual behavior patterns are all determined by the interactions of
    (a) chromosomes.
    (b) genes.
    (c) transformers.
    (d) DNA molecules.

    Answer: B Difficulty: 1 Page: 174

12. If it weren't for ____, we would all develop into ____.
    (a) androgens; females
    (b) estrogen; females
    (c) progesterone; males
    (d) oxygen ions; males

    Answer: A Difficulty: 1 Page: 174

13. SRY stands for the
    (a) sterilized X chromosome.
    (b) sterilized Y chromosome.
    (c) surrogate response on the Y gene.
    (d) sex-determining region Y gene.

    Answer: D Difficulty: 1 Page: 174

14. In male sexual differentiation, each Wolffian duct differentiates into
    (a) the penis.
    (b) an epididymus, vas deferens, and seminal vesicle.
    (c) each of the two testes.
    (d) the scrotum.

    Answer: B Difficulty: 2 Page: 175

15. Differentiation of fetal tissues into external male genitals occurs under the influence of
    (a) testosterone.
    (b) Mullerian inhibiting substance (MIS)
    (c) H-Y antigen.
    (d) dihydrotestosterone (DHT).

    Answer: D Difficulty: 2 Page: 175

16. In female sexual differentiation, which statement is correct?
    (a) The Mullerian ducts develop into the fallopian tubes, the uterus, and the upper two-thirds of the vagina.
    (b) The Mullerian ducts develop into the fallopian tubes and the Wolffian ducts develop into the uterus.
    (c) The Mullerian ducts degenerate and the Wolffian ducts develop into the labia majora, labia minora, and the vaginal opening.
    (d) The Wolffian ducts develop into the fallopian tubes, the ovaries, and the vagina.

    Answer: A Difficulty: 3 Page: 175

17. In males, the testes develop in the
    (a) scrotum.
    (b) rectum.
    (c) abdomen.
    (d) intestines.

    Answer: C Difficulty: 1 Page: 175

18. About four months after conception, the testes normally descend into the scrotal sac through the
    (a) inguinal canal.
    (b) pancreas.
    (c) adriotic canal.
    (d) prostate.

    Answer: A Difficulty: 2 Page: 175

19. Testosterone is a type of
    (a) chemical.
    (b) androgen.
    (c) gene.
    (d) fluid.

    Answer: B Difficulty: 1 Page: 175

20. For most males, the testes descend into the scrotal sac at about
    (a) 4 weeks after conception.
    (b) 7 weeks after conception.
    (c) 10 weeks after conception.
    (d) 16 weeks after conception.

    Answer: B Difficulty: 3 Page: 175

21. Failure of the testes to descend is called
    (a) Klinefelter syndrome.
    (b) Turner syndrome.
    (c) pseudo hermaphroditism.
    (d) cryptorchidism.

    Answer: D Difficulty: 1 Page: 175

22. Enrico has a genetic condition that has rendered him infertile because he cannot produce any sperm. In addition, he exhibits mild mental retardation and poor motor coordination. Enrico most likely suffers from
(a) Turner syndrome.
(b) Klinefelter syndrome.
(c) androgen-insensitivity syndrome.
(d) androgenital syndrome.

Answer: B Difficulty: 1 Page: 176

23. Turner syndrome
(a) is marked by the presence of an extra X chromosome in a male.
(b) occurs when a genetic (XX) female possesses masculinized external genitals.
(c) is marked by the loss of some genetic material from an X chromosome in a female.
(d) occurs when a male possesses an extra Y chromosome.

Answer: C Difficulty: 2 Page: 176

24. In the absence of testosterone, as in female fetuses, the hypothalamus develops sensitivity to
(a) testosterone.
(b) glycotesone.
(c) embriotic fluid.
(d) estrogen.

Answer: D Difficulty: 1 Page: 176

25. Sexual differentiation of the hypothalamus most likely occurs during the
(a) third trimester.
(b) second trimester.
(c) second half of the first trimester.
(d) first half of the first trimester.

Answer: B Difficulty: 2 Page: 176

26. Most children acquire a firm sense of gender identity by the age of
(a) one.
(b) two.
(c) three.
(d) four.

Answer: C Difficulty: 3 Page: 176

27. Hermaphroditism describes an individual who
(a) has a genetic pattern of either XXY or XYY.
(b) is a genetic (XX) female with masculinized external genitals.
(c) has one gonad from each gender or gonads that combine testicular and ovarian tissue.
(d) is a genetic male (XY) with feminized external genitals.

Answer: C Difficulty: 3 Page: 177

28. Erica was born with androgenital syndrome. She has female internal organs but a clitorus so enlarged it resembles a small penis. What is the cause of her masculinized external genitals?
(a) excessive levels of androgens
(b) a higher-than-normal sensitivity to androgens
(c) a lower-than-normal sensitivity to estrogens
(d) excessive production of estrogen and progesterone

Answer: A Difficulty: 2 Page: 177

29. Which of the following is a genetic enzyme disorder preventing masculinization of the external genitals?
    (a) Dominican Republic syndrome
    (b) Klinefelter syndrome
    (c) Turner syndrome
    (d) androgen-insensitivity syndrome

    Answer: A Difficulty: 3 Page: 177

30. Which of the following conclusions can be drawn from studies of pseudohermaphrodites?
    (a) Gender identity is fixed at birth.
    (b) Gender identity is not necessarily fixed in early childhood but is malleable.
    (c) Gender identity is largely influenced by biological factors.
    (d) Gender identity is minimally influenced by environmental factors.

    Answer: B Difficulty: 2 Page: 178

31. Studies of children who are pseudohermaphrodites suggest that
    (a) the appearance of external genitalia is the best indicator of gender identity.
    (b) greater success in coping with ambiguous genitalia results when the children are raised as females.
    (c) children should be raised as females unless their testes descend.
    (d) environmental influences may play a critical role in shaping the gender identity.

    Answer: D Difficulty: 3 Page: 178

32. Transsexuals are also called
    (a) transposed individuals.
    (b) transgendered individuals.
    (c) transassociated individuals.
    (d) transfigured individuals.

    Answer: B Difficulty: 2 Page: 179

33. The main feature of transsexualism is
    (a) cross-dressing.
    (b) homosexuality.
    (c) gender-reassignment surgery.
    (d) gender dysphoria.

    Answer: D Difficulty: 1 Page: 181

34. Experts estimate the number of transsexuals in the United States to be around
    (a) 10,000.
    (b) 15,000.
    (c) 25,000.
    (d) 35,000.

    Answer: C Difficulty: 3 Page: 181

35. Which of the following statements is true regarding transsexuals?
    (a) They are attracted to members of their own sex and regard themselves as homosexual.
    (b) Patterns of sexual attraction do not appear to be of central importance.
    (c) They are attracted to members of the opposite sex.
    (d) Most are aware of their transsexual feelings early in childhood.

    Answer: B Difficulty: 2 Page: 181

36. According to the text, transsexuals usually
    (a) show cross-gender preferences in play and dress early in childhood.
    (b) have very rigid notions of gender and the behaviors associated with gender.
    (c) are aware of their transsexual feelings very early in childhood.
    (d) do not show cross-gender preferences in play or dress until adolescence.

    Answer: A Difficulty: 2 Page: 181

37. According to psychoanalytic theory, transsexual males may have
    (a) had close-binding fathers.
    (b) had prenatal hormonal imbalances.
    (c) had close-binding mothers and detached-hostile fathers.
    (d) smaller than normal regions in the hypothalamus.

    Answer: C Difficulty: 1 Page: 182

38. Before gender reassignment surgery, transsexuals are asked to live as the desired sex for at least
    (a) 3 years.
    (b) 1 year.
    (c) 6 months.
    (d) 3 months.

    Answer: B Difficulty: 2 Page: 183

39. Which is *true* regarding sex-reassignment surgery for female to male reassignment?
    (a) The urethra is rerouted through the enlarged clitoris.
    (b) The ovaries are removed but the uterus and vagina kept intact.
    (c) An artificial penis is constructed that can become naturally erect.
    (d) The uterus and breasts are removed but the ovaries are kept intact.

    Answer: A Difficulty: 1 Page: 183

40. The Gender Identity Project in New York City's Greenwich Village helps
    (a) transsexuals.
    (b) people with Dominican Republic syndrome.
    (c) people with Turner syndrome.
    (d) pseudohermaphrodites.

    Answer: A Difficulty: 2 Page: 186

41. In reviews of the international literature on sex-reassignment surgery in 1984, what did researchers conclude?
    (a) About 90% of transsexuals who undergo gender-reassignment surgery report positive results.
    (b) Psychological adjustment is more positive for transsexuals who do not undergo gender-reassignment surgery.
    (c) Sex-reassignment surgery resulted in much higher self-esteem and social adjustment for most transsexuals.
    (d) About 50% of transsexuals having undergone reassignment surgery had disturbing outcomes ranging from requests for reversal surgery to suicide.

    Answer: A Difficulty: 2 Page: 186

42. Postoperative adjustment for transsexuals is more favorable for
    (a) males to females.
    (b) females to males.
    (c) both directions are equally favorable.
    (d) postoperative adjustment is only in its idea phase.

    Answer: B Difficulty: 1 Page: 186

43. Stephen believes that women are too emotional and easily distracted for the tough, competitive world of business. As a result, he hires many women but they always end up being assistants to the men in his company. Stephen's fixed ideas are typical of
    (a) most men.
    (b) machismo.
    (c) acculturation.
    (d) stereotyping.

    Answer: D Difficulty: 2 Page: 187

44. Gender identity is defined as
    (a) the roles or behaviors we personally identify with our sex.
    (b) an individual's self-concept of masculinity or femininity.
    (c) a culture's broad expectations of men and women.
    (d) the stereotypical behaviors associated with male or femaleness in a culture.

    Answer: B Difficulty: 1 Page: 187

45. Which of the following is a stereotype frequently used to describe women?
    (a) arrogant
    (b) affectionate
    (c) autocratic
    (d) active

    Answer: B Difficulty: 1 Page: 187

46. Which of the following is a stereotype frequently used to describe men?
    (a) understanding
    (b) talkative
    (c) imaginative
    (d) realistic

    Answer: D Difficulty: 1 Page: 187

47. John Money stated, "...a child assimilates and lives it, is inhabited by it, has it as a belonging, and manifests it to others...in word and deed" (Money, 1994, p. 166). What is the "it" that Money refers to in this statement?
    (a) gender identity
    (b) biological sex
    (c) gender role
    (d) gender polarization

    Answer: C Difficulty: 2 Page: 187

48. The Hispanic concept, *marianismo*, describes a stereotype in which
    (a) a virtuous woman is a woman who "suffers in silence."
    (b) a male is expected to be strong, virile, and dominant.
    (c) a woman is expected to disclose feelings and personal experiences.
    (d) a male is expected to be strong and virile yet expressive of his feelings.

    Answer: A Difficulty: 3 Page: 187

49. The prejudgment that gender implies certain negative traits is called
    (a) gender stereotyping.
    (b) sexism.
    (c) trait disorientation.
    (d) gender misconception.

    Answer: B Difficulty: 1 Page: 188

50. Mario sees women as incapable of making intellectual decisions and believes that their emotions will always cause them to buckle under pressure. Mario's ideas regarding women exemplify
    (a) gender identity.
    (b) gender roles.
    (c) sexism.
    (d) machismo.

    Answer: C Difficulty: 2 Page: 189

51. At about what age do children begin to show preferences for gender-typed activities?
    (a) 12 — 18 months
    (b) 2 — 3 years
    (c) 4 — 6 years
    (d) 7 — 9 years

    Answer: B Difficulty: 2 Page: 189

52. According to a 1995 Harris Poll, of working women
    (a) about half provide at least half of the family income.
    (b) about one third provide at least half the family income.
    (c) most work to simply supplement their husbands' income.
    (d) most women would prefer to be at home raising their children instead of working.

    Answer: A Difficulty: 3 Page: 189

53. Despite larger numbers of women in the workplace, how many still bear the responsibility for the children, cooking and cleaning?
    (a) 100%
    (b) 90%
    (c) 75%
    (d) 60%

    Answer: B Difficulty: 2 Page: 189

54. In terms of gender and verbal ability
    (a) females are superior at verbal skills across the life span.
    (b) early studies found no differences in abilities, but recent studies find females superior at verbal skills.
    (c) recent studies found no overall gender differences but boys are slower to develop language skills.
    (d) males excel in verbal abilities until adolescence when females begin to excel.

    Answer: C Difficulty: 2 Page: 189

55. Males generally exceed females in
    (a) verbal problem solving skills.
    (b) visual-spatial abilities.
    (c) science.
    (d) computational math during elementary school.

    Answer: B Difficulty: 1 Page: 189

56. On the SAT
    (a) twice as many boys as girls score over 500 in the mathematics test.
    (b) twice as many girls as boys score over 500 in the analogies test.
    (c) any differences between boys and girls in the mathematics test are negligible.
    (d) the new emphasis on math skills for girls is closing the gap between male and female math performance.

    Answer: A Difficulty: 2 Page: 189

57. Gender differences in intellectual abilities are best explained by
    (a) differences in innate ability.
    (b) differences in temperament.
    (c) differences in development.
    (d) differences in cultural expectations.

    Answer: D Difficulty: 2 Page: 190

58. In terms of physical strength
    (a) there is little difference, pound for pound, between male and female strength.
    (b) males have more upper body strength than females.
    (c) females have more lower body strength than males.
    (d) when matched for body weight and type, males have both more upper and lower body strength than females.

    Answer: B Difficulty: 1 Page: 190

59. Eric is rapidly approaching puberty. As a result, what body changes can he expect?
    (a) A greater amount of fat will be stored in his hips and thighs.
    (b) The density of his bones will increase and his pelvis will broaden.
    (c) He will experience a rapid increase in height, bone density, and muscle.
    (d) Testosterone production will lead to an increase in overall body fat.

    Answer: C Difficulty: 3 Page: 190

60. At puberty, female production of estrogen and progesterone results in
    (a) an increase in body fat.
    (b) an increase in lean muscle mass.
    (c) a decrease in lower body strength.
    (d) a decrease in overall heart rate.

    Answer: A Difficulty: 1 Page: 190

61. In terms of cardiovascular differences, after puberty
    (a) females have higher concentrations of hemoglobin-rich red blood cells than males.
    (b) females have lower resting heart rates than males.
    (c) males have larger heart size and a slower heart rate than females.
    (d) cardiorespiratory endurance is 28% higher for females than males.

    Answer: C Difficulty: 2 Page: 190

62. According to a meta-analysis of the research literature on male and female personality differences, females exceed males in
    (a) self-esteem.
    (b) extraversion.
    (c) assertiveness.
    (d) tough-mindedness.

    Answer: B Difficulty: 1 Page: 190

63. Which statement *best* reflects differences in communication between the genders?
    (a) Women talk more than men do but men disclose more personal experiences.
    (b) Men talk more than women do but disclose fewer personal feelings.
    (c) Boys tend to be more talkative in early childhood, but by elementary school, girls dominate the classroom.
    (d) Boys tend to verbally dominate the elementary school classroom, but by high school, girls clearly dominate.

    Answer: B Difficulty: 2 Page: 190

64. According to the ____ perspective, the story of the survival of our ancient ancestors is etched in our genes.
    (a) biological
    (b) evolutionary
    (c) psychological
    (d) social-learning

    Answer: B Difficulty: 2 Page: 191

65. The average life expectancy of men is seven years less than for females. Which statement most accurately reflects this difference?
    (a) Testosterone has more damaging effects on the body.
    (b) Females are more physically fit than males across the life span.
    (c) Men are often reluctant to seek health care.
    (d) Men tend to place themselves in more physical danger than women.

    Answer: C Difficulty: 2 Page: 191

66. Dr. Jameson believes that males are better suited to hunting because of physical attributes such as greater upper-body strength. He further believes that this attribute was selected to increase survival. What perspective is Dr. Jameson advocating?
    (a) biological
    (b) sociobiological
    (c) cross-cultural
    (d) psychological

    Answer: B Difficulty: 2 Page: 192

67. Prenatal sexual differentiation of the brain may explain why
    (a) females have a larger right hemisphere and are more verbal.
    (b) males have a larger left-hemisphere and are superior at visual-spatial tasks.
    (c) females have a larger hypothalamic region than males.
    (d) males have more growth in the right hemisphere than in the left.

    Answer: D Difficulty: 2 Page: 192

68. In Margaret Mead's studies in New Guinea, males in the Tchambuli tribe
    (a) cared for children, wore makeup, and gossiped.
    (b) cared for children alongside the females.
    (c) were aggressive and warlike.
    (d) nurtured the children but were more aggressive than females sexually.

    Answer: A Difficulty: 2 Page: 192

69. According to Freud, gender typing is best explained in terms of
    (a) the oral stage of psychosexual development.
    (b) identification with the same-gender parent.
    (c) the modeling of sex-role behaviors children witness from parents.
    (d) socialization.

    Answer: B Difficulty: 3 Page: 194

70. Five-year old Tyler came home one day wearing makeup. He and his five-year old playmate, Anna, had been playing dress-up. His father was furious, ordered his son to immediately wash off the makeup, and would not allow him to play with Anna again. What process is Tyler's father using to teach gender-typing?
    (a) modeling
    (b) identification
    (c) observational learning
    (d) socialization

    Answer: D Difficulty: 3 Page: 194

71. Social-learning theorists believe that aggression is largely influenced by
    (a) predisposition.
    (b) learning.
    (c) our genetic makeup.
    (d) environment.

    Answer: B Difficulty: 1 Page: 196

72. In Kohlberg's cognitive-developmental theory, gender typing involves three concepts
    (a) gender identity, gender stability, and gender constancy.
    (b) gender identity, extrinsic rewards, and parental identification.
    (c) gender constancy, identification, and modeling.
    (d) gender stability, gender constancy, and gender play.

    Answer: A Difficulty: 2 Page: 197

73. Julie is 2 years old. She knows that she is a girl but talks about growing up and being a daddy. She does not yet have an understanding of
    (a) gender identity.
    (b) gender stability.
    (c) gender constancy.
    (d) gender permanence.

    Answer: B Difficulty: 2 Page: 197

74. The complex cognitive network of ideas through which a child interprets and organizes information about gender is called a
    (a) sex role.
    (b) gender stereotype.
    (c) gender pattern.
    (d) gender schema.

    Answer: D Difficulty: 1 Page: 197

75. To Anika, a five-year-old, it is clear that girls do not play football, climb trees, hit others, or play "Army." Instead, girls play "Barbie," school, draw, or play hopscotch. According to Sandra Bem, Anika can be described as
    (a) sexually differentiated.
    (b) having a self-concept that is inconsistent with cultural views of femaleness.
    (c) being highly gender-schematic.
    (d) having low self-esteem.

    Answer: C Difficulty: 1 Page: 197

76. The double standard that "it is natural for men to sow their wild oats," but women who choose to do so are "nymphomaniacs," supports a long-held stereotype that women
    (a) do not enjoy sex as much as men.
    (b) are readily aroused and sexual.
    (c) know more about sex than men.
    (d) are sexually aggressive.

    Answer: A Difficulty: 2 Page: 199

77. It was widely believed in the ____ period that women were naturally asexual and "unbothered" by sexual desires.
    (a) Renaissance
    (b) Victorian
    (c) Tahitian
    (d) antediluvian

    Answer: B Difficulty: 2 Page: 199

78. Psychological androgeny is a term used to describe
    (a) males who display more feminine than masculine traits.
    (b) males and females who display high assertion and instrumental skills.
    (c) females who display more masculine than feminine traits.
    (d) males and females who display both masculine and feminine traits.

    Answer: D Difficulty: 2 Page: 199

79. Psychologically androgenous persons tend to have
    (a) higher self-esteem then people who are masculine or undifferentiated.
    (b) lower self-esteem than persons who are undifferentiated.
    (c) higher self-esteem than people who are feminine or undifferentiated.
    (d) lower self-esteem than persons who are feminine.

    Answer: C Difficulty: 2 Page: 200

MATCHING

Match the disorder with the correct description of its symptoms and/or cause.

(a) Klinefelter Syndrome

(b) Hermaphroditism

(c) Androgenital Syndrome

(d) Turner Syndrome

(e) Androgen-Insensitivity Syndrome

(f) Transsexualism

(g) Dominican Republic Syndrome

80. Males possess an extra X chromosome, resulting in enlarged breasts, poor muscular development, and infertility.

    Answer: a

81. Genetic XY males who had a lower-than-normal prenatal sensitivity to androgens.

    Answer: e

82. Females who are missing part of the genetic material on the X chromosomes and do not develop ovaries or have ovaries that fail to function normally.

    Answer: d

83. An individual who possesses either one ovary and one testicle or gonads that combine testicular and ovarian tissue.

    Answer: b

84. A genetic female with female internal structures but masculinized genitals.

    Answer: c

85. A genetic enzyme disorder that prevents testosterone from masculinizing the external genitalia.

    Answer: g

86. A feeling of incongruity between one's genital anatomy and one's gender role of identity.

Answer: f

TRUE/FALSE

87. Gender roles are stereotypes because they evoke fixed expectations of men and women.

Answer: True

88. When asked whether they would give up their work responsibilities to stay at home raising children, 48% of women said yes.

Answer: False

89. Differences in verbal, mathematical, and spatial abilities between males and females are getting larger.

Answer: False

90. Even when body fat is taken into account, males still have greater cardiorespiratory endurance than females.

Answer: True

91. Research has shown that women talk more, introduce new topics more readily, and interrupt others more often than men.

Answer: False

92. Sociobiologists believe that biology is *not* destiny, that our behavior is not dictated by our genes.

Answer: False

93. In males, testosterone spurs the growth of the right hemisphere and slows the growth of the left hemisphere.

Answer: True

94. Freud believed that through identification with the same-gender parent, children adopt gender-typed behaviors typically associated with gender.

Answer: True

95. In interactions with infants, fathers handle boy and girl infants differently.

Answer: True

96. Of the institutions children are exposed to, schools may be the biggest offenders of gender stereotyping.

Answer: True

97. In the popular media, men are often portrayed as struggling with role conflicts.

Answer: False

98. Gender stability is the recognition that people retain their genders for a lifetime.

Answer: True

99. Children who develop self-concepts that are consistent with the prominent gender schema of their culture have lower self-esteem.

Answer: False

100. The zygote, the beginning of a new human being, is only 1/175 of an inch long.

Answer: True

101. We would all develop female sexual organs if male sex hormones were not present during critical stages of prenatal development.

    Answer: True

102. Klinefelter syndrome is a sex chromosomal disorder caused by loss of some X chromosomal material.

    Answer: False

103. The boys with Dominican Republic Syndrome resembled girls at birth and were reared as females.

    Answer: True

104. Gender-reassignment surgery implants the internal reproductive organs of the other gender.

    Answer: False

105. Biological views on gender typing tend to focus on the roles of genetics and prenatal influences in predisposing men and women to gender-linked behavior patterns.

    Answer: True

106. Appropriate gender typing, in Freud's view, requires that boys come to identify with their mothers and girls with their fathers.

    Answer: False

107. The media by and large portray men and women in traditional roles.

    Answer: True

108. Lawrence Kohlberg claims that gender typing is the product of environmental influences and that children do not play an active role.

    Answer: False

109. Adolescent girls who show a number of masculine traits are less popular than girls who thoroughly adopt the traditional feminine gender role.

    Answer: False

110. Some evidence shows psychologically androgynous men and women to be more comfortable with their sexuality than masculine men and feminine women.

    Answer: True

ESSAY

111. Explain the prenatal sexual differentiation of a male. Include in your answer the roles of testosterone, H-Y antigen, Mullerian and Wolffian ducts, dihydrotestosterone (DHT), and Mullerian inhibiting substance (MIS).

    Answer:

112. Explain the prenatal sexual differentiation of a female. Include in your answer the roles of androgens, and the Wolffian and Mullerian ducts.

    Answer:

113. Differentiate between Klinefelter syndrome, Turner syndrome, androgen-insensitivity syndrome, and androgenital syndrome in terms of causes and effects.

    Answer:

114. By summarizing studies of pseudohermaphroditism, support or refute the idea that gender identity is largely determined by sexual anatomy.

    Answer:

115. Explain the psychological and physical processes involved in gender-reassignment surgery.

    Answer:

116. Identify several stereotypes attributed to females in our culture and discuss the impact of those stereotypes on female behavior.

    Answer:

117. Identify several stereotypes attributed to males in our culture and discuss the impact of those stereotypes on male behavior.

    Answer:

118. Describe the four theories of gender role development: psychoanalytic theory, social learning theory, cognitive-developmental theory, and gender schema theory.

    Answer:

Chapter 7: Attraction and Love

MULTIPLE CHOICE

1. According to the text, the key factor in considering a potential partner for dates, sex, and marriage is
   (a) intelligence.
   (b) physical appearance.
   (c) personality.
   (d) family background.

   Answer: B Difficulty: 2 Page: 207

2. Regarding beauty, research suggests
   (a) it's completely a function of the beholder.
   (b) it's partly a function of the beholder and partly a function of cultural standards.
   (c) our tastes are completely subjective.
   (d) both a & c.

   Answer: B Difficulty: 2 Page: 208

3. In the United States, which attribute do women find particularly attractive in men?
   (a) muscularity.
   (b) brown eyes.
   (c) tallness.
   (d) sculpted facial bones.

   Answer: C Difficulty: 2 Page: 208

4. How is female weight viewed?
   (a) Slender figures are valued cross-culturally.
   (b) Some pre-literate societies value plump women.
   (c) Wide hips were not found appealing in any culture.
   (d) In our culture anorexic thinness is the ideal.

   Answer: B Difficulty: 1 Page: 209

5. Which is *true* regarding the preferred female figure in the United States?
   (a) The hour-glass figure is viewed as most attractive and desirable for long-term relationships.
   (b) Wide hips and a broad pelvis are widely recognized as sexually appealing.
   (c) Very thin women are considered highly attractive and desirable.
   (d) Slender, short women are viewed as attractive and desirable for long-term relationships.

   Answer: A Difficulty: 2 Page: 209

6. Which statement is *true* about male preferences for women's breasts?
   (a) Males prefer women with larger breasts, and they prefer breast sizes larger than predicted by women.
   (b) Males prefer women with larger breasts but not nearly as large as predicted by women.
   (c) Males did not show a preference for large breasts even though women predicted they would.
   (d) Males were mixed in breast size preferences with only some preferring larger breasts.

   Answer: B Difficulty: 2 Page: 209

7. Women prefer men with
   (a) larger pectorals.
   (b) smaller pectorals.
   (c) larger pectorals, but not as large as men believe.
   (d) neither large nor small pectorals—no consensus was found.

   Answer: C Difficulty: 1 Page: 209

8. An interesting difference between the *self-perceptions* of college men and women is that most college men
   (a) felt they should gain weight.
   (b) thought they should be more muscular.
   (c) wished they were taller.
   (d) thought their physiques were close to ideal.

   Answer: D Difficulty: 3 Page: 209

9. Which is true regarding college students' perceptions and preferences concerning weight?
   (a) Women see themselves as O.K. and see men as a bit too heavy.
   (b) Women see themselves as too heavy and men as O.K.
   (c) Men prefer women a bit heavier than the women imagine they would.
   (d) Men are generally correct about the preferences of women.

   Answer: C Difficulty: 2 Page: 209

10. According to the text, people are more attractive when they are
    (a) laughing.
    (b) smiling.
    (c) looking confident.
    (d) not looking down.

    Answer: B Difficulty: 1 Page: 210

11. In terms of attractiveness, cross-cultural research suggests that
    (a) certain facial features typify beauty universally.
    (b) larger body sizes typify beauty universally.
    (c) personality is rated as the most attractive quality universally.
    (d) a fit, well-developed musculature is universally accepted as attractive.

    Answer: A Difficulty: 2 Page: 211

12. Which of the following features appears to be associated with attractiveness universally?
    (a) large eyes
    (b) wide jaw
    (c) large upper and lower lips
    (d) a small distance between the eyes

    Answer: A Difficulty: 3 Page: 211

13. Research by Cunningham on historical evidence of facial preferences among diverse cultures suggests
    (a) beauty is in the eye of the beholder.
    (b) preferences varied by culture.
    (c) few conclusions are possible about what is beautiful.
    (d) none of the above.

    Answer: D Difficulty: 3 Page: 211

14. Which is true regarding the attractiveness of smiling?
    (a) Smiling is as important in business contexts as socially.
    (b) For men smiling is more important than for women.
    (c) Smiling may be a greater determinant of attractiveness in women than in men.
    (d) Women, but not men, rate smiling faces more attractive than non-smiling faces.

    Answer: C Difficulty: 2 Page: 210

15. In addition to physical features, attractiveness appears to depend on
    (a) personality.
    (b) honesty.
    (c) gender-role expectations.
    (d) dominance.

    Answer: C Difficulty: 2 Page: 210

16. In one study, highly feminine women were more likely to be attracted to
    (a) dominant "macho" men.
    (b) demure passive men.
    (c) emotionally expressive men.
    (d) submissive men.

    Answer: A Difficulty: 3 Page: 212

17. Men who viewed videos in the Riggio and Woll (1984) study were put off by
    (a) highly feminine, demure women.
    (b) passive women.
    (c) women in traditional roles.
    (d) expressive, dominant women.

    Answer: D Difficulty: 2 Page: 212

18. According to the text, perceptions of physical attractiveness can be affected by an individual's
    (a) friends.
    (b) name.
    (c) family of origin.
    (d) political stance.

    Answer: B Difficulty: 3 Page: 212

19. Harold loves his first name—it's his late father's name. To become more attractive, he should
    (a) change it to a more acceptable name like John or Brad.
    (b) use the nickname Hal.
    (c) change it to a unisex name, like Chris or Pat.
    (d) leave it as it is.

    Answer: D Difficulty: 3 Page: 212

20. When searching for a prospective partner for a long-term, meaningful relationship, which characteristic was *not* rated as more important than physical attractiveness?
    (a) assertiveness
    (b) fidelity
    (c) sensitivity
    (d) warmth

    Answer: A Difficulty: 2 Page: 212

21. When searching for a potential sexual relationship, which quality was rated most important by college students?
    (a) physical attractiveness
    (b) fidelity
    (c) honesty
    (d) humor

    Answer: A Difficulty: 1 Page: 212

22. In long-term partners, the quality most desired by students was
    (a) warmth.
    (b) playfulness.
    (c) honesty.
    (d) sensitivity.

    Answer: C Difficulty: 2 Page: 212

23. In choosing a potential mate, women place greater emphasis than men on
    (a) frugality.
    (b) physical attractiveness.
    (c) earning potential.
    (d) youth.

    Answer: C Difficulty: 2 Page: 213

24. In choosing a potential mate, men place greater emphasis than women on
    (a) expressiveness.
    (b) physical attraction.
    (c) kindness.
    (d) earning potential.

    Answer: B Difficulty: 2 Page: 213

25. In cross-cultural studies, which statement best reflects male and female considerations when choosing a mate?
    (a) Women place more emphasis on romance than men and less emphasis on earning power or status.
    (b) Women place less emphasis on family of origin or status than men and more emphasis on physical attraction and romance.
    (c) Men place more emphasis on reproductive potential than women and less emphasis on physical attractiveness.
    (d) Men place more emphasis on romance than women and less emphasis on practical aspects.

    Answer: D Difficulty: 3 Page: 213

26. Which statement most accurately reflects mate selection by women?
    (a) Women will forego job status in favor of romance.
    (b) Women will forego family of origin in favor of attractive looks.
    (c) Women will forego attractive looks in favor of steady earning potential.
    (d) Women will forego educational background in favor of youth and attractiveness.

    Answer: C Difficulty: 2 Page: 213

27. Almost universally, men prefer
    (a) younger women.
    (b) slender women.
    (c) intelligent women.
    (d) submissive women.

    Answer: A Difficulty: 1 Page: 213

28. Almost universally, women prefer
    (a) younger men.
    (b) muscular men.
    (c) older men.
    (d) intelligent men.

    Answer: C Difficulty: 1 Page: 213

29. Sociobiologists believe that age and health may be more important to a woman's appeal because they are associated with
    (a) the ability to provide.
    (b) the ability to nurture.
    (c) reproductive capacity.
    (d) a more satisfying sex life.

    Answer: C Difficulty: 2 Page: 213

30. According to David Buss (1994), male interest in younger women
    (a) began shortly after the industrial revolution.
    (b) occurs in both preliterate and industrialized societies.
    (c) occurs mainly in preliterate and third-world societies.
    (d) is changing as we enter the new millennium.

    Answer: B Difficulty: 3 Page: 214

31. In all 37 cultures studied by David Buss, which was true for men in terms of choosing a potential mate?
    (a) Men placed great value on a female's earning potential.
    (b) Men placed great value on a female's "good looks."
    (c) Men placed more value on honesty than intelligence.
    (d) Men placed more value on fidelity than kindness.

    Answer: B Difficulty: 2 Page: 214

32. In all 37 cultures in the Buss studies, which characteristic was rated higher than earning power and physical attractiveness in mate selection?
    (a) honesty
    (b) fidelity
    (c) a sense of humor
    (d) intelligence

    Answer: D Difficulty: 2 Page: 214

33. According to sociobiologists, women tend to marry men who are similar to themselves in physical attractiveness and
    (a) age.
    (b) socioeconomic standing.
    (c) intelligence.
    (d) sexual desire.

    Answer: B Difficulty: 2 Page: 214

34. In terms of mate selection, the matching hypothesis proposes that people tend to develop romantic relationships with people who are similar in
    (a) physical attractiveness.
    (b) intelligence.
    (c) personality.
    (d) attitude.

    Answer: A Difficulty: 1 Page: 215

35. According to the text, the central motive in the matching hypothesis seems to be
    (a) financial security.
    (b) one's family of origin.
    (c) fear of rejection.
    (d) reproductive potential.

    Answer: C Difficulty: 3 Page: 215

36. Generally speaking, which of the following is similar between sex and marriage partners?
    (a) ethnicity
    (b) age
    (c) religion
    (d) all of the above

    Answer: D Difficulty: 1 Page: 215

37. In the NHSLS study, females who had a graduate degree never partnered with an individual who
    (a) was of a different race.
    (b) had not completed high school.
    (c) was of a different religion.
    (d) was more than five years older.

    Answer: B Difficulty: 2 Page: 215

38. In the NHSLS study, men reported that they almost never had sexual relationships with women who
    (a) were of a different race.
    (b) were of a different religion.
    (c) had much more or much less education than they had.
    (d) were the same age as or slightly older than they were.

    Answer: C Difficulty: 3 Page: 215

39. Sarah feels greatly admired by her partner, Susan. When Susan gives her compliments about her abilities, she feels motivated to support and compliment Susan. This type of exchange in relationships is called
    (a) social exchange.
    (b) storge.
    (c) reciprocity.
    (d) agape.

    Answer: C Difficulty: 3 Page: 216

40. The text claims that our culture "idealizes" romantic love. Which of the following best expresses what that means?
    (a) We are extremely practical about how to make love work for us.
    (b) We recognize that love must be understood within a cultural context.
    (c) We perceive love to be grand and consuming.
    (d) We recognize the place of love when raising children.

    Answer: C Difficulty: 2 Page: 216

41. The type of love that binds friends, parents, and children through attachment or deep friendship is called
    (a) agape.
    (b) storge.
    (c) philia.
    (d) eros.

    Answer: B Difficulty: 1 Page: 217

42. Michael seems to be always "in love." In the last several years, he has been "head over heels" three times for three different women. The relationships generally last months because as the passion dies down a bit, Michael becomes bored and begins to insist that he has "fallen out of love." Michael's approach to love can best be described as
    (a) eros.
    (b) agape.
    (c) ludus.
    (d) philia.

    Answer: A Difficulty: 3 Page: 217

43. Love that is characterized by selfless giving is called
    (a) eros.
    (b) agape.
    (c) ludus.
    (d) pragma.

    Answer: B Difficulty: 1 Page: 217

44. Which type of love is rarely seen between adults in committed relationships?
    (a) storge
    (b) pragma
    (c) eros
    (d) agape

    Answer: D Difficulty: 1 Page: 217

45. Love that is based on liking and respect rather than sexual desire is called
    (a) storge.
    (b) eros.
    (c) agape.
    (d) philia.

    Answer: D Difficulty: 1 Page: 217

46. Aaron and Marcos have been friends for years, sharing intimate conversations and interests. Lately they have both noticed a growing sexual component in their feelings for each other. In their relationship, Aaron and Marcos may be experiencing a shift from
    (a) eros love to storge love.
    (b) philia love to agape love.
    (c) storge love to eros love.
    (d) storge love to agape love.

    Answer: C Difficulty: 2 Page: 217

47. Which of the following is true of the experience of romantic love during adolescence?
    (a) It is strongly influenced by culture.
    (b) It is partly arousal and partly a fanciful image of the object of our affection.
    (c) It is perhaps more accurately called lust.
    (d) All of the above.

    Answer: D Difficulty: 1 Page: 217

48. According to the Janus and Janus (1993) survey, which group rated themselves as the *most* romantic?
    (a) single women
    (b) single men
    (c) married men
    (d) married women

    Answer: B Difficulty: 2 Page: 218

49. Which of the following is true of romantic love?
    (a) It is always even keeled.
    (b) It's the result of long-term infatuation.
    (c) It leads to agape.
    (d) It can teeter between ecstasy and misery.

    Answer: D Difficulty: 1 Page: 219

50. Margaret and Terry have just fallen in love. They feel an intense desire to be close to each other and spend as much time together as possible. When not together, both feel intensely excited and anxious. Generally their time is spent fantasizing about their next date. What stage of love are Margaret and Terry experiencing?
    (a) companionate love
    (b) realistic love
    (c) infatuation
    (d) consummate love

    Answer: C Difficulty: 3 Page: 220

51. Intense absorption in another person accompanied by sexual desire, general physiological arousal, or excitement is called
    (a) consummate love.
    (b) empty love.
    (c) selfless love.
    (d) infatuation.

    Answer: D Difficulty: 1 Page: 220

52. What distinguishes infatuation from a lasting romantic love?
    (a) Partners view each other more romantically.
    (b) Partners view each other more realistically.
    (c) Sexual desire increases.
    (d) Sexual desire decreases.

    Answer: B Difficulty: 2 Page: 220

53. Which of the following is true about infatuation and a lasting mutual love?
    (a) Infatuation is not a necessary first step.
    (b) Infatuation is a necessary first step.
    (c) Lasting mutual love always follows infatuation.
    (d) If only one partner is infatuated, the relationship cannot move on to a lasting mutual love.

    Answer: A Difficulty: 1 Page: 220

54. According to Clyde and Susan Hendricks, game-playing love is similar to the Greek style of love called
    (a) storge.
    (b) pragma.
    (c) ludus.
    (d) philia.

    Answer: C Difficulty: 2 Page: 221

55. Julia gets incensed whenever she sees her boyfriend look at another woman. They often wind up in huge arguments because Julia is so suspicious of his every move. Julia's style of love is referred to as
    (a) agape.
    (b) mania.
    (c) eros.
    (d) storge.

    Answer: B Difficulty: 3 Page: 221

56. Satisfying love relationships are characterized by high levels of
    (a) eros and mania.
    (b) ludus and agape.
    (c) agape and eros.
    (d) philia and pragma.

    Answer: C Difficulty: 2 Page: 221

57. A love relationship based on practical aspects such as potential parenting skills, and societal status is an example of
    (a) agape.
    (b) ludus.
    (c) storge.
    (d) pragma.

    Answer: D Difficulty: 2 Page: 221

58. "I am willing to share myself and my possessions with my partner," is an example of
    (a) intimacy.
    (b) passion.
    (c) commitment.
    (d) infatuation.

    Answer: A Difficulty: 1 Page: 221

59. "I will always feel a strong responsibility for my partner," is an example of
    (a) intimacy.
    (b) passion.
    (c) commitment.
    (d) infatuation.

    Answer: C Difficulty: 1 Page: 221

60. "My partner is able to count on me in times of need," is a statement typical of
    (a) commitment.
    (b) intimacy.
    (c) infatuation.
    (d) passion.

    Answer: B Difficulty: 1 Page: 221

61. "I cannot imagine another person making me as happy as my partner does," is a statement typical of
    (a) intimacy.
    (b) infatuation.
    (c) commitment.
    (d) passion.

    Answer: D Difficulty: 1 Page: 221

62. Which is not a style of love presented by Clyde and Susan Hendrick?
    (a) romantic love
    (b) dating love
    (c) selfless love
    (d) logical love

    Answer: B Difficulty: 1 Page: 221

63. According to Sternberg's model, what leads to a good match?
    (a) similar taste in food
    (b) similar religious and political views
    (c) closely matched commitments with differing needs for intimacy
    (d) perfectly congruent triangles

    Answer: D Difficulty: 2 Page: 221

64. According to Robert Sternberg, which of the following statements is true?
    (a) Romantic love has passion, intimacy, and commitment.
    (b) Romantic love has passion and intimacy but lacks commitment.
    (c) Consummate love has commitment and intimacy but lacks passion.
    (d) Consummate love has passion and commitment but lacks intimacy.

    Answer: B Difficulty: 2 Page: 222

65. A relationship that has both passion and commitment but lacks intimacy is called
    (a) empty love.
    (b) companionate love.
    (c) consummate love.
    (d) fatuous love.

    Answer: D Difficulty: 1 Page: 222

66. A relationship that has both passion and intimacy but lacks commitment is called
    (a) empty love.
    (b) romantic love.
    (c) fatuous love.
    (d) consummate love.

    Answer: B Difficulty: 1 Page: 223

67. Roger and Cherise stay together for the sake of the children. Though their marriage no longer has intimacy or passion, they feel a deep sense of commitment to raising their children in a two-parent home. What type of love do Robert and Cherise display?
    (a) empty love
    (b) consummate love
    (c) fatuous love
    (d) companionate love

    Answer: A Difficulty: 2 Page: 223

68. According to Robert Sternberg, love in which intimacy and commitment are strong but passion is lacking is called
    (a) empty love.
    (b) consummate love.
    (c) companionate love.
    (d) fatuous love.

    Answer: C Difficulty: 2 Page: 223

69. Marriages based in deep and abiding friendship but lacking in passion are described by Sternberg as high in
    (a) fatuous love.
    (b) consummate love.
    (c) empty love.
    (d) companionate love.

    Answer: D Difficulty: 1 Page: 223

70. A loving experience with another person or a friendship in which intimacy is present but passion and commitment are lacking is called
    (a) romantic love.
    (b) nonlove.
    (c) liking.
    (d) infatuation.

    Answer: C Difficulty: 1 Page: 223

71. Most couples strive to attain a love characterized by a complete combination of passion, intimacy, and commitment. Sternberg called this type of love
    (a) consummate.
    (b) companionate.
    (c) romantic.
    (d) fatuous.

    Answer: A Difficulty: 1 Page: 223

72. Which of the following is true about *liking*?
    (a) Liking is a basis for friendship.
    (b) Liking consists of closeness and passion.
    (c) Liking is often felt toward passing acquaintances.
    (d) Liking does not generally lead to long-term relationships.

    Answer: A Difficulty: 2 Page: 223

73. Suzy and Donna shared physical intimacy but were unwilling to share information about their religious backgrounds. Which of the following is probably true?
    (a) They lack the quality most often associated with true friendship.
    (b) They have a consummate love for one another.
    (c) Their relationship is best characterized as romantic love.
    (d) Their relationship is best described as nonlove.

    Answer: A Difficulty: 2 Page: 223

74. In Sternberg's model which is true of an ideal marriage?
    (a) An ideal marriage is considered to be exclusively romantic love.
    (b) There is a healthy dose of passion, intimacy and commitment.
    (c) There is mostly passion with some intimacy and commitment.
    (d) Commitment is the most important characteristic.

    Answer: B Difficulty: 1 Page: 223

75. In research testing facets of Sternberg's triangular theory, some studies report that
    (a) married men and women both report declines in passion over time.
    (b) married men and women report no decline in passion over time.
    (c) married women but not men reported a decline in passion over time.
    (d) married men but not women reported a decline in passion over time.

    Answer: C Difficulty: 3 Page: 225

76. Critics of Sternberg's model state that his model
    (a) has vastly advanced our understanding of love.
    (b) does not fully address the intimacy component of love.
    (c) focuses too heavily on passion and not enough on companionate love.
    (d) tells us little about the goals or sources of love.

    Answer: D Difficulty: 2 Page: 226

MATCHING

For each of Sternberg's types of love, match the type with its correct description.

(a) empty love

(b) companionate love

(c) liking

(d) fatuous love

(e) consummate love

(f) romantic love

(g) nonlove

(h) infatuation

77. A relationship in which intimacy, passion, and commitment are lacking—casual interaction with another person.

    Answer: g

78. The type of love associated with whirlwind romance—passion and commitment are high but intimacy is lacking.

    Answer: d

79. A loving relationship high in passion and intimacy but lacking in commitment.

    Answer: f

80. Characteristic of "love at first sight," passion is high but both intimacy and commitment are lacking.

    Answer: h

81. A loving experience with another in which intimacy is present but commitment and passion are lacking.

    Answer: c

82. A relationship that is stagnant with little of the intimacy or passion that may have once existed, while still maintaining a sense of commitment.

    Answer: a

83. A complete type of love involving three components: intimacy, passion, and commitment.

    Answer: e

84. A love that can occur in marriages in which passion has waned and been replaced by a committed friendship.

    Answer: b

Chapter 7: Attraction and Love

TRUE/FALSE

85. In the United States, both men and women find slenderness an important component of physical attraction.

    Answer: True

86. College women generally see themselves as heavier than the ideal feminine form but even heavier than the figure they perceive as most alluring to men.

    Answer: False

87. A smile may be a great determinant of attractiveness in women.

    Answer: True

88. In Nevid's studies involving attraction, men considered cooking ability and frugality when choosing a female partner.

    Answer: True

89. Cross-culturally, women are more romantic than men.

    Answer: False

90. On average, men in the United States are 3 years older than the women they marry.

    Answer: False

91. It is normal for passionate love to evolve into a more intimate and committed love in long-term relationships.

    Answer: True

92. Sternberg's triangle model is used primarily to determine if a relationship will have longevity.

    Answer: False

93. College men would like women to be thinner than women want to be.

    Answer: False

94. College women prefer men who are thinner than the men imagine the women prefer.

    Answer: True

95. Women who are randomly assigned unique names like Harriet and Gertrude are rated as more attractive than women assigned names like Kathy and Jennifer.

    Answer: False

96. Physical appeal is the most important trait people seek in partners for long-term relationships.

    Answer: False

97. The evolutionary view of gender differences in preferences for mates is largely speculative and not fully consistent with the evidence.

    Answer: True

98. According to the text, we are more likely to be attracted to people who disagree with our views and tastes than to people who share them.

    Answer: False

99. Infatuation is typified by strong sexual desire but not by intimacy and commitment.

    Answer: True

100. The single most highly prized quality students want in a long-term partner is honesty.

     Answer: True

101. Physical appeal seems to play a filtering role in relationships; when someone meets minimum physical standards, people look for more meaningful traits.

     Answer: True

102. Men are more willing than women to marry someone of a different race.

     Answer: True

103. Women are more likely than men to marry someone who has more education than they do.

     Answer: True

104. In societies where women are economically dependent on men, a man's appeal may depend more on this money than his physical appeal.

     Answer: True

ESSAY

105. Discuss the similarities and differences between traits that men find attractive and traits that women find attractive in choosing a potential partner for a relationship.

     Answer:

106. Explain the matching hypothesis in terms of the old adage "opposites attract?"

     Answer:

107. Discuss the similarities and differences between storge, agape, philia, and eros love. Give an example of each type of love.

     Answer:

108. Discuss the three distinct components of love in Robert Sternberg's triangular theory of love and how each component relates to a successful or unsuccessful relationship.

     Answer:

109. Discuss the components of 5 of the 8 types of love identified by Sternberg.

     Answer:

Chapter 8: Relationships and Communication

MULTIPLE CHOICE

1. Initial feelings of attraction for another individual are generally based on
   (a) mutual interests.
   (b) visual impressions.
   (c) similar attitudes.
   (d) mutual friends.

   Answer: B Difficulty: 1 Page: 231

2. According to Levinger, which stage of the relationship begins when two people find one another appealing?
   (a) continuation
   (b) building
   (c) attraction
   (d) excitement

   Answer: C Difficulty: 1 Page: 231

3. The second stage of George Levinger's (1980) *ABCDE* model of relationships is
   (a) building.
   (b) continuation.
   (c) attraction.
   (d) deterioration.

   Answer: A Difficulty: 1 Page: 231

4. In Levinger's relationship model, attraction is followed by
   (a) commitment.
   (b) building.
   (c) continuation.
   (d) bonding.

   Answer: B Difficulty: 1 Page: 231

5. According to the NHSLS study, 35% of married people met their spouses through
   (a) family members.
   (b) self-introduction.
   (c) mutual friends.
   (d) coworkers.

   Answer: C Difficulty: 2 Page: 231

6. The majority of people seeking mates on the Internet are
   (a) divorced individuals between the ages of 40 and 50.
   (b) single mothers seeking potential fathers.
   (c) affluent, educated professionals.
   (d) young adults in their early twenties.

   Answer: C Difficulty: 2 Page: 232

7. Neil participates in online chat rooms. He pretends sometimes he is a women. This is an example of
   (a) gender bending.
   (b) gender replacement.
   (c) gender discrimination.
   (d) none of the above.

   Answer: A Difficulty: 1 Page: 232

8. Building a relationship includes the following except
   (a) small talk.
   (b) initial attraction.
   (c) surface contact.
   (d) honesty.

   Answer: B Difficulty: 1 Page: 232

9. Probing for common ground by investigating overlapping attitudes and interests is called
   (a) attraction.
   (b) surface contact.
   (c) small talk.
   (d) self-disclosure.

   Answer: B Difficulty: 1 Page: 233

10. Exchanging information according to breadth of topic coverage but not depth is referred to as
    (a) self-disclosure.
    (b) surface contact.
    (c) evaluation.
    (d) small talk.

    Answer: D Difficulty: 1 Page: 233

11. Bob sees Nancy at a social event. He tries to make eye contact with her, but she doesn't respond. Nancy could be
    (a) shy.
    (b) not interested in Bob.
    (c) unaware of Bob.
    (d) all of the above.

    Answer: D Difficulty: 2 Page: 234

12. Early exchanges with a potential partner are likely to involve all of the following *except*
    (a) occupation.
    (b) hometown.
    (c) dating history.
    (d) marital status.

    Answer: C Difficulty: 2 Page: 234

13. The exchange of personal or intimate information is called
    (a) surface contact.
    (b) small talk.
    (c) self-disclosure.
    (d) the opening line.

    Answer: C Difficulty: 2 Page: 234

14. The authors of your text suggest that if you are turned down twice for a date, you should
    (a) not ask a third time.
    (b) ask the person straight out if he/she is interested in you.
    (c) suggest a "group date" rather than a one-to-one date.
    (d) ask the person to tell you why they are not interested in you.

    Answer: A Difficulty: 2 Page: 234

15. Self-disclosure is central to building
    (a) casual relationships.
    (b) intimate relationships.
    (c) small talk.
    (d) none of the above.

    Answer: B Difficulty: 1 Page: 234

16. Building social skills by practicing easy to more difficult skills in graduated steps is called
    (a) self-disclosure.
    (b) successive approximations.
    (c) small talk.
    (d) surface talk.

    Answer: B Difficulty: 3 Page: 235

17. In studies investigating self-disclosure, researchers found that
    (a) early self-disclosure hastened the bonding process.
    (b) early disclosers were seen as immature.
    (c) late disclosers were rated as guarded and cold.
    (d) late disclosers were rated as less well-adjusted.

    Answer: B Difficulty: 2 Page: 235

18. In regard to self-disclosure, researchers find that women
    (a) are only slightly more disclosing than men.
    (b) tend to "hold back" before disclosing any intimate feelings.
    (c) are ten times more likely than men to disclose intimacies.
    (d) wait for cues from the male before disclosing personal information.

    Answer: A Difficulty: 2 Page: 237

19. When couples begin to see themselves as more "we" than "I," they enter a relationship phase called
    (a) social exchange.
    (b) mutuality.
    (c) building.
    (d) attraction.

    Answer: B Difficulty: 2 Page: 238

20. To keep their relationship interesting, Merrill and Mitch try one new activity each month. To date they have tried roller-skating, skeet-shooting, and chess. They discover that they both like skeet-shooting and chess, but neither cares much for roller-skating. Merrill and Mitch's activities demonstrate that they are in the
    (a) attraction phase of their relationship.
    (b) building phase of their relationship.
    (c) commitment phase of their relationship.
    (d) continuation phase of their relationship.

    Answer: D Difficulty: 2 Page: 238

21. According to Levinger, when couples seek ways to introduce variety into their relationships, they enter a phase called
    (a) mutuality.
    (b) building.
    (c) continuation.
    (d) commitment.

    Answer: C Difficulty: 1 Page: 238

22. Which of the following is *true* regarding jealousy?
    (a) In a survey of 103 women, 75% described themselves as jealous.
    (b) Jealousy, even in large amounts, is good for a relationship.
    (c) Jealousy is more common in cultures that stress a *machismo* tradition.
    (d) For men, feelings of inadequacy lead to jealousy.

    Answer: C Difficulty: 2 Page: 238

23. Jealousy leads to feelings of
    (a) insecurity.
    (b) rejection.
    (c) anxiety.
    (d) all of the above.

    Answer: D Difficulty: 1 Page: 238

24. What is a factor that encourages the continuation stage of a relationship?
    (a) seeking ways to introduce variety
    (b) perceiving fairness
    (c) showing a lack of jealousy
    (d) all of the above

    Answer: D Difficulty: 1 Page: 238

25. Researchers have found gender differences in jealousy. Males seem to be most upset by ____, whereas females seem to be more upset by ____.
    (a) sexual infidelity; time spent away from home and family
    (b) emotional infidelity; sexual infidelity
    (c) sexual infidelity; emotional infidelity
    (d) psychological infidelity; emotional infidelity

    Answer: C Difficulty: 2 Page: 239

26. John and Sue are a couple. John sometimes plays jealous games with her——he flirts openly with other girls. Why might John be playing games?
    (a) He wants more attention from Sue.
    (b) He wants to test their relationship.
    (c) He wants to inflict pain on Sue.
    (d) All of the above.

    Answer: D Difficulty: 1 Page: 239

27. The fourth stage in a relationship according to the text is
    (a) a new beginning.
    (b) problem solving.
    (c) plateau.
    (d) deterioration.

    Answer: D Difficulty: 1 Page: 239

28. Which of the following does *not* cause jealousy?
    (a) experience with former partners who cheated
    (b) a lack of self-confidence
    (c) fear of not being able to find another partner
    (d) having an extremely independent personality

    Answer: D Difficulty: 2 Page: 239

29. Kevin knows that his relationship with Mario is slipping away. He feels at a loss as to what to do, so he simply does nothing. Kevin's actions demonstrate
    (a) a passive response to relationship deterioration.
    (b) an active response to relationship ending.
    (c) a passive response to relationship continuation.
    (d) an active response to relationship building.

    Answer: A Difficulty: 3 Page: 239

30. Which factor will do little to deter or slow deterioration in a relationship?
    (a) a commitment to maintaining the relationship
    (b) a belief in the ability to overcome difficulties
    (c) seeking professional help
    (d) waiting for things to improve on their own

    Answer: D Difficulty: 2 Page: 239

31. According to social-exchange theory, individuals are *especially* likely to leave a relationship when
    (a) financial constraints are manageable.
    (b) alternative partners are available.
    (c) they no longer derive satisfaction from the relationship.
    (d) the risk of social sanctions is low.

    Answer: B Difficulty: 2 Page: 239

32. According to social-exchange theory, relationships draw to a close when
    (a) partners find little satisfaction in the affiliation.
    (b) barriers to leave the relationship are low.
    (c) alternative partners are available.
    (d) all of the above

    Answer: D Difficulty: 1 Page: 241

33. Loneliness is defined as a state of
    (a) solitude.
    (b) being alone.
    (c) painful isolation.
    (d) introspection.

    Answer: C Difficulty: 1 Page: 244

34. Loneliness tends to peak during
    (a) adolescence.
    (b) young adulthood.
    (c) middle adulthood.
    (d) late adulthood.

    Answer: A Difficulty: 1 Page: 244

35. Which statement is *true* about loneliness?
    (a) Loneliness tends to peak around mid-life.
    (b) Married couples rarely speak of feeling lonely.
    (c) Loneliness is a matter of choice.
    (d) Lonely people tend to have shallow friendships.

    Answer: D Difficulty: 3 Page: 244

36. Andrea complains of being lonely. She admits that she sees others as relatively unfriendly and concerned only about themselves. Several times she has made the statement that the "world is full of people who wouldn't hesitate to step on their best friend just to get ahead." Andrea is probably lonely because of her
    (a) lack of empathy.
    (b) cynicism about human nature.
    (c) lack of social skills.
    (d) failure to disclose personal information.

    Answer: B Difficulty: 2 Page: 244

37. Mark complains of being lonely. He feels that he has been plagued by bad luck and that the right circumstances never present themselves for meeting new people. Mark is probably lonely because he
    (a) lacks social skills.
    (b) is cynical about human nature.
    (c) has an external locus of control.
    (d) lacks empathy.

    Answer: C Difficulty: 3 Page: 244

38. Which of the following is *not* noted to be a cause of loneliness?
    (a) lack of social skills
    (b) an internal locus of control
    (c) lack of empathy
    (d) general pessimism

    Answer: B Difficulty: 1 Page: 244

39. In terms of loneliness, self-criticism and expectations of failure are often connected to
    (a) lack of empathy.
    (b) lack of interest in other people.
    (c) a fear of rejection.
    (d) demanding too much too soon.

    Answer: C Difficulty: 1 Page: 244

40. Which is not a solution in trying to cope with loneliness?
    (a) challenging feelings of pessimism
    (b) being assertive
    (c) hire a prostitute
    (d) become a good listener

    Answer: C Difficulty: 2 Page: 245

41. Which is regarded by Sternberg as the basic component of romantic love?
    (a) sexual relations
    (b) passion
    (c) commitment
    (d) intimacy

    Answer: D Difficulty: 2 Page: 246

42. According to Sternberg, sexual involvement does not necessarily mean a relationship has
    (a) intimacy.
    (b) commitment.
    (c) self-disclosure.
    (d) trust.

    Answer: A Difficulty: 2 Page: 246

43. Which is *true* regarding intimacy?
    (a) People who are sexually involved are intimately involved.
    (b) Some married people share greater emotional intimacy with friends than their spouses.
    (c) Emotional intimacy between friends is discouraged in most cultures.
    (d) Sexual intimacy is a necessary component of any emotionally intimate relationship.

    Answer: B Difficulty: 2 Page: 246

44. The core feature of intimacy is
    (a) trust.
    (b) sex.
    (c) disclosing everything about yourself.
    (d) talking.

    Answer: A Difficulty: 2 Page: 246

45. Commitment and trust in a relationship can be seen as developing according to
    (a) situational growth.
    (b) mutual cyclical growth.
    (c) coping mechanisms.
    (d) iterative growth mechanisms.

    Answer: B Difficulty: 3 Page: 247

46. Social scientists suggest that the most important initial step in developing intimacy is to
    (a) disclose all your intimate secrets to your friend or partner.
    (b) always say what's on your mind as issues arise.
    (c) get to know and like yourself.
    (d) become an excellent listener and allow others to freely disclose.

    Answer: C Difficulty: 2 Page: 248

47. Relationships tend to prosper when couples have a mutual level of
    (a) sexual interest.
    (b) honesty.
    (c) commitment.
    (d) education.

    Answer: C Difficulty: 3 Page: 248

48. In healthy committed relationships
    (a) couples spend the majority of their time together.
    (b) all decisions are joint decisions.
    (c) friends of each individual become friends of the "couple."
    (d) each partner maintains his/her individual interests and needs.

    Answer: D Difficulty: 2 Page: 248

49. What describes the tendency for one's partner to help "sculpt" one in the direction of his or her ideal self?
    (a) idealism
    (b) Michelangelo phenomenon
    (c) Renaissance
    (d) Michelangelo theorem

    Answer: A Difficulty: 2 Page: 248

50. In committed relationships, a delicate balance exists between
    (a) intimacy and sex.
    (b) individuality and mutuality.
    (c) affection and stability.
    (d) honesty and confidentiality.

    Answer: B Difficulty: 2 Page: 248

51. In the United States, we tend to assume that good communication means
    (a) talking a lot.
    (b) being a good listener.
    (c) using lots of expression.
    (d) using lots of gestures.

    Answer: A Difficulty: 1 Page: 249

52. Sarah is extremely upset with her partner, Kathleen. Three days ago she asked Kathleen to pay the phone bill as soon as possible. When she confronts Kathleen, Kathleen states that she didn't think Sarah meant immediately. Sarah and Kathleen's miscommunication is a problem involving
    (a) a mismatch between the speaker's words and tone of voice.
    (b) the speaker being unable to find the right words.
    (c) poor listening.
    (d) the speaker's word choice and the listener's interpretation.

    Answer: D Difficulty: 2 Page: 249

53. Sometimes the *best* way to communicate how we feel is not through words but
    (a) letters.
    (b) touch.
    (c) silence.
    (d) voice tone.

    Answer: B Difficulty: 1 Page: 249

54. Which of the following is a powerful form of communication?
    (a) touching
    (b) verbal
    (c) non-verbal
    (d) all of the above

    Answer: D Difficulty: 1 Page: 249

55. Though couples talk about many of their interests, attitudes, and concerns, the area most often overlooked is
    (a) finances.
    (b) religion.
    (c) sex.
    (d) work.

    Answer: C Difficulty: 1 Page: 250

56. Which statement represents a common irrational belief about relationships and sex?
    (a) Men naturally know what to do to please their partners sexually.
    (b) Even in intimate relationships, partners need to discuss what pleases them.
    (c) Women will naturally let partners know what their sexual needs are.
    (d) Couples know that they must speak openly about sexual wants and needs.

    Answer: A Difficulty: 3 Page: 250

57. When communicating about difficult issues, such as sex, it is especially important to
    (a) bring it up immediately.
    (b) limit the discussion to the bedroom.
    (c) choose the right time and place.
    (d) let the other person know not to interrupt you.

    Answer: C Difficulty: 2 Page: 251

58. The statement, "There's something I need to talk about. Is now a good time?" represents a communication suggestion called
    (a) broaching the topic.
    (b) requesting permission to bring up a topic.
    (c) active listening.
    (d) reinforcing the other person.

    Answer: B Difficulty: 2 Page: 251

59. Which statement best represents the communication suggestion, "giving your partner permission to say something that might be upsetting to you?"
    (a) "I know you don't want to hurt my feelings, but I'm wondering if this position is not comfortable for you?"
    (b) "I've always found it rather awkward to talk about sex."
    (c) "How come you never say anything when we're making love?"
    (d) "I love you very much but it annoys me when you don't come to bed when I do."

    Answer: A Difficulty: 3 Page: 252

60. Skilled listening involves
    (a) the use of reinforcement.
    (b) paraphrasing.
    (c) active listening.
    (d) all of the above.

    Answer: D Difficulty: 1 Page: 252

61. Active listening involves
    (a) being quiet.
    (b) listening for the facts of the conversation.
    (c) listening for the meaning of the speaker's words.
    (d) getting ready to answer when the speaker finishes talking.

    Answer: C Difficulty: 2 Page: 252

62. In healthy communication, it is more important to
    (a) bring subjects up right away rather than waiting.
    (b) let your partner know when he/she does something wrong rather than right.
    (c) speak than to listen.
    (d) reward positive efforts than criticize mistakes.

    Answer: D Difficulty: 3 Page: 252

63. What is not an exercise used by sex therapists to help couples with sexual dysfunction?
    (a) taking turns petting
    (b) audio stimulation
    (c) directing your partner
    (d) signaling

    Answer: B Difficulty: 2 Page: 253

64. Jenna hopes to improve her relationship with Mark. She begins by telling him he is "disrespectful" and requests that he show "more respect for her." What is wrong with Jenna's request?
    (a) It is too demanding.
    (b) It is not specific enough.
    (c) It is judgmental.
    (d) She is being too nice.

    Answer: B Difficulty: 3 Page: 254

65. Andrew wants Maggio to come home after work and to stop going to the bars for drinks first. He confronts Maggio by stating, "If you really cared about me, you'd respect me and be home for dinner." What is wrong with Andrew's request?
    (a) He failed to use an "I" statement.
    (b) He is not being specific.
    (c) He is choosing the wrong time to deliver his message.
    (d) He is too aggressive.

    Answer: A Difficulty: 2 Page: 254

66. The *most* important question to ask yourself before confronting a partner is
    (a) "Is it worth it?"
    (b) "Is my goal to hurt or to help?"
    (c) "Is this the right time?"
    (d) "Is this an old or a new issue?"

    Answer: B Difficulty: 2 Page: 255

67. In the middle of an argument, Jack says to Kristina, "You are always so irresponsible. Last Christmas you did the same thing and the Christmas cards never got delivered to my employees. Last week you said you'd pick up my dry cleaning but decided to stop at your mother's on the way. By the time you got done gossiping with her, the dry cleaners were closed!" What is wrong with Jack's approach?
    (a) He is too passive.
    (b) He is not being specific.
    (c) He has picked the wrong time.
    (d) He is bringing up the past.

    Answer: D Difficulty: 3 Page: 255

68. When Linnea says, "Can I show you how I'd like the laundry folded?" she is using the suggestion of
    (a) right timing.
    (b) evaluating her motives.
    (c) constructive criticism.
    (d) expressing displeasure in terms of her own feelings.

    Answer: C Difficulty: 1 Page: 255

69. If you find yourself getting defensive when your partner criticizes, the best advice is to
    (a) take a few moments to stop and think.
    (b) walk away.
    (c) admit you're wrong.
    (d) give in.

    Answer: A Difficulty: 1 Page: 257

70. To prevent criticism from becoming a major argument, you should
    (a) walk away and cool off.
    (b) acknowledge the criticism and validate your partner's feelings.
    (c) reject the criticism.
    (d) be sure your partner understands it's "our problem" and not "my problem."

    Answer: B Difficulty: 2 Page: 257

71. When you feel your partner is unjustified in his/her criticism, it is important that you
    (a) express your anger openly.
    (b) tell your partner he/she is wrong.
    (c) find others to support your position.
    (d) avoid retaliation.

    Answer: D Difficulty: 3 Page: 257

72. Sometimes when couples reach an impasse, it is best to
    (a) take a break and set the issue aside for awhile.
    (b) avoid the issue altogether.
    (c) stay with the issue, even if it takes days to resolve.
    (d) try to get the person to see your point of view.

    Answer: A Difficulty: 2 Page: 257

73. In regards to difficult issues in relationships, which statement is true?
    (a) When all else fails you can agree to disagree.
    (b) There are no issues that can't be resolved if couples are truly committed to each other.
    (c) Most couples need professional assistance with the really tough issues.
    (d) Given enough time, most partners come around to the other's point of view.

    Answer: A Difficulty: 2 Page: 257

MATCHING

For each of the following sample statements, match the statement with the communication skill the statement demonstrates.

(a) Acknowledging the criticism

(b) Talking about talking

(c) Being specific

(d) Requesting permission to bring up a topic

(e) Expressing criticism constructively

(f) Reinforcing the other person for communicating

(g) Using "I" talk

(h) Using self-disclosure

(i) Asking questions to draw the person out

(j) Asking clarifying questions

74. "There's something I need to talk about, but I'm not sure how to bring it up. Can you help me?"

    Answer: d

75. "You know, I think other people have an easier time than I do when it comes to talking about some things."

    Answer: b

76. "Could you give an example of what you mean?"

    Answer: j

77. "I really appreciate that you are concerned about our relationship."

    Answer: f

78. "Sometimes I feel that I disappoint you when we make love. Should I be doing something differently?"

    Answer: h

79. "Do you think I do things that bug you?"

    Answer: i

80. "You can show me consideration by taking the time to have a cup of coffee with me before we head to work in the morning."

    Answer: c

81. "I feel afraid when you raise your voice."

    Answer: g

82. "Can I take your hand and show you what I'd like?"

    Answer: e

83. "You're right. I was so busy I never got the grocery shopping done."

Answer: a

TRUE/FALSE

84. Small talk is an insincere method of starting a relationship.

Answer: False

85. Social exchange theory involves evaluating a relationship on a reward-cost basis.

Answer: True

86. Family members and coworkers are the most common means of meeting potential mates.

Answer: False

87. A concern about Internet romance is that individuals tend to change or omit truths about themselves.

Answer: True

88. Premature self-disclosure may actually repel the other person.

Answer: True

89. In contrast to the United States, self-disclosure in relationships occurs more frequently and earlier in Japanese society.

Answer: True

90. Mild forms of jealousy are not necessarily destructive in relationships.

Answer: True

91. In women, feelings of jealousy give rise to feelings of inadequacy while in men, feelings of inadequacy give rise to feelings of jealousy.

Answer: False

92. If you are sexually intimate with a person, you are also emotionally intimate.

Answer: False

93. Research suggests that we should refrain from disclosing certain types of information too rapidly if we want to make a good impression on someone.

Answer: True

94. Intimate relationships usually involve balances in which some things are revealed and others are not.

Answer: True

95. Relationships tend to prosper when one side has a stronger commitment.

Answer: False

96. Swift self-disclosure of intimate information is a way to enhance romance in a new relationship.

Answer: False

97. An external locus of control implies that people do not see themselves as capable of taking their lives into their own hands and achieving goals.

Answer: True

98. People cannot have intimate relationships without being sexually intimate.

    Answer: False

99. The two most important ingredients of an intimate relationship are affection and stability.

    Answer: False

100. Feelings of trust increase the willingness of the partners to concede that they need each other and the relationship.

    Answer: True

101. Intimate relationships involve balances in which some things are revealed and others are not.

    Answer: True

ESSAY

102. Identify and discuss what occurs in each stage of Levinger's *ABCDE* model of relationships.

    Answer:

103. Discuss six of the eleven suggestions offered by the authors to combat loneliness.

    Answer:

104. Identify at least four factors central to building and maintaining intimate relationships and explain the importance of each factor.

    Answer:

105. Discuss the factors that make communication about sex difficult and offer suggestions that can help increase a couple's comfort level when communicating about sex.

    Answer:

106. What non-verbal techniques can couples use to enhance communication about sex?

    Answer:

107. Assume that your partner is prepared to offer you some criticism regarding your recent behavior. What suggestions should you consider as the receiver in order to enhance communication?

    Answer:

108. Assume that you are preparing to confront your partner about his/her recent behavior. What suggestions should you consider as the sender in order to enhance communication?

    Answer:

Chapter 9: Sexual Techniques and Behavior Patterns

1. In the NHSLS study, the majority of both men and women reported that they use masturbation
   (a) to relax.
   (b) to relieve sexual tension.
   (c) to relieve boredom.
   (d) when a partner does not want to engage in sex.

   Answer: B Difficulty: 1 Page: 263

2. In the NHSLS study, the reason reported *least* often by both men and women for masturbation was using masturbation as a means to
   (a) aid in sleep.
   (b) relieve boredom.
   (c) induce relaxation.
   (d) cope with the fear of AIDS and other STDs.

   Answer: D Difficulty: 2 Page: 263

3. The practice of withdrawing the penis prior to ejaculation during sexual intercourse is called
   (a) fellatio.
   (b) coitus interruptus.
   (c) escaping.
   (d) the retreat method.

   Answer: B Difficulty: 2 Page: 263

4. In the early Judeo-Christian tradition, masturbation was known as
   (a) fellatio.
   (b) cunnilingus.
   (c) onanism.
   (d) coitus interruptus.

   Answer: C Difficulty: 1 Page: 263

5. In the Book of Genesis, Onan "sinned" because he was unhappy with the Biblical law requiring a younger brother to
   (a) marry his brother's widow and father children for the elder brother if he died and was without an heir.
   (b) raise the elder brother's children if he died.
   (c) financially support his elder brother's wife and children if he died.
   (d) give his first born child to the widow of his elder brother to raise as his elder brother's son.

   Answer: A Difficulty: 3 Page: 263

6. The most likely reason that early Jews and Christians condemned masturbation is because
   (a) the Bible condemns it.
   (b) it did nothing to help increase the population.
   (c) of the belief that it led to physical illness.
   (d) of the belief that it caused mental illness.

   Answer: D Difficulty: 2 Page: 263

7. The belief that masturbation caused tuberculosis, nervous disease, poor eyesight, memory loss, and epilepsy was advocated by
   (a) Richard von Krafft-Ebing and Havelock Ellis.
   (b) S.A.D. Tissot and Benjamin Rush.
   (c) Sylvester Graham and J.H. Kellogg.
   (d) William Masters and Virginia Johnson.

   Answer: B Difficulty: 3 Page: 263

8. In the 19th century, graham crackers and corn flakes were advocated as
   (a) foods to improve circulation.
   (b) measures to prevent colon cancer.
   (c) anti-masturbation foods.
   (d) sexual stimulants.

   Answer: C Difficulty: 2 Page: 264

9. Krafft-Ebing linked masturbation with
   (a) male homosexuality.
   (b) frigidity.
   (c) blindness.
   (d) female homosexuality.

   Answer: A Difficulty: 2 Page: 264

10. Krafft-Ebing believed that masturbation led to
    (a) depression.
    (b) sexual addiction.
    (c) inhibited orgasm.
    (d) impotence with women.

    Answer: D Difficulty: 2 Page: 264

11. Masturbation may be a sign of an adjustment problem if
    (a) a person masturbates more than once a day.
    (b) it is used as an exclusive sexual outlet when opportunities for sexual relationships are available.
    (c) it is used in conjunction with pornographic materials as sexual stimulants.
    (d) a child younger than age twelve engages in masturbation.

    Answer: B Difficulty: 3 Page: 264

12. In earlier centuries the diagnosis of hysteria in women might be treated by
    (a) progressive relaxation.
    (b) visits to a spa.
    (c) bringing them to orgasm.
    (d) all of the above.

    Answer: C Difficulty: 2 Page: 265

13. What did the New England college survey show about masturbation?
    (a) The percentage of men and women who masturbate is about the same.
    (b) The percentage of men who masturbate is about twice as high as that of women.
    (c) The percentage of women who masturbate is actually higher than that of men.
    (d) Ninety-eight percent of men reported they masturbated while only twenty-three percent of women reported doing so.

    Answer: B Difficulty: 2 Page: 265

14. In the Kinsey studies, what was the reported incidence of masturbation in the United States?
    (a) About half the men and one third of the women reported they had masturbated at some time.
    (b) Seventy-five percent of the men but only forty-five percent of the women reported they had masturbated at some time.
    (c) Nearly all the men and about two-thirds of the women reported they had masturbated at some time.
    (d) About sixty-five percent of both men and women reported they had masturbated at some time.

    Answer: C Difficulty: 2 Page: 265

15. When comparing the Kinsey studies and the NHSLS study, what differences were found in terms of masturbation in the United States?
    (a) Both studies were very similar in the reported incidence of masturbation for both males and females.
    (b) The reported incidence of masturbation for both males and females was much lower in the NHSLS study than in the Kinsey studies.
    (c) The reported incidence of masturbation was higher for both men and women in the NHSLS study than in the Kinsey studies.
    (d) The reported incidence of masturbation was much higher for women but significantly lower for men in the NHSLS study than in the Kinsey studies.

    Answer: B Difficulty: 2 Page: 267

16. Which was found to be a liberating influence on masturbation?
    (a) religion
    (b) age
    (c) higher education
    (d) race

    Answer: C Difficulty: 1 Page: 266

17. In terms of race or ethnicity, which group had the lowest reported incidence of masturbation by the NHSLS study?
    (a) African Americans
    (b) White Americans
    (c) Hispanic Americans
    (d) Asian Americans

    Answer: A Difficulty: 2 Page: 266

18. In terms of religion, which group had the lowest reported incidence of masturbation by the NHSLS study?
    (a) those practicing no religion
    (b) liberal or moderate Protestants
    (c) conservative Protestants
    (d) Catholics

    Answer: C Difficulty: 3 Page: 266

19. Research suggests that _____ correlation exists for women between prior masturbation and sexual _____ in marriage.
    (a) a positive; satisfaction
    (b) a positive; frustration
    (c) a negative; satisfaction
    (d) no; satisfaction

    Answer: A Difficulty: 2 Page: 267

20. According to several studies, women who had masturbated in adolescence were more likely as adults to
(a) have difficulty achieving orgasm with a partner.
(b) be sexually promiscuous.
(c) find marital intercourse gratifying.
(d) replace intercourse with masturbation in their marriages.

Answer: C Difficulty: 2 Page: 267

21. Masters and Johnson and Hite reported that women achieve orgasm more reliably through
(a) masturbation involving the clitoral area.
(b) intercourse with a partner.
(c) insertion of the fingers or objects in the vagina.
(d) masturbation combined with intercourse.

Answer: A Difficulty: 3 Page: 267

22. Typically, how long does it take a male to reach orgasm through masturbation?
(a) 30 seconds
(b) 1-2 minutes
(c) 5-10 minutes
(d) 15-20 minutes

Answer: B Difficulty: 2 Page: 268

23. Although masturbation techniques vary widely, most men report that they masturbate by
(a) rubbing the penis and testicles against clothing or bedding.
(b) using electronic devices such as vibrators.
(c) using "artificial vaginas" or "sex dolls."
(d) manual manipulation of the penis.

Answer: D Difficulty: 1 Page: 268

24. As a prelude to masturbation, most men use
(a) electric vibrators.
(b) fantasy, erotic photos, or videos.
(c) artificial vaginas.
(d) a rubbing motion of the penis against clothing or bedding.

Answer: B Difficulty: 1 Page: 269

25. During male masturbation, as orgasm approaches
(a) less pressure is applied to the shaft of the penis.
(b) the glans becomes sensitive and is avoided.
(c) less speed is used to stroke the penis.
(d) the glans becomes relatively insensitive to stimulation.

Answer: B Difficulty: 2 Page: 268

26. Regarding the techniques of female masturbation, Masters and Johnson reported that
(a) all women stimulate their breasts as well as their genitals.
(b) most women stroke the glans of the clitorus until they reach orgasm.
(c) most women did not use fantasy while masturbating.
(d) they never observed two women masturbating in the same way.

Answer: D Difficulty: 3 Page: 269

27. In female masturbation, most women
    (a) use their fingers or objects to simulate a penis.
    (b) insert a finger in the anus to heighten orgasmic sensations.
    (c) use a circular motion to massage the glans of the clitoris until orgasm.
    (d) massage the mons, labia majora, and clitoral region.

    Answer: D Difficulty: 2 Page: 269

28. Which is not true of women who masturbate?
    (a) some touch the glans lightly
    (b) most prefer to insert a soft object into the vagina
    (c) many masturbate while bathing
    (d) some massage their breasts

    Answer: B Difficulty: 2 Page: 270

29. Masturbation for both men and women generally requires
    (a) erotic videos.
    (b) some form of cognitive stimulation.
    (c) fantasies involving emotional involvement.
    (d) fantasies involving dominance.

    Answer: B Difficulty: 1 Page: 271

30. In women, sexual daydreaming or fantasy was associated with
    (a) a greater sex drive and more positive attitude about sex.
    (b) a greater sex drive but less positive attitude about sex.
    (c) a lower sex drive and less overall sexual activity.
    (d) a greater sex drive but less overall sexual activity.

    Answer: A Difficulty: 2 Page: 271

31. In contrast to men's sexual fantasies, women
    (a) are more likely to fantasize about strangers.
    (b) are more likely to fantasize about assuming an aggressive role in sexual activity.
    (c) are more likely to focus on emotional aspects of the fantasy.
    (d) are more likely to fantasize about same-gender sexual encounters.

    Answer: C Difficulty: 2 Page: 271

32. Which is true about sexual fantasies?
    (a) Most psychologists consider fantasizing with acquaintances a precursor to
        inappropriate behavior.
    (b) Fantasizing about behavior you would never act out is probably harmless.
    (c) Fantasies that lead to excitement are generally a reflection of what one would do if
        the opportunity were available.
    (d) Only those with deficient sex lives engage in sexual fantasies.

    Answer: B Difficulty: 2 Page: 271

33. The most common masturbation fantasy reported by both genders in the *Playboy* sample was
    (a) "having intercourse with a stranger."
    (b) "having a sexual encounter with two men or two women."
    (c) "having intercourse with a loved one."
    (d) "assuming a dominant or aggressive role in a sexual encounter."

    Answer: C Difficulty: 1 Page: 271

34. Maria is concerned about her own sexual fantasies. She fantasizes quite a lot both during masturbation and during intercourse with her partner. She is concerned that she shouldn't be fantasizing so much to achieve orgasm and that her fantasies often involve sexual aggression. What should Maria know?
    (a) Aggressive fantasies will lead to unhealthy experimentation with rape or sadistic sexual behavior.
    (b) Fantasizing too much will cause her to lose her grip on reality and create unrealistic expectations in her sexual relations with her partner.
    (c) Most people do not intend to and never will act out their sexual fantasies.
    (d) Fantasizing reinforces traditional gender roles and gender stereotypes.

    Answer: C Difficulty: 2 Page: 272

35. Which is *true* regarding masturbation fantasies?
    (a) Masturbation fantasies allow people to rehearse sexual encounters.
    (b) Masturbation fantasies reinforce traditional gender roles and stereotypes.
    (c) Masturbation fantasies increase sexual promiscuity and infidelity.
    (d) Masturbation fantasies decrease sexual arousal with partners.

    Answer: A Difficulty: 2 Page: 272

36. In terms of foreplay, the *most* important sexual technique is
    (a) touching.
    (b) kissing.
    (c) communication.
    (d) fellatio.

    Answer: C Difficulty: 1 Page: 272

37. Which statement is *true* regarding sexual foreplay?
    (a) Humans are unique in that other animals do not use foreplay prior to intercourse.
    (b) In the United States, women desire longer periods of foreplay and afterplay than men.
    (c) The pattern and duration of foreplay is largely uniform across cultures.
    (d) Kissing is an important part of sexual foreplay in all cultures.

    Answer: B Difficulty: 3 Page: 272

38. Which is true of kissing?
    (a) It's universal.
    (b) The Balinese rub noses to kiss.
    (c) Sustained kissing on the lips is usually an erotic gesture.
    (d) It is not practiced in Japan.

    Answer: C Difficulty: 2 Page: 273

39. In sexual foreplay involving the breasts, many women prefer
    (a) men to kiss or suck on their breasts immediately.
    (b) a hard sucking action on the nipples to stimulate the clitoris.
    (c) not to have their breasts kissed or caressed.
    (d) several minutes of body contact or gentle caresses before breast stimulation.

    Answer: D Difficulty: 2 Page: 273

40. Which is true of touching?
    (a) It's a common form of foreplay.
    (b) Women, but not men, like their genitals to be touched as a prelude to intercourse.
    (c) Women generally prefer not to be touched in the sensitive area around the clitoris.
    (d) Holding hands is not sexually stimulating as the hands have few nerve endings.

    Answer: A Difficulty: 2 Page: 273

41. Ahmed's wife does not seem happy with their sexual activity. Ahmed does not understand why. He generally initiates sex by immediately stroking his wife's genital area. What should Ahmed be aware of?
    (a) Most women prefer immediate oral-genital contact.
    (b) Most women prefer immediate breast stimulation followed by genital stimulation.
    (c) Most women prefer holding, hugging, and nongenital massage prior to genital stimulation.
    (d) Most women prefer immediate penetration of the penis in the vagina.

    Answer: C Difficulty: 3 Page: 274

42. According to Masters and Johnson, what do men prefer as a form of foreplay?
    (a) direct stroking of the genitals
    (b) whole body caresses
    (c) intimate talk followed by deep kissing
    (d) breast stimulation followed by stroking of the genitals

    Answer: A Difficulty: 2 Page: 274

43. Manual stimulation of the clitoris
    (a) should focus on the glans.
    (b) is more effective without lubrication.
    (c) should focus on the shaft or region surrounding the shaft.
    (d) is best if combined with penetration of the fingers in the vagina.

    Answer: C Difficulty: 2 Page: 274

44. Which statement is *true* about breast stimulation?
    (a) Most women prefer breast stimulation over clitoral stimulation.
    (b) Some women can achieve orgasm through breast stimulation alone.
    (c) Most male breasts are not sensitive to erotic stimulation.
    (d) Most men enjoy breast stimulation as much as women.

    Answer: B Difficulty: 1 Page: 275

45. Slang terms such as "blow job," "sucking off" or "giving head" refer to
    (a) cunnilingus.
    (b) anilingus.
    (c) coitus.
    (d) fellatio.

    Answer: D Difficulty: 1 Page: 275

46. Oral stimulation of the female genitals is called
    (a) coitus.
    (b) anilingus.
    (c) cunnilingus.
    (d) fellatio.

    Answer: C Difficulty: 1 Page: 275

47. Which statement best summarizes the differences found in the Kinsey studies and the NHSLS study regarding oral sex?
    (a) Kinsey found that less than 20% of couples had engaged in oral sex while the NHSLS study found over 90% of couples had engaged in oral sex.
    (b) Kinsey found that more women had engaged in oral sex and the NHSLS study found that more men had engaged in oral sex.
    (c) Kinsey found that 60% of married, college-educated couples engaged in oral sex and the NHSLS study found that 71-80% of married couples engaged in oral sex.
    (d) Kinsey found that 60% of couples, regardless of educational level, engaged in oral sex and the NHSLS study found a much higher proportion of oral sex among colege-educated adults.

    Answer: C Difficulty: 2 Page: 275

48. Which ethnic group is less likely to engage in oral sex?
    (a) White Americans
    (b) African Americans
    (c) Hispanic Americans
    (d) Native Americans

    Answer: B Difficulty: 2 Page: 275

49. Which ethnic group is more likely to engage in oral sex?
    (a) White Americans
    (b) African Americans
    (c) Hispanic Americans
    (d) Asian Americans

    Answer: A Difficulty: 2 Page: 275

50. Which statement most accurately reflects the relationship between education and experience with oral sex in the NHSLS study?
    (a) High school graduates had the lowest reported incidences of oral sex.
    (b) Individuals with college degrees reported the highest incidences of oral sex but those with advanced degrees reported many fewer incidences.
    (c) Individuals who did not graduate from high school had the highest incidences of oral sex.
    (d) The reported incidences of oral sex increased proportionately with education level.

    Answer: D Difficulty: 2 Page: 276

51. Males or females should not swallow a man's semen
    (a) if they are unsure of their partner's sexual history.
    (b) because swallowing semen will lead to gagging.
    (c) because the taste of semen is offensive.
    (d) because it is against the law in most states.

    Answer: A Difficulty: 1 Page: 276

52. Which is/are effective ways of fellating a man?
    (a) Vary the pressure and the movements of the mouth.
    (b) Gently pull the penis with the teeth.
    (c) Suck briskly on the meatus.
    (d) All of the above.

    Answer: A Difficulty: 2 Page: 277

53. How can gagging be avoided during fellatio?
    (a) It is an automatic reflex—difficult to avoid.
    (b) The giver can grasp the base of his/her partner's shaft in order to control penetration.
    (c) The receiver should be on top.
    (d) The giver should be on top.

    Answer: B Difficulty: 2 Page: 277

54. Which is/are true of semen?
    (a) Swallowing semen is encouraged as a way to enhance intimacy.
    (b) While it is rare, pregnancy can occur by swallowing semen.
    (c) A teaspoon of semen contains about 13 grams of fat.
    (d) None of the above.

    Answer: D Difficulty: 1 Page: 277

55. When couples engage in simultaneous oral-genital stimulation, the position used is called
    (a) rear-entry.
    (b) the missionary position.
    (c) anilingus.
    (d) sixty-nine.

    Answer: D Difficulty: 1 Page: 277

56. In a survey of college students, which reasons were most frequently given for not engaging in oral sex?
    (a) offensiveness and repulsion
    (b) genital odors and genital tastes
    (c) shyness and embarrassment
    (d) misinformation and stubbornness

    Answer: C Difficulty: 2 Page: 278

57. Which is true of coitus?
    (a) It is the same as sexual intercourse.
    (b) It includes all forms of sexual contact, including felattio, cunnilingus, and intercourse.
    (c) It is best undertaken in the missionary position.
    (d) The penis may or may not be aligned with the vagina.

    Answer: A Difficulty: 2 Page: 279

58. The most commonly used coital position is
    (a) the male-superior position.
    (b) the female-superior position.
    (c) the rear-entry position.
    (d) the lateral-entry position.

    Answer: A Difficulty: 1 Page: 279

59. A disadvantage of the male-superior coital position is that
    (a) couples cannot see each other's faces.
    (b) it is difficult for the man to caress his partner.
    (c) the position is not very stimulating for the man.
    (d) women cannot orgasm in this position.

    Answer: B Difficulty: 1 Page: 280

60. The coital position that best favors orgasm for the woman and ejaculatory control for the man is the
    (a) rear-entry position.
    (b) lateral-entry position.
    (c) male-superior position.
    (d) female-superior position.

    Answer: D Difficulty: 3 Page: 280

61. Benjamin has difficulty with ejaculatory control. Which intercourse position should he probably avoid until he gains more control?
    (a) male-superior
    (b) female-superior
    (c) rear-entry
    (d) lateral-entry

    Answer: B Difficulty: 2 Page: 280

62. Which intercourse position allows the greatest freedom to touch and caress the body for both males and females?
    (a) male-superior
    (b) rear-entry
    (c) lateral-entry
    (d) female-superior

    Answer: D Difficulty: 2 Page: 280

63. The advantages to the lateral-entry position do not include which of the following?
    (a) Each partner has relatively free movement
    (b) Each partner can kiss freely
    (c) Making noises is easier than in other sexual positions
    (d) It is not as physically taxing as other positions

    Answer: C Difficulty: 1 Page: 280

64. A significant disadvantage of the lateral-entry position is that
    (a) the woman will often orgasm well before the man.
    (b) deep penile penetration is difficult to achieve.
    (c) it is impersonal because couples don't face one another.
    (d) the position can easily fatigue the man and the woman.

    Answer: B Difficulty: 2 Page: 282

65. Elza is eight months pregnant. Which intercourse position will be least risky to the developing fetus and most comfortable for Elza?
    (a) rear-entry with both partners lying side-by-side
    (b) lateral-entry with she and her partner lying side by side
    (c) rear-entry with Elza on her hands and knees
    (d) male-superior

    Answer: A Difficulty: 2 Page: 282

66. Which intercourse position is sometimes thought of as the most impersonal?
    (a) lateral-entry
    (b) rear-entry
    (c) female-superior
    (d) male-superior

    Answer: B Difficulty: 1 Page: 282

67. Disadvantages to the use of fantasy during coitus include
    (a) fantasizing detracts from the authenticity of the encounter.
    (b) fantasizing belittles one's partner.
    (c) fantasizing leads to sexual dissatisfaction.
    (d) none of the above.

    Answer: D Difficulty: 1 Page: 283

68. The 1988 National Survey of Family Growth found that
    (a) African American women were more likely than White American women to have had 15 or
        more sexual partners.
    (b) African American women were more likely to have had their first sexual experience
        at an earlier age than Asian American women.
    (c) White American women were more likely to have had 10 or more sex partners than
        African American women.
    (d) African American women and Native American women were both more likely to have had
        12 or more sex partners than White American women.

    Answer: C Difficulty: 3 Page: 284

69. Which is the most frequently reported coital fantasy among married women?
    (a) I imagine that I am being forced to expose my body to a seducer.
    (b) My thoughts center around feelings of weakness or helplessness.
    (c) I pretend that I am a whore or prostitute.
    (d) Thoughts of an imaginary man enter my mind.

    Answer: D Difficulty: 1 Page: 283

70. Which is *true* regarding the relationship between coital fantasy and sexual satisfaction?
    (a) The use of fantasies during intercourse is related to marital dissatisfaction.
    (b) There is no connection between marital dissatisfaction and the use of coital
        fantasies.
    (c) Women who use coital fantasies report they cannot be sufficiently aroused by their
        partners.
    (d) Most married couples do not use sexual fantasies to enhance their sexual arousal.

    Answer: B Difficulty: 2 Page: 285

71. Dave and his partner Tim enjoy making love in the "Greek style." What is it they enjoy?
    (a) the fact that one or both are bisexual
    (b) coitus in unusual places
    (c) inserting the penis in each other's rectum
    (d) multiple orgasms

    Answer: C Difficulty: 2 Page: 285

72. Why might a woman want her partner's finger in her anus at the moment of orgasm?
    (a) It can heighten sexual sensation.
    (b) It relieves tension.
    (c) It reduces the possibility of transmitting a disease.
    (d) It reduces the embarrassing sound of uncontrolled flatulence.

    Answer: A Difficulty: 2 Page: 286

73. The NHSLS study reported the incidence of anal sex was highest among
    (a) African Americans.
    (b) college-educated Americans.
    (c) high-school educated Americans.
    (d) lower economic groups.

    Answer: B Difficulty: 2 Page: 286

74. When all demographic factors are taken into consideration, what is the approximate percent of persons in the United States who report experience with anal intercourse?
    (a) 10 percent
    (b) 25 percent
    (c) 45 percent
    (d) 60 percent

    Answer: C Difficulty: 3 Page: 286

75. Which statement most accurately reflects a legitimate concern about anal sex?
    (a) Oral-anal activity carries a serious health risk.
    (b) Even in couples with no history of sexually transmitted disease, anal intercourse can cause serious infections.
    (c) Anal intercourse is unnatural and morally unacceptable behavior for all human beings.
    (d) Anal intercourse is acceptable for homosexual males but not appropriate for heterosexual couples.

    Answer: A Difficulty: 2 Page: 287

MATCHING

Match the appropriate intercourse (coital) position with its correct advantages and disadvantages. Answers may be used more than once.

(a) male-superior

(b) female-superior

(c) lateral-entry

(d) rear-entry

76. Manual stimulation of the clitoris by the male is most difficult in this position.

    Answer: a

77. This position is less stimulating for the male but may help with ejaculatory control.

    Answer: b

78. The best position for prolonged intercourse.

    Answer: c

79. This position is best when both partners are fatigued.

    Answer: c

80. This position may introduce air into the vagina.

    Answer: d

81. In this position, insertion of the penis is most difficult.

    Answer: c

82. In this position, it may be difficult to keep the penis in the vagina.

    Answer: d

83. This position may create a sense of emotional distance.

    Answer: d

84. It can be difficult to achieve deep penetration of the penis in this position.

    Answer: c

85. This position often facilitates a feeling of control for the female.

    Answer: b

TRUE/FALSE

86. Masturbation among married people signifies a troubled relationship.

    Answer: False

87. Regarding manual stimulation of the genitals, variability in technique is desirable.

    Answer: True

88. In the NHSLS study, the most frequently cited reason for masturbation was lack of a sexual partner.

    Answer: False

89. For both genders, people with more education reported more frequent masturbation.

    Answer: True

90. In sexual fantasies, women are more apt to fantasize about being aggressive or sexually dominant.

    Answer: False

91. It is natural for heterosexual individuals to fantasize periodically about sexual activity with the same gender.

    Answer: True

92. Deep kissing is the same as French kissing and soul kissing.

    Answer: True

93. Sex therapists encourage clients to use fantasies to enhance sexual arousal.

    Answer: True

94. A majority of men masturbate by rubbing their genitals against inflatable dolls.

    Answer: False

95. Touching is a common form of foreplay.

    Answer: True

96. African American women are more likely to masturbate than European American women.

    Answer: False

97. In the Judeo-Christian tradition, any sexual contact that does not lead to procreation has been considered sinful.

    Answer: True

98. The word masturbation derives from the Latin word *masturbari*.

    Answer: True

99. African American men are more likely to masturbate than European men.

    Answer: False

100. Women are more likely to reach orgasm through masturbation than coitus.

    Answer: True

101. Most women masturbate by inserting a finger or other object into the vagina.

    Answer: False

102. Virtually all species of mammals, from horses to dogs, engage in some kind of sexual foreplay.

    Answer: True

103. Kissing is unknown in some cultures, including those of the Thonga of Africa and the Siriono of Bolivia.

    Answer: True

104. Research and evidence show that partners who fantasize during coitus have a troubled relationship.

    Answer: False

ESSAY

105. Identify the key figures and opinions that formed the medical and psychological views of masturbation in the eighteenth and nineteenth centuries.

    Answer:

106. Discuss the implications of "interactive sex" or "cybersex" in terms of the social and political impact of this technology in the new millennium.

    Answer:

107. Identify and discuss the advantages and disadvantages of the four intercourse positions in the text.

    Answer:

108. Summarize the studies investigating the use of sexual fantasy during intercourse. Discuss the frequency and impact of coital fantasies on overall sexual functioning within a relationship.

    Answer:

109. Summarize the frequency of anal intercourse among couples. What factors influence a couple to engage or not engage in anal intercourse?

    Answer:

Chapter 10: Sexual Orientation

1. Sexual orientation is defined as an individual's
   (a) erotic attraction and sexual activity with members of the same or other gender.
   (b) erotic attraction toward and romantic interest in members of the same or other gender.
   (c) sexual activity with members of the same or other gender.
   (d) preference for particular sexual activities with one's own gender.

   Answer: B Difficulty: 1 Page: 290

2. Many gay people object to the term "homosexual" because
   (a) it draws attention to sexual behavior, bears a social stigma, and is ambiguous.
   (b) it is a derivative of the word "homophile" which focuses only on sexual behavior.
   (c) it is a term that is historically outdated.
   (d) it is so clinical.

   Answer: A Difficulty: 1 Page: 291

3. The term "homophile" suggests
   (a) an unnatural relationship.
   (b) love and friendship to member of one's own gender.
   (c) a fear of same-gender orientation.
   (d) ambiguity.

   Answer: B Difficulty: 1 Page: 292

4. Which is *true* of gay males and lesbians?
   (a) Their gender identities are consistent with their anatomical genders.
   (b) They generally are uncomfortable with their anatomical gender.
   (c) They focus more on the sexual aspects of relationships than heterosexual couples.
   (d) Sexual activity, not romantic or erotic attraction, defines their sexual interests.

   Answer: A Difficulty: 2 Page: 292

5. How do heterosexuals tend to perceive male-male relationships?
   (a) Heterosexuals see them as remarkably similar to their own, heterosexual relationships.
   (b) Heterosexuals focus mostly on the sexual aspects of male-male relationships.
   (c) Heterosexuals usually notice the caring bond among gays.
   (d) Heterosexuals tend to underestimate the time gays spend in sexual activity.

   Answer: B Difficulty: 2 Page: 292

6. Concerning sexual orientation, which of the following is not accurate?
   (a) While some people are exclusively gay, and some are exclusively straight, some fall in between.
   (b) Determining a person's sexual orientation is not a clear-cut task.
   (c) If an alleged straight person has had a sexual experience with someone of his/her own gender, he/she is bi-sexual.
   (d) Some people are exclusively gay.

   Answer: C Difficulty: 2 Page: 292

7. That prison inmates maintain their heterosexual identity while engaging in male-male sexual, is evidence that
   (a) they confuse sexuality with power.
   (b) sexual experiences do not necessarily determine sexual identity.
   (c) all men lie on a continuum between homo- and heterosexuality.
   (d) male and female inmates should be granted more visitation privileges.

   Answer: B Difficulty: 2 Page: 293

8. Which of the following is evidence that sexual orientation is not necessarily expressed in sexual behavior?
   (a) Some gay men and women have sex more often than their heterosexual counterparts.
   (b) Once released from prison, former inmates choose to have sex with other-gender partners.
   (c) Some people enjoy hugging others, regardless of others' gender.
   (d) Some people remain celibate for religious reasons.

   Answer: D Difficulty: 2 Page: 293

9. Which of the following is most accurate regarding attraction to others?
   (a) Bi-sexuality is politically correct rhetoric; in reality, people are attracted either to one gender or the other.
   (b) A correct model of sexuality would have three corners: gay, heterosexual, and experimenters.
   (c) The boundary between homo- and heterosexuality is sometimes blurry.
   (d) With the exception of prison inmates, attraction to one's own or the other gender is mutually exclusive.

   Answer: C Difficulty: 3 Page: 293

10. Engaging in sexual activity with members of the same sex
    (a) does not mean an individual is a gay male or lesbian.
    (b) is indicative of gender dysphoria.
    (c) indicates a same-gender sexual orientation that is fixed.
    (d) will eventually alter sexual orientation.

    Answer: A Difficulty: 2 Page: 293

11. Which of the following is *true* regarding sexual fantasies and sexual orientation?
    (a) Heterosexual adults rarely fantasize about sexual activity with their own gender.
    (b) Gay males and lesbians frequently fantasize about sexual activity with the opposite gender.
    (c) When heterosexuals fantasize about sexual activity with the same gender, it indicates a bisexual orientation.
    (d) When homosexual fantasize about sexual activity with the opposite gender, they are unsure of their homosexual orientation.

    Answer: B Difficulty: 3 Page: 293

12. In the Kinsey studies, what percent of male respondents were exclusively gay?
    (a) 1%
    (b) 4%
    (c) 10%
    (d) 22%

    Answer: B Difficulty: 2 Page: 293

13. In interpreting the original Kinsey studies, it is important to keep in mind that
    (a) Kinsey's sample was not a random, and this makes it impossible to know if the results can be generalized.
    (b) his sample consisted of more gay men and lesbian women than heterosexuals.
    (c) he did not include prison populations or ethnic minorities.
    (d) results may be biased by the researcher's personal beliefs.

    Answer: A Difficulty: 2 Page: 295

14. In comparing Kinsey's first studies with later studies on sexual orientation, it can be said that
    (a) the initial Kinsey studies vastly overestimated the incidence of same-sex behavior.
    (b) the initial Kinsey studies underestimated the percent of exclusively gay or lesbian orientations.
    (c) the initial Kinsey studies underestimated the incidence of same-sex behavior.
    (d) the estimates of same-sex behavior and sexual orientation in the initial Kinsey studies are similar to later studies.

    Answer: D Difficulty: 2 Page: 295

15. Statistics concerning *past* sexual activity with a member of one's own gender must be interpreted with caution because
    (a) people tend to repress memories of same-sex experiences.
    (b) the experience may have been a brief experimental period in a person's life.
    (c) recalling previous sexual experiences can be harmful.
    (d) researchers do not get the opportunity to interview people in person.

    Answer: B Difficulty: 2 Page: 295

16. Kinsey's data indicated that patterns of sexual behavior
    (a) remain fixed throughout the life span.
    (b) usually change between adolescence and adulthood.
    (c) change for gay males and lesbians more often than for heterosexuals.
    (d) can sometimes change.

    Answer: D Difficulty: 2 Page: 295

17. Which of the following is most accurate regarding current estimates of the number of gays?
    (a) Kinsey's figure of 10% is accurate.
    (b) If one counts those who have engaged in at least one sexual activity with someone of the same gender since adolescence, roughly 18% of males would qualify as gay.
    (c) They are lower than Kinsey's estimates.
    (d) Kinsey's estimate is about right for the U.S., but much too low for Asia and the Pacific island countries.

    Answer: C Difficulty: 3 Page: 295

18. Cross-cultural studies indicate the following trends among gays and lesbians
    (a) Gays and lesbians are unwilling to report engaging in sexual behavior.
    (b) A certain percentage of gays and lesbians identify themselves as such, and an even higher percentage of people report some sexual attraction to members of their own gender.
    (c) Only those who identify themselves as gay report attraction to members of their own gender.
    (d) The percentage of lesbians is consistently somewhat higher than the percentage of gay men.

    Answer: B Difficulty: 3 Page: 295

19. The author points out several factors that affect survey results. Which of the following is not among them?
    (a) the region of the country where the survey was conducted
    (b) the phrasing of the questions
    (c) the manner in which the survey was conducted, such as personal interviews, phone calls, or written surveys
    (d) the gender of the interviewer

    Answer: A Difficulty: 3 Page: 296

20. Not all sex researchers accept Kinsey's continuum because
    (a) there are too few markings along the continuum.
    (b) it promotes bias among the respondents.
    (c) the true incidence of bi-sexuality is so small.
    (d) gay and heterosexual orientations may not be opposites.

    Answer: D Difficulty: 3 Page: 296

21. According to Michael Storms, a person who is high in both heteroeroticism and homoeroticism may exhibit a
    (a) heterosexual orientation.
    (b) homosexual orientation but choose to participate in heterosexual activities.
    (c) predominantly homosexual orientation.
    (d) bisexual orientation.

    Answer: D Difficulty: 1 Page: 296

22. Elza is low in both heteroeroticism and homoeroticism. According to Michael Storms, Elza might be described as
    (a) exclusively heterosexual.
    (b) asexual.
    (c) bisexual.
    (d) largely homosexual.

    Answer: B Difficulty: 1 Page: 296

23. Regarding bi-sexuality Kinsey and Storms's models made different predictions. Which of the following is most accurate?
    (a) Kinsey was right.
    (b) Storms was right.
    (c) Kinsey was right about heterosexuals, but Storms was right about gays.
    (d) Neither was right since heterosexuals are reluctant to report same-gender fantasies.

    Answer: B Difficulty: 3 Page: 296

24. Which of the following is true, according to NHSLS study?
    (a) Some 15% of the respondents feel attracted to both genders.
    (b) About 15% of the respondents reported having a bisexual identity.
    (c) A bisexual identity is more common than attraction to both genders.
    (d) Attraction to both genders is more common than a bisexual identity.

    Answer: D Difficulty: 2 Page: 297

25. Depending on the definition of bisexuality, it is probably safe to say that approximately
    (a) 1% - 4% of the population is bisexual.
    (b) 5% - 8% of the population is bisexual.
    (c) 8% - 12% of the population is bisexual.
    (d) 13% - 15% of the population is bisexual.

    Answer: A Difficulty: 3 Page: 297

26. Which statement is *true* about bisexuality?
    (a) Bisexual people use bisexuality as a cover for a gay male or lesbian sexual orientation.
    (b) Heterosexual people, gay males, and lesbians ostracize bisexual people.
    (c) The vast majority of bisexual people are in heterosexual marriages.
    (d) Bisexuality is simply a form of sexual experimentation by predominantly heterosexuals.

    Answer: B Difficulty: 2 Page: 298

27. Which is true of a bisexual?
    (a) Some can lead a lifestyle permitting them to satisfy their dual inclinations.
    (b) Some are pressured to commit themselves to just one gender
    (c) Some are gay but are looking for a way to mask their orientation.
    (d) All of the above.

    Answer: D Difficulty: 2 Page: 298

28. Which is true of gay male and lesbian sexual orientations throughout history?
    (a) They have always met with strong condemnation.
    (b) In Western culture they have been widely condemned.
    (c) In Judeo-Christian tradition they have been allowed, but not openly encouraged.
    (d) Our legal system maintains criminal penalties for men, but not for lesbians.

    Answer: B Difficulty: 3 Page: 298

29. Which was true in early Christianity regarding sexual activity?
    (a) Sexual activity within one's own gender was neither encouraged nor discouraged.
    (b) All non-procreative sex was thought to be sinful.
    (c) A double standard existed: male/male activity was condemned; female/female activity was not.
    (d) Sexual activity was not addressed by the early church.

    Answer: B Difficulty: 3 Page: 298

30. By late Middle Ages, most laws in Western Europe contained
    (a) penalties for anal but not oral sex.
    (b) penalties for bestiality unless the husband had become a widower.
    (c) penalties for too frequent vaginal intercourse.
    (d) penalties for masturbation.

    Answer: D Difficulty: 3 Page: 298

31. Regarding church response to gay orientation, which is true?
    (a) The Roman Catholic Church condemns orientation and activity.
    (b) The Roman Catholic Church claims no righteous man or women can have a homosexual orientation.
    (c) Some pastors bless gay unions because the demand exceeds the demand for male/female unions.
    (d) Some pastors bless gay unions because God did not intend for people to live alone.

    Answer: D Difficulty: 3 Page: 299

32. Male-male sexual activity is more common in societies that
    (a) encourage competition between males.
    (b) highly value female virginity.
    (c) place less value on traditional gender roles.
    (d) place less value on the institution of marriage.

    Answer: B Difficulty: 2 Page: 299

33. Initiating young males into adulthood through male-male sexual activity sometimes centers on the belief that
    (a) older men are the best teachers of sexual techniques.
    (b) females are contaminated.
    (c) sexual orientation is flexible.
    (d) semen boosts strength and virility.

    Answer: D Difficulty: 2 Page: 299

34. In a number of preliterate societies, male-male sexual activity is limited to
    (a) rites of passage into manhood.
    (b) unmarriageable boys.
    (c) males in lower social hierarchies.
    (d) adulthood.

    Answer: A Difficulty: 3 Page: 299

35. In Sambia, a ten-year-old boy is encouraged to engage in fellatio with an older male because
    (a) it teaches him how to give sexual pleasure.
    (b) he learns how older men delay ejaculation.
    (c) semen is believed to give rise to puberty and acquire fierce manhood.
    (d) it teaches him the dominance hierarchy in Sambian society.

    Answer: C Difficulty: 2 Page: 299

36. Which statement most accurately reflects who discriminates against gay males and lesbians?
    (a) Ethnic minorities as a whole are more tolerant of gay males and lesbians.
    (b) Disabled people show more compassion for gay males and lesbians.
    (c) Asian Americans and Hispanic people are more tolerant of gay males and lesbians.
    (d) Both majority and minority groups display strong intolerance for gay males and
        lesbians.

    Answer: D Difficulty: 2 Page: 301

37. Which statement represents a *false* assumption about male-male sexual behavior in animals of other species?
    (a) The behavior may represent dominance rituals.
    (b) The behavior clearly represents same-sex orientation.
    (c) The behavior may occur as a means of seeking favors from dominant males.
    (d) The behaviors may be a form of play.

    Answer: B Difficulty: 2 Page: 301

38. In a national survey of males in their late teens, how many felt sex between men was "disgusting?"
    (a) 90%
    (b) 60%
    (c) 30%
    (d) 0%

    Answer: A Difficulty: 1 Page: 302

39. Which group is harshest in their judgments of gay males and lesbians?
    (a) teenage females
    (b) males over the age of fifty
    (c) males between 15 and 19
    (d) both males and females over the age of forty

    Answer: C Difficulty: 2 Page: 302

40. From a 1998 national poll, which conclusion about homosexuality is accurate?
    (a) Most adults believe it is wrong.
    (b) Most adults believe it is O.K.
    (c) Most adults said they didn't know.
    (d) Slightly more adults believe it is O.K. than those who believe it is wrong.

    Answer: A Difficulty: 2 Page: 302

41. Between 1977 and 1996, the number of Americans endorsing equal opportunity employment rights for gay males and lesbians
    (a) declined substantially.
    (b) declined very slightly.
    (c) increased substantially.
    (d) stayed even.

    Answer: C Difficulty: 3 Page: 302

42. Despite increases in overall tolerance of gay people, the majority of American adults still believe that
    (a) gay men and women are born gay.
    (b) gay men and women should not have equal access to jobs.
    (c) gay couples should not raise children.
    (d) gay individuals will molest young children.

    Answer: C Difficulty: 2 Page: 303

43. Those *most* likely to be homophobic are
    (a) people who support traditional gender roles and hold a fundamentalist religious orientation.
    (b) males who hold liberal political positions.
    (c) well-educated heterosexual men and women.
    (d) males who deny their own homosexuality.

    Answer: A Difficulty: 1 Page: 304

44. Jerry is homophobic. If Jerry were to participate in plethysmograph studies while viewing sexually explicit videos, what might be expected?
    (a) Jerry would only be aroused by male-female sexual activity but deny this arousal.
    (b) Jerry would be aroused by male-female and female-female sexual activity and report this arousal.
    (c) Jerry would be aroused by male-female, male-male, and female-female sexual activity but deny arousal that results from male-male activity.
    (d) Jerry would be aroused by male-female and male-male sexual activity and report this arousal.

    Answer: C Difficulty: 2 Page: 304

45. In a survey at Pennsylvania State University, how many gay males and lesbians reported that they had been physically assaulted because of their orientation?
    (a) 5%
    (b) 20%
    (c) 50%
    (d) 80%

    Answer: B Difficulty: 2 Page: 305

46. The anti-gay sentiment has recently been fueled by
    (a) challenges to sodomy laws.
    (b) an increase in child molestation cases.
    (c) evidence supporting a biological basis for sexual orientation.
    (d) the AIDS epidemic.

    Answer: D Difficulty: 2 Page: 305

47. The 1986 Supreme Court decision (*Hardwick vs. Bowers*) was a blow to gay rights because
(a) marriage between gay persons was banned.
(b) the sodomy laws in Georgia were upheld.
(c) gays were banned from military service.
(d) employers were given the right not to hire gay individuals.

Answer: B Difficulty: 3 Page: 306

48. "Outing" is the practice of
(a) revealing one's gay or lesbian orientation to friends and family.
(b) bringing gay issues into the political arena.
(c) unmasking other gay people without their consent.
(d) frequenting gay bars and bathhouses.

Answer: C Difficulty: 3 Page: 306

49. Which statement regarding monozygotic twins (MT) and dizygotic twins (DT) is most accurate?
(a) If one twin is gay, it is probable that his DT is gay.
(b) If one twin is gay, it is probable that his MT is gay.
(c) Since DT are more likely than MT to be dressed and treated alike, a higher concordance for gay sexual orientation is expected among DTs.
(d) Because MTs share 50% of their heredity, one would expect a concordance rate of 50% for sexual orientation.

Answer: B Difficulty: 3 Page: 307

50. Researchers at the National Cancer Institute found evidence linking a gay male sexual orientation to
(a) an extra 13th chromosome.
(b) an area at the tip of the X chromosome.
(c) the interstitial nucleus of the hypothalamus.
(d) prenatal exposure to excess estrogens.

Answer: B Difficulty: 2 Page: 307

51. According to LeVay's research, which area of the brain might be linked to same-sex orientation?
(a) the frontal lobes
(b) the posterior cerebellum
(c) the cingulate gyrus
(d) the anterior hypothalamus

Answer: D Difficulty: 2 Page: 309

52. What does polymorphously perverse mean?
(a) engaging in sadomasochistic sexual activity
(b) being open to all forms of sexual stimulation
(c) limiting sexual gratification to anal intercourse
(d) adopting a bisexual orientation

Answer: B Difficulty: 1 Page: 309

53. According to the research of Richard Pillard and his colleagues, gay males described themselves as
(a) having distant relationships with their fathers as children.
(b) having smothering relationships with their mothers.
(c) overly masculine children.
(d) having alcoholic fathers and distant mothers.

Answer: A Difficulty: 2 Page: 311

54. Angelica is a lesbian. According to learning theorists, what is the most likely explanation for the development of her lesbian orientation?
    (a) She had a cold and distant relationship with her mother.
    (b) She was extremely close to her father and had all male playmates as a small child.
    (c) Because she never learned to get along with females, she lacks experience with behaviors associated with the female gender.
    (d) She experimented with same-gender sexual behavior, and the experiences were pleasurable.

    Answer: D Difficulty: 3 Page: 311

55. In terms of close relationships and satisfaction, researchers have found that gay males and lesbians
    (a) have more difficulty with satisfactory relationships than heterosexual couples.
    (b) experience similar levels of satisfaction as heterosexual couples.
    (c) experience high levels of attachment but lower levels of intimacy than heterosexual couples.
    (d) experience higher levels of intimacy but lower levels of commitment than heterosexual couples.

    Answer: B Difficulty: 2 Page: 312

56. For gay individuals who sought therapy to change their sexual orientation, the key factor in a successful outcome appeared to be
    (a) a high motivation to change.
    (b) sex reassignment surgery.
    (c) hormone treatments.
    (d) the type of therapy.

    Answer: A Difficulty: 3 Page: 315

57. In comparing the sexual techniques of male-female partners and male-male partners, it appears that gay males
    (a) spend more time concentrating on the genital area.
    (b) almost always use anal intercourse as the means for orgasm and ejaculation.
    (c) spend more time caressing their partners' bodies before approaching the genitals.
    (d) frequently use a practice called "fisting."

    Answer: C Difficulty: 2 Page: 318

58. Genital apposition is a sexual technique where
    (a) males insert a fist or hand into the rectum.
    (b) lesbians position themselves to rub their genitals together rhythmically.
    (c) gay males simultaneously perform fellatio on each other.
    (d) lesbians use a dildo or penis-shaped object to stimulate their partner.

    Answer: B Difficulty: 2 Page: 318

59. Which of the following statements best characterizes President Clinton's 1993 policy regarding gays in the military?
    (a) The policy admits gays into the military but their advancement in rank is limited.
    (b) Gay men and women may serve as enlisted members but not as officers.
    (c) Gay men and women must be admitted and allowed to reveal their sexual orientation if they so desire.
    (d) Gay men and women can serve but are prohibited from revealing their sexual orientation.

    Answer: D Difficulty: 2 Page: 320

MATCHING

For each of the following descriptions of a gay couple's relationship, match the description with Bell and Weinberg's relationship lifestyle.

(a) Dysfunctionals

(b) Close Coupled

(c) Functionals

(d) Open Coupled

(e) Asexuals

60. Mark and Stephanos have lived together as a couple for about six years. Both occasionally engage in sexual relations with other men.

    Answer: d

61. Alesha has known since she turned twenty that she is attracted to women. She had a brief relationship with another female around age thirty. Since then she has lived alone and has had no further sexual relationships.

    Answer: e

62. Marcos is the life of the party. He frequents gay bars and social clubs, often bringing home a new lover once or twice every few weeks. He is satisfied with his love life.

    Answer: c

63. Jennifer seems to be constantly searching for the right woman. She frequently initiates new relationships, but as soon as sex becomes part of the relationship, she cuts it off and begins searching for another partner.

    Answer: a

64. Richard and Michael were married in a church ceremony last year. Prior to taking this step, they had lived together as a couple for six years. As part of their marriage vows, they agreed to complete fidelity as a couple.

    Answer: b

TRUE/FALSE

65. In a survey investigating extracurricular sexual activity, almost 80% of gay males living with a partner reported having sex with another partner in the last year.

    Answer: True

66. Research has failed to find a connection between sexual orientation and differences in levels of male or female sex hormones in adulthood.

    Answer: True

67. According to Freud, same-gender sexual orientation results from early childhood experiences with a "close-binding" father and a "detached-hostile" mother.

    Answer: False

68. Gay males are generally fearful or repulsed by the idea of sexual activity with a female.

    Answer: False

69. The majority of gay males and lesbians report that they preferred opposite sex activities and toys as children.

    Answer: True

70. Today, it is clear that sexual orientation is largely the result of biological factors.

    Answer: False

71. As a general group, gay males and lesbians are more highly educated than most Americans.

    Answer: True

72. If given the opportunity and means, Bell and Weinberg found that the majority of gay men and women would change their orientation to heterosexual.

    Answer: False

73. About 20% of gay males and lesbians enter a heterosexual marriage at least once.

    Answer: True

74. Gay men and women are more likely than the general population to use personal computers, modems, and online services.

    Answer: True

75. Gay men and women may engage in male-female activity while maintaining a gay sexual orientation.

    Answer: True

76. Because same-sex orientation carries a social stigma, survey results probably tend to over-report the number of respondents who report same-sex desires.

    Answer: False

ESSAY

77. Compare and contrast the Kinsey continuum of sexual orientation and Michael Storm's two-dimensional model of sexual orientation.

    Answer:

78. Discuss studies investigating sexual fantasies and the relationship between opposite or same-gender sexual fantasies and sexual orientation.

    Answer:

79. Explain the role of religions in past and current perceptions of same-gender sexual behavior.

    Answer:

80. Using examples of religious upbringing, ethnicities, and gender roles, relate these ideas to intolerance and prejudice against gay men and women.

    Answer:

81. Using the concepts of polymorphously perverse, the Oedipal complex, castration anxiety, and penis envy, explain Freud's theory of sexual orientation.

    Answer:

82. Discuss the various aspects of coming out.

    Answer:

83. Identify and discuss three lifestyle differences between gay males and lesbians.

    Answer:

Chapter 11: Conception, Pregnancy, and Childbirth

MULTIPLE CHOICE

1. What is a zygote?
   (a) a new ovum
   (b) a fertilized ovum
   (c) an unfertilized ovum
   (d) a premature ovum

   Answer: B Difficulty: 2 Page: 328

2. Elainie is age 37. Four months into her pregnancy, Elaine obtains _____ in order to check for the presence of chromosomal abnormalities.
   (a) an X-ray screening
   (b) amniocentesis
   (c) an ultra sound
   (d) a spinal tap

   Answer: B Difficulty: 2 Page: 328

3. Amniocentesis is a procedure used to
   (a) check for chromosomal abnormalities.
   (b) determine ovulation.
   (c) treat postpartum depression.
   (d) treat blood disorders in newborns.

   Answer: A Difficulty: 2 Page: 328

4. Ray has a chromosomal abnormality, caused by an extra chromosome on the 21st pair. This abnormality has retarded Ray's mental growth and is called
   (a) Down syndrome.
   (b) Klinefelters syndrome.
   (c) XYY syndrome.
   (d) FSH.

   Answer: A Difficulty: 1 Page: 328

5. What is the gelatinous layer that surrounds an ovum?
   (a) zona pellucida
   (b) hyaluronidase
   (c) epiovum
   (d) gonadotropin

   Answer: A Difficulty: 2 Page: 329

6. Hyaluronidase is a(n)
   (a) treatment for cervical cancer.
   (b) enzyme.
   (c) bacterium.
   (d) abnormal growth.

   Answer: B Difficulty: 1 Page: 329

7. Shettle's approach to controlling gender selection is based on this fact.
   (a) Sperm bearing the Y sex chromosome are faster swimmers.
   (b) Sperm bearing the Y sex chromosome prefer a more acidic environment.
   (c) Sperm bearing the X sex chromosome prefer a slightly higher temperature.
   (d) Sperm bearing the X sex chromosome live somewhat longer than Y sex chromosomes.

   Answer: B Difficulty: 3 Page: 330

8. Just prior to ovulation, basal body temperature
   (a) rises slightly and remains higher for three to four days.
   (b) dips slightly then rises and remains elevated until menstruation.
   (c) rises slightly then dips and remains slightly lower until menstruation.
   (d) dips slightly and remains lower until menstruation ends.

   Answer: B Difficulty: 2 Page: 332

9. John and his wife are trying to conceive. John knows that his sperm count is slightly low. Which recommendation should John follow for the best chance of conception?
   (a) John and his wife should have intercourse every day for the entire week.
   (b) John and his wife should have intercourse twice a day for the entire week.
   (c) John and his wife should engage in intercourse every 72 hours and John should masturbate every day to increase his sperm count.
   (d) John and his wife should have intercourse every 48 hours.

   Answer: D Difficulty: 2 Page: 332

10. Over-the-counter ovulation kits analyze the urine or saliva for the presence of
    (a) luteinizing hormone.
    (b) estrogen.
    (c) follicle stimulating hormone.
    (d) progesterone.

    Answer: A Difficulty: 1 Page: 332

11. A few days before ovulation, cervical mucus
    (a) thickens and takes on a yellowish color.
    (b) becomes thin, slippery, and clear.
    (c) becomes thick, white, and takes on a cottage-cheese like texture.
    (d) thickens and takes on a milky white color.

    Answer: B Difficulty: 2 Page: 332

12. Women can improve their chances of conception by using the
    (a) lateral-entry coital position.
    (b) lateral rear-entry coital position.
    (c) male-superior coital position.
    (d) female-superior coital position.

    Answer: C Difficulty: 1 Page: 332

13. How long should a couple have tried to conceive before being considered infertile?
    (a) 3 months
    (b) 6 months
    (c) 10 months
    (d) 12 months

    Answer: D Difficulty: 3 Page: 333

14. Which causes fertility problems for men?
    (a) a low sperm count
    (b) thyroid disease
    (c) a pituitary imbalance
    (d) all of the above

    Answer: D Difficulty: 2 Page: 333

15. Of couples who experience infertility problems, how many will eventually succeed in conceiving a child?
    (a) 20%
    (b) 35%
    (c) 50%
    (d) 60%

    Answer: C Difficulty: 3 Page: 333

16. What is the most common fertility problem for men?
    (a) a pituitary imbalance
    (b) low sperm count
    (c) diabetes
    (d) thyroid disease

    Answer: B Difficulty: 2 Page: 333

17. All of the following may lower a man's sperm count except
    (a) electric blankets.
    (b) hot baths.
    (c) prolonged athletic activity.
    (d) infrequent ejaculation.

    Answer: D Difficulty: 2 Page: 333

18. Which of the following does not cause infertility in women?
    (a) irregular ovulation
    (b) endometriosis
    (c) low blood sugar
    (d) declining hormone levels

    Answer: C Difficulty: 2 Page: 334

19. To be considered normal, how long should sperm be able to swim after ejaculation?
    (a) ten minutes
    (b) five hours
    (c) two hours
    (d) sixty minutes

    Answer: C Difficulty: 2 Page: 334

20. Sperm counts have been increased by
    (a) a high fiber diet.
    (b) surgical repair of the varicose veins in the scrotum.
    (c) a steady cardio-vascular routine.
    (d) all of the above.

    Answer: B Difficulty: 1 Page: 334

21. For men whose sperm lack a tail, which procedure produces the best chance of conception?
    (a) removal of sperm from the testes and in vitro fertilization
    (b) pooling of several ejaculates and injection of the sperm into the uterus
    (c) pooling of several ejaculates and injection of the sperm near the cervix
    (d) small injections of estrogens to increase sperm count and viability

    Answer: A Difficulty: 3 Page: 334

22. How many women are estimated to be infertile because they fail to ovulate?
    (a) 3% to 5%
    (b) 7% to 8%
    (c) 10% to 15%
    (d) 20% to 25%

    Answer: C Difficulty: 3 Page: 334

23. The drug *clomiphene* works by stimulating the release of
    (a) estrogen in non-ovulating women.
    (b) testosterone in men with low sperm counts.
    (c) follicle-stimulating hormone in men with low sperm counts.
    (d) follicle-stimulating hormone and luteinizing hormone in non-ovulating women.

    Answer: D Difficulty: 2 Page: 334

24. Endometriosis occurs when
    (a) infectious agents scar the fallopian tubes.
    (b) cells break away from the uterine lining, implant, and grow elsewhere.
    (c) hormonal imbalances prevent ovulation.
    (d) malnutrition causes hormonal imbalances and prevents ovulation.

    Answer: B Difficulty: 1 Page: 335

25. Laparoscopy is
    (a) an abnormal condition in which endometrial tissue swells beyond the abdominal cavity.
    (b) a medical procedure in which a long, narrow tube is inserted through an incision in the naval, permitting the visual inspection of organs in the pelvic cavity.
    (c) a test in which carbon dioxide gas is blown through the cervix and its progress through the reproductive tract is tracked to determine whether fallopian tubes are blocked.
    (d) a test in which a dye is injected into the reproductive tract and its progress is tracked by X-rays to determine whether the fallopian tubes are blocked.

    Answer: B Difficulty: 2 Page: 335

26. In a Rubin test
    (a) carbon dioxide is blown into the uterus to check for blocked fallopian tubes.
    (b) blood is drawn to check for anemia due to excessive blood loss during menstruation.
    (c) dye is injected into the uterus to look for uterine tumors.
    (d) sperm are checked for motility by measuring their rate and duration of swimming.

    Answer: A Difficulty: 2 Page: 335

27. In vitro fertilization is a procedure in which
    (a) donor sperm is injected near the cervix or in the uterus.
    (b) sperm are removed from a man's testes and injected in the uterus.
    (c) eggs are removed from the ovary, fertilized, and implanted in the uterus.
    (d) sperm are amplified and injected directly into the fallopian tube.

    Answer: C Difficulty: 3 Page: 336

28. Which procedure involves placing the parents' zygote in the mother's fallopian tube?
    (a) IVF
    (b) donor IVF
    (c) GIFT
    (d) ZIFT

    Answer: D Difficulty: 3 Page: 336

29. Charlene and her husband want to have a baby, but Charlene cannot produce any ova in her ovaries. Which procedure will Charlene have to try in order to give birth?
    (a) ZIFT
    (b) donor IVF
    (c) GIFT
    (d) IVF

    Answer: B Difficulty: 2 Page: 336

30. _____ is a method of conception in which a woman volunteer is artificially inseminated by the male partner of the intended mother, after which the embryo is removed from the volunteer and inserted into the uterus of the intended mother.
    (a) Embryonic transfer
    (b) Gamete intrafallopian transfer
    (c) Intracytoplasmic transfer
    (d) Zygote intrafallopian transfer

    Answer: A Difficulty: 2 Page: 336

31. Intracytoplasmic sperm injection may be associated with
    (a) a lower risk of birth defects.
    (b) a higher rate of multiple births.
    (c) a higher risk of birth defects.
    (d) a lower rate of implantation.

    Answer: C Difficulty: 2 Page: 336

32. For many women the first sign of pregnancy is
    (a) missing a period.
    (b) morning sickness.
    (c) retaining water.
    (d) a faint vaginal twinge.

    Answer: A Difficulty: 1 Page: 338

33. What is the hormone produced by women shortly after conception, which stimulates the corpus luteum to continue to produce progesterone?
    (a) testosterone
    (b) human chorionic gonadotropin
    (c) estrogen
    (d) endosterone

    Answer: B Difficulty: 2 Page: 338

34. The *beta subunit HCG radioimmunoassay* can detect pregnancy about
    (a) six weeks after conception.
    (b) eight days after conception.
    (c) three weeks after conception.
    (d) four weeks after conception.

    Answer: B Difficulty: 2 Page: 339

35. Over-the-counter pregnancy tests are intended to detect
    (a) luteinizing hormone in the urine.
    (b) lower than normal estrogen levels in the blood.
    (c) higher than normal follicle-stimulating hormone levels in the urine.
    (d) human chorionic gonadotropin in the urine.

    Answer: D Difficulty: 1 Page: 339

36. In pregnant women, Hegar's sign means the
    (a) labia have turned a darker color.
    (b) cervix has taken on a bluish appearance.
    (c) uterus has softened between the uterine body and the cervix.
    (d) veins under the skin of the breasts are more pronounced.

    Answer: C Difficulty: 2 Page: 339

37. In most women, morning sickness usually subsides by the
    (a) twelfth week of pregnancy.
    (b) eighth week of pregnancy.
    (c) sixth week of pregnancy.
    (d) fourth week of pregnancy.

    Answer: A Difficulty: 3 Page: 340

38. Provided that the pregnancy is progressing normally and the woman has no history of miscarriage, how long is it safe to have intercourse?
    (a) Intercourse is never safe during pregnancy.
    (b) Intercourse is safe up until labor.
    (c) Intercourse should stop three weeks before the baby's due date.
    (d) Intercourse should stop during the last trimester.

    Answer: B Difficulty: 2 Page: 340

39. The experiencing of a number of signs of pregnancy by the father is called
    (a) harmonic pregnancy.
    (b) sympathetic pregnancy.
    (c) intuitive pregnancy.
    (d) male pregnancy.

    Answer: B Difficulty: 2 Page: 341

40. The germinal stage of pregnancy refers to the first
    (a) trimester.
    (b) six weeks after conception.
    (c) two months after conception.
    (d) two weeks.

    Answer: D Difficulty: 2 Page: 343

41. Several days into the germinal stage, the cell mass takes the form of a fluid-filled ball of cells, which is called a
    (a) follicle.
    (b) blastocyst.
    (c) morula.
    (d) zygote.

    Answer: B Difficulty: 2 Page: 343

42. How long does it take a zygote to reach the uterus?
    (a) 24 hours
    (b) 3 to 4 days
    (c) 7 to 8 days
    (d) 10 days

    Answer: B Difficulty: 2 Page: 343

43. In cell differentiation, the trophoblast will eventually become the
    (a) heart and lungs.
    (b) spinal cord and brain.
    (c) amniotic sac, placenta, and umbilical cord.
    (d) limb buds.

    Answer: C Difficulty: 1 Page: 344

44. Development of organs near the spinal axis before limbs is referred to as
    (a) proximodistal development.
    (b) trophocystic development.
    (c) endoderm development.
    (d) cephalocaudal development.

    Answer: A Difficulty: 3 Page: 345

45. The respiratory and digestive systems in the embryo develop from the
    (a) ectoderm of the embryonic disk.
    (b) neural tube.
    (c) endoderm of the embryonic disk.
    (d) mesoderm of the embryonic disk.

    Answer: C Difficulty: 2 Page: 345

46. In what week of development does the heart begin beating?
    (a) the second week
    (b) the fourth week
    (c) the sixth week
    (d) the seventh week

    Answer: B Difficulty: 1 Page: 345

47. The protective environment in which the fetus grows is called the
    (a) placenta.
    (b) amniotic sac.
    (c) fallopian tubes.
    (d) ovum.

    Answer: B Difficulty: 1 Page: 345

48. Which is *not* a function of the placenta?
    (a) It delivers oxygen from the mother to the fetus.
    (b) It acts as a barrier for toxins such as alcohol, aspirin, and nicotine.
    (c) It secretes estrogen and progesterone.
    (d) It secretes human chorionic gonadotropin.

    Answer: B Difficulty: 2 Page: 345

49. The fetal stage begins in the
    (a) third week of pregnancy.
    (b) sixth week of pregnancy.
    (c) ninth week of pregnancy.
    (d) twelfth week of pregnancy.

    Answer: C Difficulty: 2 Page: 346

50. When do pregnant women generally begin to feel fetal movement?
    (a) three weeks after conception
    (b) nine weeks after conception
    (c) twelve weeks after conception
    (d) sixteen weeks after conception

    Answer: D Difficulty: 2 Page: 346

51. A cephalic presentation means the baby's
    (a) feet are down.
    (b) head is down.
    (c) buttocks are down.
    (d) left or right shoulder is down.

    Answer: B Difficulty: 1 Page: 346

52. Environmental influences or agents that can harm the embryo or fetus are called
    (a) bacteria.
    (b) teratogens.
    (c) steroid fluids.
    (d) antigens.

    Answer: B Difficulty: 1 Page: 346

53. Fetal arms and legs are most vulnerable to teratogens during the
    (a) second to third week after conception.
    (b) third to fifth week after conception.
    (c) fourth to eighth week after conception.
    (d) eighth to tenth week after conception.

    Answer: C Difficulty: 2 Page: 347

54. The critical period of vulnerability is a period of time during which an embryo or fetus is vulnerable to the effects of
    (a) estrogen.
    (b) teratogens.
    (c) bacteria.
    (d) illness.

    Answer: B Difficulty: 2 Page: 347

55. Marianne is seven months pregnant. She was recently exposed to the measles and was never immunized as a child. She is concerned about the risk to her baby if she contracts the virus. What should Marianne know?
    (a) She can request an immediate immunization from her obstetrician.
    (b) The highest risk of fetal damage from measles occurs in the first eight weeks of pregnancy.
    (c) The highest risk to her baby will occur in the eighth month of pregnancy.
    (d) Rubella cannot cross the placenta so there is no risk to her baby.

    Answer: B Difficulty: 2 Page: 348

56. Cherisse is four weeks pregnant. Routine blood screening reveals that she is carrying syphilis. What should Cherisse know?
    (a) Maternal syphilis cannot cross the placenta.
    (b) She can be treated with antibiotics before the fourth month of her pregnancy.
    (c) She must wait until the sixth month, and then she can be treated with antibiotics.
    (d) The syphilis organism can only cross the placenta in the first two months of her pregnancy.

    Answer: B Difficulty: 3 Page: 348

57. Life-threatening high blood pressure during pregnancy may indicate
    (a) toxemia.
    (b) Rubella.
    (c) ectopic pregnancy.
    (d) syphilis.

    Answer: A Difficulty: 2 Page: 348

58. Toxemia appears to be linked to
    (a) diabetes.
    (b) HIV/AIDS.
    (c) malnutrition.
    (d) RH incompatibility.

    Answer: C Difficulty: 1 Page: 348

59. Most ectopic pregnancies occur in the
    (a) vagina.
    (b) fallopian tubes.
    (c) abdomen.
    (d) cervix.

    Answer: B Difficulty: 1 Page: 348

60. In RH incompatibility
    (a) fetal antibodies attack the mother's red blood cells.
    (b) the father's antibodies attack the mother's red blood cells.
    (c) the mother's antibodies attack the fetus' red blood cells.
    (d) the fetus's red blood cells attack the mother's antibodies.

    Answer: C Difficulty: 2 Page: 349

61. Fetal erythroblastosis can be a result of
    (a) toxemia.
    (b) RH incompatibility.
    (c) HIV transfer from the mother to the fetus.
    (d) sickle cell anemia.

    Answer: B Difficulty: 2 Page: 349

62. Diethylstilbestrol (DES) was given to women
    (a) as a prenatal vitamin.
    (b) who are at risk of having a miscarriage.
    (c) to decrease birth defects.
    (d) with a viral infection.

    Answer: B Difficulty: 2 Page: 350

63. Baby M is small for her gestational age. She has a noticeably flattened nose and widely-spaced eyes, and her brain size is smaller than average. What would cause these characteristics?
    (a) marijuana
    (b) alcohol
    (c) heroin
    (d) LSD

    Answer: B Difficulty: 3 Page: 351

64. Maternal smoking produces all of the following *except*
    (a) a higher risk of low birth weight.
    (b) decreased lung function in the newborn.
    (c) decreased fetal heart rate.
    (d) an increased risk for sudden infant death syndrome.

    Answer: C Difficulty: 2 Page: 351

65. Braxton-Hicks contractions
    (a) widen the cervix.
    (b) advance the baby through the birth canal.
    (c) become intense and frequent.
    (d) are false labor contractions.

    Answer: D Difficulty: 2 Page: 354

66. Which two hormones cause uterine contractions during labor?
    (a) progesterone and oxytocin
    (b) prostaglandins and estrogen
    (c) oxytocin and prolactin
    (d) prostaglandins and oxytocin

    Answer: D Difficulty: 1 Page: 355

67. In the first stage of labor, the cervix dilates to about
    (a) 3 cm.
    (b) 10 cm.
    (c) 5 cm.
    (d) 4 cm.

    Answer: B Difficulty: 2 Page: 355

68. During the third stage of labor, the
    (a) placenta is expelled.
    (b) baby moves down the birth canal.
    (c) baby is born.
    (d) cervix fully dilates.

    Answer: A Difficulty: 2 Page: 357

69. To temporarily numb the mother's body below the waist, a physician may administer
    (a) a narcotic such as Demoral.
    (b) an epidural block.
    (c) general anesthesia.
    (d) a pudendal block.

    Answer: B Difficulty: 2 Page: 358

70. Lamaze method
    (a) was named after a French obstetrician.
    (b) aids a father in the delivery room.
    (c) eliminates use of anesthesia.
    (d) is a yoga exercise; designed to facilitate delivery.

    Answer: A Difficulty: 2 Page: 358

71. Which is not true about anoxia?
    (a) It causes various problems in the neonate.
    (b) It is the process through which the baby receives oxygen.
    (c) It sometimes causes death.
    (d) It can be monitored.

    Answer: B Difficulty: 1 Page: 365

72. In preterm infants, respiratory distress syndrome frequently results from
    (a) insufficient surfactant.
    (b) heart defects.
    (c) an inability to control body temperature.
    (d) an underdeveloped immune system.

    Answer: A Difficulty: 2 Page: 366

73. Which hormone stimulates the production of milk?
    (a) prostaglandins
    (b) oxytocin
    (c) progesterone
    (d) prolactin

    Answer: D Difficulty: 2 Page: 367

74. According to obstetricians, how long should women wait after childbirth before resuming intercourse?
    (a) 2 weeks
    (b) 12 weeks
    (c) 3 months
    (d) 6 weeks

    Answer: D Difficulty: 3 Page: 368

TRUE/FALSE

75. The highest risk of birth defects from rubella occurs in the first trimester.

    Answer: True

76. A fetus will probably not contract syphilis if the mother is treated with antibiotics in the first three months of her pregnancy.

    Answer: True

77. The majority of babies born to mothers infected with HIV do not become infected with the virus.

    Answer: True

78. Rh incompatibility adversely affects a first child but is less dangerous to subsequent children.

    Answer: False

79. Deficiencies of vitamin K and vitamin D have been linked to cleft palate, eye damage, and mental retardation.

    Answer: True

80. Nearly 40% of children whose mothers drank heavily during pregnancy develop fetal alcohol syndrome.

    Answer: True

81. Among women who smoke cigarettes, nearly 60% quit smoking when they become pregnant.

    Answer: False

82. For most women, the amniotic sac breaks about 24 hours before labor begins.

    Answer: False

83. Transition is the process that occurs when the cervix becomes nearly fully dilated and the head moves into the birth canal.

    Answer: True

84. Women with postpartum depression are more likely than those with "maternity blues" to have been depressed before and during their pregnancies.

    Answer: True

85. Spontaneous abortion is more prevalent among older mothers.

    Answer: True

86. Low birth weight is the most common risk factor for infant disease and mortality.

    Answer: True

87. Fertiltiy problems stem from the male about 75% of the time.

    Answer: False

88. Very few women have irregular menstrual cycles.

    Answer: False

89. Sperm counts of 10 million to 40 million sperm per milliliter of semen are considered normal.

    Answer: False

90. There is an all-female species of lizard that lays unfertilized eggs that develop into identical females generation after generation.

    Answer: True

91. A test-tube baby is grown in a large laboratory dish throughout the nine month gestation period.

    Answer: False

92. Although morning sickness tends to decrease as a pregnancy progresses, it is limited to the first trimester.

    Answer: False

93. The embryonic stage is the period from implantation until about the eighth week of development.

    Answer: True

94. Nutrients and waste products are exchanged between mother and embryo through a mass of tissue called the amniotic sac.

    Answer: False

95. Nearly 15% of women in the United States had rubella as children and so acquired immunity.

    Answer: False

96. Rh is a blood protein found in some people's red blood cells.

    Answer: True

97. Pregnant women can only have two alcoholic beverages a day without harming their babies.

    Answer: False

98. X-rays increase the risk of malformed organs in a fetus, especially within a month and a half after conception.

    Answer: True

99. Fertility problems stem from the male about 30% of the time.

    Answer: True

MATCHING

Match the description of the chromosomal or genetic abnormality with the appropriate name.

(a) Cystic fibrosis

(b) Huntington's chorea

(c) Tay-Sach's disease

(d) Hemophilia

(e) Spina bifida

(f) PKU

(g) Down's syndrome

(h) Retina blastoma

(i) Sickle cell anemia

100. A disorder where part of the spine is exposed or missing

Answer: e

101. A form of blindness caused by a dominant gene

Answer: h

102. Mental retardation that is the result of an extra 21st chromosome

Answer: g

103. A form of mental retardation in which children cannot metabolize phenylalanine

Answer: f

104. A fatal neurological disorder, the onset of which begins in middle adulthood

Answer: b

105. A sex-linked disorder in which the blood fails to clot

Answer: d

106. A genetic disease in which the lungs and pancreas become clogged with mucus

Answer: a

107. A fatal neurological disorder that primarily afflicts Jews of European descent

Answer: c

108. A blood disorder that mostly afflicts African Americans, decreasing the ability of red blood cells to carry oxygen

Answer: i

ESSAY

109. Explain methods couples can use to optimize the chances of conception.

Answer:

110. Describe both folklore and modern methods for selecting the sex of a child.

    Answer:

111. List the major causes of infertility in men and women. Describe two procedures for each gender that can be used to increase the chances of conception.

    Answer:

112. Differentiate between in vitro fertilization, gamete intrafallopian transfer, zygote intrafallopian transfer, embryonic transfer, and intracytoplasmic sperm injection.

    Answer:

113. Summarize the ethical concerns associated with sperm and egg donations and how those donations are dispersed.

    Answer:

114. Outline the developmental changes that occur during each of the three trimesters of pregnancy.

    Answer:

115. Describe the effects of maternal cigarette smoking on the developing fetus.

    Answer:

116. Describe the events that occur in each of the three stages of labor.

    Answer:

117. Summarize the pros and cons of breast-feeding versus bottle-feeding.

    Answer:

Chapter 12: Contraception and Abortion

1. Which statement best describes early contraceptive use?
   (a) The only method available was coitus interruptus.
   (b) Though not very effective in preventing pregnancy, numerous methods were tried.
   (c) Crude condoms did not come into existence until the 1800s.
   (d) Numerous methods were available that were highly effective in preventing pregnancy.

   Answer: B Difficulty: 2 Page: 375

2. In Greek and Roman times what was used for contraception?
   (a) something similar to the present day condom
   (b) absorbent materials
   (c) drugs
   (d) flushing fluids

   Answer: B Difficulty: 2 Page: 375

3. The term condom was not used to describe penile sheaths until
   (a) paternity was clearly established.
   (b) the late middle ages.
   (c) the eighteenth century.
   (d) the late twentieth century.

   Answer: B Difficulty: 2 Page: 375

4. The Comstock Law
   (a) placed contraceptive devices under the obscenity codes.
   (b) allowed only physicians to dispense information about contraception.
   (c) opened the doors for the legal sale of contraceptive devices.
   (d) allowed physicians to dispense information about sexually transmitted disease.

   Answer: A Difficulty: 1 Page: 375

5. In what year did Margaret Sanger establish the National Birth Control League?
   (a) 1876
   (b) 1899
   (c) 1904
   (d) 1914

   Answer: D Difficulty: 3 Page: 375

6. In 1918, the courts finally
   (a) repealed the Comstock law.
   (b) allowed Margaret Sanger to open a birth-control clinic.
   (c) ruled to allow physicians to discuss the prevention and cure of sexually transmitted disease.
   (d) ruled to allow research into safe abortion methods.

   Answer: C Difficulty: 2 Page: 375

7. In what year was the birth control pill introduced to the public?
   (a) 1942
   (b) 1956
   (c) 1960
   (d) 1965

   Answer: C Difficulty: 3 Page: 376

8. The biggest obstacle to the effective use of contraception is
   (a) lack of availability.
   (b) trying to choose between too many alternatives.
   (c) finding the right time and place to discuss the topic.
   (d) lack of planning.

   Answer: D Difficulty: 2 Page: 377

9. Approximately how many pregnancies are the result of contraceptive failure?
   (a) 50%
   (b) 65%
   (c) 32%
   (d) 45%

   Answer: A Difficulty: 2 Page: 378

10. A *perfect* failure rate for a contraceptive method takes into account
    (a) incorrect use.
    (b) consistent and correct use.
    (c) inconsistent use.
    (d) human error.

    Answer: B Difficulty: 1 Page: 378

11. Combination pills contain
    (a) estrogen only.
    (b) progesterone only.
    (c) both estrogen and progesterone.
    (d) both estrogen and prostaglandins.

    Answer: C Difficulty: 2 Page: 380

12. Which of the following is not a form of contraception?
    (a) diaphragms
    (b) cervical caps
    (c) Norplant
    (d) condrotine

    Answer: D Difficulty: 1 Page: 380

13. Oral contraceptives are most commonly referred to as
    (a) Norplant.
    (b) cunnilingus.
    (c) the pill.
    (d) intrauterine devices.

    Answer: C Difficulty: 1 Page: 380

14. Which is not a type of combination pill?
    (a) Ortho-novum
    (b) Minipill
    (c) Ovcon
    (d) Loestrin

    Answer: B Difficulty: 2 Page: 380

15. The most popular form of birth control for single women of child-bearing age is
    (a) the birth control pill.
    (b) the condom.
    (c) the diaphragm.
    (d) withdrawal.

    Answer: A Difficulty: 1 Page: 380

16. Birth control pills work by
    (a) preventing the production of estrogen.
    (b) preventing the production of progesterone and thus ovulation.
    (c) preventing a fertilized egg from implanting in the uterus.
    (d) preventing the release of FSH and LH.

    Answer: D Difficulty: 2 Page: 380

17. The progestin in combination pills
    (a) inhibits the production of LH and increases the thickness and acidity of cervical mucus.
    (b) inhibits the production of FSH.
    (c) decreases the thickness and acidity of cervical mucus.
    (d) inhibits the production of both FSH and LH.

    Answer: A Difficulty: 2 Page: 380

18. Progestin
    (a) lowers estrogen levels.
    (b) increases the thickness and acidity of the cervical mucus.
    (c) delays ovulation.
    (d) increases progesterone levels.

    Answer: B Difficulty: 2 Page: 380

19. Besides thickening the cervical mucus, the minipill also
    (a) makes the fallopian tubes too acidic for an egg.
    (b) suppresses ovulation.
    (c) renders the inner lining of the uterus less receptive to a fertilized egg.
    (d) increases progesterone levels.

    Answer: C Difficulty: 3 Page: 380

20. Robert and Serika are devoted pro-life supporters. Because of their strong beliefs, which method of birth control should they be advised against?
    (a) combination pills
    (b) the condom
    (c) progestin-only pills
    (d) cervical cap

    Answer: C Difficulty: 2 Page: 380

21. Which statement is *true* regarding perfect and typical failure rates with the birth control pill?
    (a) Perfect failure rate is only .1% but typical failure rate is 20%.
    (b) Perfect failure rate is about 1% and typical failure rate climbs to 10%.
    (c) Perfect failure rate is about .5% and typical failure rate is closer to 3%.
    (d) Perfect failure rate is about 10% but typical failure rate climbs to 30%.

    Answer: C Difficulty: 2 Page: 381

22. After stopping the use of oral contraceptives, nine out of ten women begin ovulating regularly within
    (a) three weeks.
    (b) three months.
    (c) six months.
    (d) one year.

    Answer: B Difficulty: 2 Page: 381

23. Which is a healthy side effect from birth-control pills?
    (a) They reduce the risk of pelvic inflammatory disease.
    (b) They make menstrual cycles consistent.
    (c) They reduce menstrual cramping and premenstrual discomfort.
    (d) All of the above.

    Answer: D Difficulty: 1 Page: 381

24. Which is not a disadvantage for women who take birth-control pills?
    (a) heightens the risk of breast cancer
    (b) increases cholesterol levels
    (c) reduces the effectiveness of antibiotics used to treat STIs
    (d) weight gain

    Answer: B Difficulty: 2 Page: 381

25. Of the following, which is *not* noted to be a benefit of oral contraceptive use?
    (a) reduction in the risk of pelvic inflammatory disease
    (b) reduction in the risk of benign ovarian cysts
    (c) reduction in facial acne
    (d) reduction in high blood pressure

    Answer: D Difficulty: 3 Page: 381

26. With combination pills, estrogen can increase a woman's weight by causing
    (a) fluid retention.
    (b) an increase in appetite.
    (c) the development of more muscle mass.
    (d) an increased need for sleep.

    Answer: A Difficulty: 2 Page: 381

27. Many women in their mid- to late thirties switch from oral contraceptives to other birth control methods
    (a) because they have sex less often.
    (b) to decrease the risk of endometrial cancer.
    (c) because of an increased risk of cardiovascular complications.
    (d) to decrease the risk of ovarian cancer.

    Answer: C Difficulty: 2 Page: 382

28. Which of the following is not the result of women taking progestin?
    (a) getting facial hair
    (b) vaginal dryness
    (c) enlarged breast size
    (d) irregular bleeding

    Answer: C Difficulty: 3 Page: 383

29. How is the "morning-after" pill different from the minipill?
    (a) The morning-after pill is a progestin-only pill, and the minipill is an estrogen-only pill.
    (b) The morning-after pill contains very high doses of estrogen and progestin, and the minipill is a progestin-only pill.
    (c) The morning-after pill prevents ovulation, and the minipill prevents implantation.
    (d) The morning-after pill is taken every day of the month, and the minipill is taken only after unprotected intercourse.

    Answer: B Difficulty: 2 Page: 384

30. Health professionals caution that if the morning-after pill fails,
    (a) the fetus might be damaged by exposure to the hormones the pill contains.
    (b) the pregnancy will be much more difficult throughout the first trimester.
    (c) the woman will be unable to ovulate regularly for at least six months.
    (d) the woman will experience severe nausea and experience amenorrhea.

    Answer: A Difficulty: 2 Page: 384

31. The morning-after pill
    (a) has a lower hormone content than most birth-control pills.
    (b) in some cases is recommended as a regular form of birth control.
    (c) causes nausea in 70% of its users.
    (d) prevents the ovum from passing through the fallopian tube.

    Answer: C Difficulty: 3 Page: 384

32. Which is not true about Norplant?
    (a) It consists of six matchstick-sized silicone tubes.
    (b) It contains progestin.
    (c) It is inserted into a woman's thigh.
    (d) It suppresses ovulation and thickens mucus so that sperm cannot pass.

    Answer: C Difficulty: 2 Page: 384

33. *Norplant* is a(n)
    (a) estrogen-only implant.
    (b) estrogen and progesterone injection.
    (c) progestin-only implant.
    (d) progestin-only injection.

    Answer: C Difficulty: 1 Page: 384

34. Norplant 2
    (a) consists of two hormone releasing tubes.
    (b) provides up to 8 years of protection.
    (c) carries estrogen.
    (d) cannot be reversed.

    Answer: A Difficulty: 1 Page: 384

35. What is true about intrauterine devices?
    (a) They are large devices to interpret a women's menstrual period.
    (b) They are the most popular form of birth control in the United States.
    (c) Their failure rate during the first year is about 23%.
    (d) They have been used by humans since Greek times.

    Answer: D Difficulty: 2 Page: 386

36. Nina is concerned about the effectiveness of *Norplant* as a contraceptive device. What should you tell Nina about the failure rate?
    (a) The failure rate is similar to that of the diaphragm.
    (b) The failure rate is only about 7%.
    (c) The failure rate is lower than the IUD but higher than oral contraceptives.
    (d) The failure rate is comparable to sterilization.

    Answer: D Difficulty: 3 Page: 385

37. Worldwide, the highest rate of IUD use is in
    (a) the United States.
    (b) China.
    (c) Great Britain.
    (d) India.

    Answer: B Difficulty: 1 Page: 386

38. What percentage of married women in the United States use IUDs?
    (a) 12%
    (b) 3%
    (c) 34%
    (d) 28%

    Answer: B Difficulty: 3 Page: 386

39. Research has shown that the IUD prevents pregnancy
    (a) by irritating the uterine lining.
    (b) by stimulating the immune system to create antibodies against sperm.
    (c) by preventing implantation of a fertilized ovum.
    (d) through some mechanism that isn't entirely clear.

    Answer: D Difficulty: 2 Page: 386

40. An advantage of the *ParaGard* IUD over oral contraceptives is that the IUD
    (a) allows for greater spontaneity in sexual activity.
    (b) has lower perfect and typical failure rates than oral contraceptives.
    (c) does not interfere with a woman's normal production of hormones.
    (d) only alters estrogen levels and does not interfere with progesterone production.

    Answer: C Difficulty: 3 Page: 387

41. What is a potential problem with the use of IUDs?
    (a) They can irritate the muscular layer of the uterine wall.
    (b) They can increase blood pressure.
    (c) They can fall out during athletic activities.
    (d) They can cause a mucous discharge.

    Answer: A Difficulty: 2 Page: 387

42. What can decrease the effectiveness of IUDs?
    (a) a high caloric diet
    (b) aspirin
    (c) vitamin C
    (d) an inactive lifestyle

    Answer: B Difficulty: 1 Page: 387

43. What is not an advantage of IUDs?
    (a) They help maintain a healthy PH balance in the vagina.
    (b) They are highly effective.
    (c) They do not diminish sexual spontaneity.
    (d) Once in place, there is no need to do more to prevent pregnancy.

    Answer: A Difficulty: 2 Page: 387

44. Research suggests that women who use the IUD have an increased risk of
    (a) pelvic inflammatory disease.
    (b) hormonal imbalances.
    (c) toxic shock syndrome.
    (d) uterine cancer.

    Answer: A Difficulty: 2 Page: 387

45. Jessica has become pregnant with an IUD in place. What are the chances that Jessica will have a miscarriage?
    (a) 50%
    (b) 35%
    (c) 26%
    (d) 10%

    Answer: A Difficulty: 3 Page: 388

46. The diaphragm's main function is to
    (a) prevent sperm from reaching the uterus.
    (b) alter the acidity in the vagina.
    (c) keep spermicide in place.
    (d) prevent implantation of a fertilized egg.

    Answer: C Difficulty: 2 Page: 388

47. PID can produce scar tissue that blocks the fallopian tubes, causing
    (a) cancer.
    (b) infertility.
    (c) infection.
    (d) bloating.

    Answer: B Difficulty: 1 Page: 387

48. IUD use is not recommended for women with a history of
    (a) high blood pressure.
    (b) bladder infections.
    (c) ectopic pregnancy.
    (d) endometriosis.

    Answer: C Difficulty: 1 Page: 388

49. Marcus and Venessa have planned a romantic evening of dinner and dancing. In preparation for the fact that they will make love later in the evening, Venessa inserts her diaphragm before leaving the house at seven. After dancing, she expects to arrive at home with Marcus around midnight. What should Venessa know?
    (a) Dancing might dislodge the diaphragm.
    (b) Her spermicide is only good for two hours after she inserts it.
    (c) The diaphragm should only be inserted just before intercourse.
    (d) She is using her diaphragm correctly.

    Answer: B Difficulty: 2 Page: 388

50. What is not true about diaphragms?
    (a) They were once used by about one third of U.S. couples who practiced birth control.
    (b) They protect women against STIs.
    (c) They are made of thin latex rubber.
    (d) They come in different sizes.

    Answer: B Difficulty: 1 Page: 388

51. How long must a diaphragm be kept in place after intercourse?
    (a) 1 hour
    (b) 3 hours
    (c) 5 hours
    (d) 6 hours

    Answer: D Difficulty: 2 Page: 388

52. In typical use, the failure rate of the diaphragm is about
    (a) 18%.
    (b) 25%.
    (c) 10%.
    (d) 3%.

    Answer: A Difficulty: 3 Page: 388

53. Spermicidal suppositories should be inserted
    (a) about 3 hours before intercourse.
    (b) about 2 hours before intercourse.
    (c) no less than an hour before intercourse.
    (d) no less than 10-15 minutes before intercourse.

    Answer: D Difficulty: 3 Page: 388

54. Which is true about nonoxynol-9?
    (a) It is harmful as a microbicide.
    (b) It is one of the most healthy forms of contraception.
    (c) It is a foamy substance.
    (d) It provides direct protection from trichomoniasis.

    Answer: A Difficulty: 1 Page: 391

55. Microbicides are
    (a) antibiotics that fight STIs.
    (b) chemical substances that kill viruses and bacteria.
    (c) harmful bacteria.
    (d) virus-fighting agents in the body.

    Answer: B Difficulty: 2 Page: 391

56. In contrast to the diaphragm, the cervical cap
    (a) is larger and does not require the use of a spermicide.
    (b) is smaller and can provide protection for up to 48 hours.
    (c) is less likely to dislodge with the thrusting of the penis.
    (d) has a much lower typical use failure rate.

    Answer: B Difficulty: 2 Page: 391

57. Which is not true about cervical caps?
    (a) They are smaller than a diaphragm.
    (b) They provide continuous protection for nearly 48 hours.
    (c) They are intended to be used with a spermicide.
    (d) They sometimes cause irritation to the uterus.

    Answer: D Difficulty: 2 Page: 391

58. According to the text which is not a term for condom?
    (a) safes
    (b) booties
    (c) rubbers
    (d) skins

    Answer: B Difficulty: 1 Page: 392

59. Today, the condom is making a comeback as a contraceptive device largely because
    (a) it protects from STIs and HIV.
    (b) of concerns about the side effects of the pill.
    (c) of concerns about the high failure rates in other barrier methods.
    (d) of large-scale advertising efforts.

    Answer: A Difficulty: 2 Page: 392

60. Hendrick is considering becoming sexually active. He wants to use condoms to protect against the possibility of contracting an STI or HIV. Which type of condom should he use?
    (a) He should only use condoms made from the intestinal membranes of lambs.
    (b) He should only use condoms made of latex.
    (c) He can use either latex or polyurethane condoms.
    (d) All types of condoms will protect from STI and HIV.

    Answer: B Difficulty: 2 Page: 392

61. Of the following lubricants, which is safe to use with a condom?
    (a) baby oil
    (b) vaseline
    (c) K-Y jelly
    (d) hand lotion

    Answer: C Difficulty: 2 Page: 393

62. For *maximum* protection from pregnancy, partners using condoms should
    (a) never carry the condom in a pants pocket or wallet.
    (b) combine condom use with a spermicide.
    (c) never open the condom package until ready to use.
    (d) never use a scissors or teeth to open a condom package.

    Answer: B Difficulty: 1 Page: 393

63. Douching after intercourse may
    (a) actually propel sperm toward the uterus.
    (b) decrease the chance of pregnancy by about 85%.
    (c) restore the natural chemical balance of the vagina.
    (d) decrease the risk of contracting an STI or HIV.

    Answer: A Difficulty: 1 Page: 395

64. On which days is intercourse avoided with the calendar method?
    (a) days 1-13 of the menstrual cycle
    (b) days 5-14 of the menstrual cycle
    (c) days 14-21 of the menstrual cycle
    (d) days 10-17 of the menstrual cycle

    Answer: D Difficulty: 2 Page: 396

65. Most women who follow the calendar method need to abstain from coitus for at least
    (a) 5 days.
    (b) 10 days.
    (c) 7 days.
    (d) 13 days.

    Answer: B Difficulty: 2 Page: 396

66. In the menstrual cycle, basal body temperature
    (a) rises just prior to ovulation and then falls three days after ovulation.
    (b) dips slightly just before ovulation and remains slightly lower until menstruation.
    (c) dips slightly just before ovulation and then rises and remains elevated until menstruation.
    (d) rises just before ovulation, remains elevated through ovulation, and then drops slightly until menstruation.

    Answer: C Difficulty: 2 Page: 396

67. The ovulation method of contraception
    (a) is the same as the withdrawal method.
    (b) tracks changes in the viscosity of the cervical mucus.
    (c) is very ineffective.
    (d) all of the above.

    Answer: B Difficulty: 1 Page: 397

68. In a cervical mucus check, ovulation is indicated by
    (a) slippery, clear mucus.
    (b) thick, white mucus.
    (c) thick, yellow mucus.
    (d) slippery, white mucus.

    Answer: A Difficulty: 1 Page: 397

69. In natural family planning methods, the estimated first year failure rate in typical use
    is about
    (a) 50%.
    (b) 40%.
    (c) 35%.
    (d) 20%.

    Answer: D Difficulty: 3 Page: 397

70. Besides abstinence which is the most effective form of contraception?
    (a) condoms
    (b) sterilization
    (c) withdrawal
    (d) diaphragms

    Answer: B Difficulty: 2 Page: 398

71. The most widely used birth control method in couples over the age of 30 is
    (a) the diaphragm.
    (b) sterilization.
    (c) condoms.
    (d) combination oral contraceptives.

    Answer: B Difficulty: 3 Page: 398

72. The male sterilization procedure used today is the
    (a) vasectomy.
    (b) vasovasotomy.
    (c) circumcision.
    (d) none of the above.

    Answer: A Difficulty: 1 Page: 398

73. In a vasectomy
    (a) each vas deferens is severed.
    (b) each epididymus is severed.
    (c) the seminiferous tubules are tied shut.
    (d) the seminal vesicles are tied shut.

    Answer: A Difficulty: 2 Page: 398

74. Studies show that men who had vasectomies more than 20 years ago faced
    (a) a slightly increased risk of prostate cancer.
    (b) no negative side effects.
    (c) a slight reduction in sensational arousal.
    (d) higher vulnerability towards STIs.

    Answer: A Difficulty: 2 Page: 399

75. Female sterilization involves
    (a) the removal of the uterus and ovaries.
    (b) the removal of the uterus.
    (c) cutting and tying the fallopian tubes.
    (d) cutting the fallopian tubes and removing the ovaries.

    Answer: C Difficulty: 2 Page: 400

76. Tubal sterilization
    (a) is also called tubal ligation.
    (b) is the most common form of female sterilization.
    (c) prevents ova and sperm from passing through the fallopian tubes.
    (d) all of the above.

    Answer: D Difficulty: 2 Page: 400

77. Most of the deaths attributed to female sterilization result from
    (a) excessive bleeding.
    (b) abdominal infections.
    (c) anesthesia.
    (d) accidental punctures of nearby organs.

    Answer: C Difficulty: 3 Page: 401

78. The female condom is made of
    (a) latex.
    (b) polyurethane.
    (c) silicone.
    (d) calf skin.

    Answer: B Difficulty: 1 Page: 401

79. Which is not a form of contraception?
    (a) hormonal method
    (b) vaginal ring
    (c) douching
    (d) Depo-provera

    Answer: C Difficulty: 2 Page: 402

80. A woman using *Depo-Provera* must receive an injection
    (a) every month.
    (b) every six months.
    (c) every three months.
    (d) once a year.

    Answer: C Difficulty: 3 Page: 402

81. Which of the following holds promise as a male contraceptive?
    (a) testosterone
    (b) progestin
    (c) inhibin
    (d) small doses of estrogen

    Answer: A Difficulty: 2 Page: 403

82. What percentage of abortions in the United States occur during the first trimester?
    (a) 30%
    (b) 50%
    (c) 70%
    (d) 90%

    Answer: D Difficulty: 3 Page: 404

83. In terms of statistics, which of the following women is *most* likely to have an abortion?
    (a) a 30-year-old Hispanic American
    (b) a 20-year-old White single mother
    (c) a 28-year-old married African American
    (d) an 18-year-old single Hispanic American

    Answer: B Difficulty: 3 Page: 404

84. Brain wave patterns typical of children do not begin until about the ____ week of pregnancy.
    (a) 30th
    (b) 35th
    (c) 25th
    (d) 20th

    Answer: A Difficulty: 2 Page: 406

85. Which statement is *true* regarding the history of abortion?
    (a) The Bible specifically prohibits abortion.
    (b) In 1869, Pope Pius IX declared that human life begins 40 days after conception.
    (c) In the United States, abortion was legalized in 1965.
    (d) Abortion was legal in the United States from 1607 to 1828.

    Answer: D Difficulty: 2 Page: 407

86. The safest and most common method of abortion is
    (a) dilation and curettage.
    (b) vacuum aspiration.
    (c) dilation and evacuation.
    (d) intra-amniotic infusion.

    Answer: B Difficulty: 1 Page: 410

87. The abortion method most commonly used in the second trimester is
    (a) vacuum aspiration.
    (b) dilation and curettage.
    (c) dilation and evacuation.
    (d) hysterotomy.

    Answer: C Difficulty: 2 Page: 410

88. During the 2nd trimester of pregnancy, what is the most common method of abortion?
    (a) vacuum aspiration
    (b) dilation and evacuation
    (c) intra-amniotic
    (d) none of the above

    Answer: B Difficulty: 2 Page: 410

89. Which of the following abortion methods does *not* require general anesthesia?
    (a) vacuum aspiration
    (b) hysterotomy
    (c) dilation and curettage
    (d) intact D and X

    Answer: A Difficulty: 2 Page: 410

90. In the drug RU-486, *mifepristone* is a chemical that induces abortion by
    (a) dramatically reducing estrogen levels.
    (b) blocking the effects of progesterone.
    (c) stimulating the release of luteinizing hormone.
    (d) augmenting the effects of progesterone.

    Answer: B Difficulty: 3 Page: 412

91. The abortion pill has not yet been introduced in the United States because
    (a) of opposition by pro-life groups.
    (b) of the high cost of the pill.
    (c) other methods of abortion are safer.
    (d) the Food and Drug Administration has not yet endorsed it as safe and effective.

    Answer: A Difficulty: 1 Page: 412

92. A combination of the cancer drug methotrexate and ____ can be used to terminate early pregnancy.
    (a) trophoblastic
    (b) misoprostol
    (c) intra-amnione
    (d) mifepristone

    Answer: B Difficulty: 3 Page: 412

MATCHING

Match the description of each of these contraceptive methods with the appropriate name.

(a) Norplant

(b) IUD

(c) Female condom

(d) Minipill

(e) Depo-Provera

(f) Gossypol

(g) Combination pill

(h) Diaphragm

93. An oral contraceptive that combines both estrogen and progesterone.

    Answer: g

94. Six match-stick sized silicone tubes containing progesterone are implanted in the upper arm.

    Answer: a

95. A shallow cup or dome made of thin latex rubber with a flexible metal ring covered in rubber.

    Answer: h

96. A copper-based device that is inserted into the uterus.

    Answer: b

97. A polyurethane sheath held in place with a flexible plastic ring.

    Answer: c

98. An progestin-only oral contraceptive that is taken every day of the menstrual cycle.

    Answer: d

99. A long-lasting, synthetic form of progesterone administered by injection.

    Answer: e

100. A male contraceptive extracted from the cotton plant.

    Answer: f

TRUE/FALSE

101. The Italian adventurer and writer, Giovanni Casanova (1725-1798), was strongly opposed to the use of condoms.

    Answer: False

102. The estrogen in combination pills prohibits the pituitary gland's secretion of luteinizing hormone (LH).

    Answer: False

103. Because of the strength of the dosage, the morning-after pill is not recommended as a regular form of birth control.

    Answer: True

104. IUDs have been used by humans since early Greek times.

    Answer: True

105. Recent studies in Africa did not find that nonoxynol-9 offers protection against STIs and HIV.

    Answer: True

106. The cervical cap should be kept in place for at least 8 hours after intercourse.

    Answer: True

107. A condom should only be removed after an erection has subsided.

    Answer: False

108. Natural family planning works best for women who have very regular menstrual cycles.

    Answer: True

109. More than 15% of men in the United States have had vasectomies.

    Answer: True

110. In culpotomy, the fallopian tubes are approached through an incision just below the navel.

    Answer: False

111. About 90% of abortions are performed in the first trimester.

    Answer: True

112. In 1977, the Hyde amendment required Medicaid to fund abortions for poor women receiving public assistance.

    Answer: False

113. The minipill contains synthetic progesterone only.

    Answer: True

114. Many women have avoided using birth-control pills because of the risk of blood clots.

    Answer: True

115. The diaphragm has almost a perfect record for contraception, with just under a 2% pregnancy rate among users.

    Answer: False

116. Douching can be an effective method of contraception after coitus.

    Answer: False

117. Vasectomy does not diminish sex drive or result in any change in sexual arousal, erectile or ejaculatory ability, or sensations of ejaculation.

    Answer: True

118. Vasectomies are not reversible.

    Answer: False

119. Use of Depo-Provera has been linked to osteoporosis, a condition involving bone loss that can cause bones to become brittle.

    Answer: True

120. Some men are infertile because they produce antibodies that destroy their own sperm.

    Answer: True

ESSAY

121. Your best friend shares that he/she is considering entering a sexual relationship but feels uncomfortable about broaching the subject of contraception with his/her partner. Counsel your friend by suggesting at least three of the communication guidelines offered in your text.

    Answer:

122. Discuss six of the eight points one should consider when choosing a contraceptive method.

    Answer:

123. Compare the advantages and disadvantages of combination oral contraceptives and progesterone-only oral contraceptives.

    Answer:

124. Compare and contrast the diaphragm with the cervical cap. What are the advantages and disadvantages of each method?

    Answer:

125. Explain how to properly use and store condoms.

    Answer:

126. Explain how the calendar method, basal body temperature, and cervical mucus check can be combined for effective natural family planning.

   Answer:

127. Identify and discuss three potential contraceptives being investigated for potential use in the new millennium.

   Answer:

128. Summarize the history of abortion from the period of Greece and Rome to the *Roe vs. Wade* decision.

   Answer:

Chapter 13: Sexuality in Childhood and Adolescence

MULTIPLE CHOICE

1. Many boys experience their first erections
   (a) at birth.
   (b) in the womb.
   (c) at about four years old.
   (d) between the ages of six and eight.

   Answer: B Difficulty: 2 Page: 420

2. Which is *true* regarding early childhood erections and vaginal lubrication?
   (a) These responses indicate early sexual interest.
   (b) These responses may be an expression of affection for adults.
   (c) These responses are reflexes and do not necessarily indicate sexual interest.
   (d) These responses indicate the beginnings of the phallic stage of development.

   Answer: C Difficulty: 2 Page: 420

3. Infants often engage in pelvic thrusting at
   (a) 8 to 10 months
   (b) 2 years old
   (c) 3 months
   (d) never

   Answer: A Difficulty: 2 Page: 421

4. Kinsey and his colleagues noted that baby girls show behaviors that resemble adult orgasm by as early as
   (a) 1 month.
   (b) 3 months.
   (c) 4 months.
   (d) 7 months.

   Answer: C Difficulty: 2 Page: 421

5. In cross-cultural studies of premarital sex, which statement *best* reflects gender differences?
   (a) Despite social prohibitions, about two-thirds of females engaged in premarital sex as opposed to about 80% of males.
   (b) About 20% of the cultures studied permitted premarital sex for females as opposed to 50% for males.
   (c) Premarital sex was discouraged for both men and women in 80% of the cultures studied.
   (d) 80% of the cultures disallowed premarital sex for females as opposed to 75% for males.

   Answer: A Difficulty: 2 Page: 421

6. In which culture do adults believe that childhood sexual experimentation is necessary for adult fertility?
   (a) the Chewu of South Africa
   (b) the Seniang of Oceania
   (c) the Trobrianders of the South Pacific
   (d) the Trukese of the South Pacific

   Answer: A Difficulty: 3 Page: 421

7. What is true about the Trukese of the South Pacific?
   (a) Children learn about sex by observing and asking adults.
   (b) Children are not introduced to sex until adulthood.
   (c) Children are given sexual partners at an early age.
   (d) None of the above.

   Answer: A Difficulty: 1 Page: 421

8. In which culture are girls initiated into intercourse between 6 and 8 years of age and boys between 10 and 12?
   (a) the Lecha of the Himalayas
   (b) the Trobrianders of the South Pacific
   (c) the Muria Gond of India
   (d) the Seniang of Oceania

   Answer: B Difficulty: 3 Page: 421

9. Children generally begin masturbating between
   (a) 1 and 2 months of age.
   (b) age 6 and age 8.
   (c) age 4 and age 5.
   (d) 6 and 12 months of age.

   Answer: D Difficulty: 2 Page: 421

10. Children in the United States typically do not engage in genital play with others until about the age of
    (a) 2.
    (b) 4.
    (c) 6.
    (d) 8.

    Answer: A Difficulty: 2 Page: 422

11. William Friedrich suggests that behavior that occurs in at least ____ of children is normal from a statistical point of view.
    (a) 20%
    (b) 36.8%
    (c) 59%
    (d) 85%

    Answer: A Difficulty: 3 Page: 423

12. Games like "show me yours" and "playing doctor" become most common between the ages of
    (a) 2 and 3.
    (b) 3 and 4.
    (c) 5 and 6.
    (d) 6 and 10.

    Answer: D Difficulty: 2 Page: 423

13. Same-gender sexual behavior in childhood
    (a) may influence sexual orientation.
    (b) is indicative of gender confusion.
    (c) may be more common than heterosexual play.
    (d) is a relatively rare occurrence.

    Answer: C Difficulty: 1 Page: 423

14. Parents who are unaware that masturbation is commonplace among children may
(a) erroneously assume that children who masturbate are oversexed or aberrant.
(b) pull a child's hands away and scold her or him.
(c) fail to acknowledge the behavior openly.
(d) all of the above.

Answer: D Difficulty: 1 Page: 424

15. Mary Calderone and Eric Johnson suggest that adults who feel guilty about sex may have
(a) experimented too much as children.
(b) had parents who were religious.
(c) had parents who punished them for masturbation.
(d) had parents who discouraged masturbation in public.

Answer: C Difficulty: 1 Page: 424

16. Jeremiah is 10 years old. If he is typical of most preadolescents, he is likely to
(a) think that girls are "dorks."
(b) begin to play in cross-integrated groups.
(c) develop a close, platonic relationship with a girl.
(d) be unconcerned about how his peers perceive him.

Answer: A Difficulty: 2 Page: 425

17. Sigmund Freud theorized that sexual impulses are ____ during preadolescence, but many preadolescents are quite active sexually.
(a) hidden
(b) open
(c) not clear
(d) dormant

Answer: A Difficulty: 2 Page: 425

18. Kinsey and his colleagues found that among preadolescents,
(a) 45% of males and 15% of females masturbate.
(b) most quit masturbating only to resume the activity in adolescence.
(c) 80% of males and 60% of females masturbate.
(d) equal numbers of males and females masturbate.

Answer: A Difficulty: 3 Page: 425

19. In the survey by Coles & Stokes, what percentage of teens reported going to their parents for information on sex?.
(a) 12%
(b) 36%
(c) 48%
(d) 56%

Answer: B Difficulty: 2 Page: 426

20. Today, what percentage of parents want teachers to discuss sexual orientation with their teenagers?
(a) 76%
(b) 36%
(c) 12%
(d) 89%

Answer: A Difficulty: 3 Page: 429

21. According to the survey done by Ramon C. Cortines, what is the most popular topic in sex education among parents of teens?
    (a) the basics of reproduction and birth control
    (b) HIV/AIDS and other sexually transmitted infections
    (c) how to use and where to get birth control devices
    (d) how to use condoms

    Answer: B Difficulty: 1 Page: 429

22. Puberty begins with
    (a) the appearance of secondary sex characteristics.
    (b) the first erection for boys.
    (c) breasts getting larger for girls.
    (d) the age of 8.

    Answer: A Difficulty: 2 Page: 431

23. Puberty ends when
    (a) a child turns seventeen.
    (b) menstruation and sperm production begin.
    (c) the long bones stop growing in length.
    (d) the vagina and penis stop growing.

    Answer: C Difficulty: 2 Page: 431

24. From the mid-1800s to today, the average age of menarche has changed from
    (a) age 11 to age 13.
    (b) age 13 to age 16.
    (c) age 17 to age 13.
    (d) age 18 to age 10.

    Answer: C Difficulty: 3 Page: 431

25. What hypothesis suggests that girls must reach a certain body weight to trigger pubertal changes such as menarche?
    (a) critical fat
    (b) pubertal
    (c) estrogen cycle
    (d) none of the above

    Answer: A Difficulty: 1 Page: 431

26. During puberty, ovaries begin to secrete estrogen in response to
    (a) the adrenal gland's secretion of testosterone.
    (b) the hypothalamus' secretion of luteinizing hormone.
    (c) the pituitary gland's secretion of growth hormone.
    (d) the pituitary gland's secretion of follicle stimulating hormone.

    Answer: D Difficulty: 3 Page: 431

27. Which of the following physical changes is/are not caused by increased estrogen production?
    (a) thickening of the vaginal lining
    (b) pubic and underarm hair growth
    (c) growth of the uterus
    (d) growth of fat and supporting tissue in the hips

    Answer: B Difficulty: 3 Page: 431

28. During puberty, estrogens cause the labia to grow, but androgens
    (a) cause the clitoris to grow.
    (b) stimulate the growth of the uterus.
    (c) cause the development of fat in the hips.
    (d) stimulate breast development.

    Answer: A Difficulty: 2 Page: 433

29. In male puberty, which of the following *accelerates* testosterone production?
    (a) growth of the penis
    (b) testicle growth
    (c) FSH production
    (d) masturbation to ejaculation

    Answer: B Difficulty: 1 Page: 434

30. Caleb has just experienced his first ejaculation. If he is *typical* of most boys, how old is he?
    (a) age 6
    (b) age 10
    (c) age 13
    (d) age 16

    Answer: C Difficulty: 3 Page: 435

31. In adolescent boys, mature sperm are usually not found in the ejaculate until
    (a) age 13.
    (b) two years after the first ejaculation.
    (c) age 17.
    (d) a year after the first ejaculation.

    Answer: D Difficulty: 3 Page: 435

32. About a year after first ejaculation, boys may also begin to experience
    (a) nocturnal emissions.
    (b) anovulatory responses.
    (c) gynecomastia.
    (d) an oral fixation.

    Answer: A Difficulty: 2 Page: 435

33. Underarm hair for boys appears on average at age
    (a) 15.
    (b) 9.
    (c) 18.
    (d) 11.

    Answer: A Difficulty: 2 Page: 436

34. Benjamin has noticed that his voice is starting to crack and that it changes from a high-pitched soprano to a lower tone with little warning. If Benjamin is *typical* of most boys, how old is he?
    (a) between age 10 and 11
    (b) between age 11 and 13
    (c) between age 14 and 15
    (d) between age 16 and 18

    Answer: C Difficulty: 3 Page: 436

35. In young men approaching age 18, which of the following hormones prevents any further increases in height?
    (a) testosterone
    (b) estrogen
    (c) interstitial cell (ISCH)
    (d) follicle stimulating hormone (FSH)

    Answer: B Difficulty: 1 Page: 436

36. In pubescent boys, a temporary enlargement of the breasts is caused by
    (a) estrogen production.
    (b) testosterone production.
    (c) inhibin production.
    (d) interstitial cell (ISCH) production.

    Answer: A Difficulty: 1 Page: 436

37. What percentage of teenagers sampled by Coles and Stokes had engaged in kissing by the age of 15?
    (a) 97%
    (b) 80%
    (c) 54%
    (d) 13%

    Answer: A Difficulty: 2 Page: 436

38. Since Kinsey's time, the incidence of premarital oral sex among teens has
    (a) decreased slightly.
    (b) increased dramatically.
    (c) stayed the same.
    (d) increased slightly.

    Answer: B Difficulty: 2 Page: 437

39. According to a 1998 federal survey, how many high school students are sexually active?
    (a) 25%
    (b) 88%
    (c) 74%
    (d) 50%

    Answer: D Difficulty: 3 Page: 438

40. Premarital intercourse is motivated by
    (a) sex hormones.
    (b) seeking peer recognition.
    (c) curiosity.
    (d) all of the above.

    Answer: D Difficulty: 1 Page: 438

41. Compared with Kinsey's data, the incidence of premarital sex among teenage girls has increased from
    (a) 5% to about 52%.
    (b) 12% to about 52%.
    (c) 20% to about 78%.
    (d) 30% to about 89%.

    Answer: C Difficulty: 2 Page: 439

42. Today in the United States, the average age of first intercourse for girls is
    (a) 13.
    (b) 14.
    (c) 15.
    (d) 16.

    Answer: D Difficulty: 3 Page: 439

43. In the NHSLS study, which statement accurately reflects data about first intercourse?
    (a) 65% of the male adolescents cited being "in love" as the primary reason for first intercourse.
    (b) About 75% of the female adolescents stated they "went along with intercourse" because their partner pressured them.
    (c) About 25% of both male and female adolescents said their first intercourse experience was spurred by curiosity.
    (d) About 48% of the females and 25% of the males said their first intercourse experience occurred because they were "in love."

    Answer: D Difficulty: 3 Page: 439

44. For teens who abstain from sex, which of the following is not cited as a reason?
    (a) fear of being caught
    (b) abstinence-only sex education
    (c) fear of pregnancy
    (d) religious values

    Answer: B Difficulty: 2 Page: 440

45. In regard to first intercourse, Coles and Stokes (1985) reported that
    (a) most adolescent boys felt "glad" while most girls felt "ambivalent."
    (b) most adolescent girls felt "sorry" while most boys felt "ambivalent."
    (c) most adolescent boys felt "ashamed" while most girls felt "dirty."
    (d) most adolescent girls and adolescent boys felt "glad."

    Answer: A Difficulty: 2 Page: 441

46. In Coles and Stokes' (1985) national survey, how many adolescents reported sexual experiences with people of their own gender?
    (a) 5%
    (b) 12%
    (c) 1%
    (d) 17%

    Answer: A Difficulty: 3 Page: 442

47. What is the belief that one's feelings and ideas are special, even unique, and that one is invulnerable?
    (a) personal fable
    (b) ego centricity
    (c) teenage infallibility
    (d) superego fixation

    Answer: A Difficulty: 2 Page: 443

48. Approximately how many teenage girls become pregnant each year?
    (a) 5%
    (b) 16%
    (c) 10%
    (d) 3%

    Answer: C Difficulty: 3 Page: 443

49. Lai is 15 and pregnant. If she is typical of many teenage mothers, which outcome is likely?
    (a) She is likely to quit school and likely to become pregnant again before age 20.
    (b) She will probably complete high school but then go on public assistance.
    (c) If she completes high school, she will avoid poverty and become successful.
    (d) She is likely to quit school but not likely to become pregnant again until she can maintain a stable financial future.

    Answer: A Difficulty: 2 Page: 444

50. Among teenage girls who become pregnant, how many will become pregnant again within a year?
    (a) one in thirty
    (b) one in ten
    (c) one in five
    (d) one in three

    Answer: C Difficulty: 3 Page: 444

51. How many teenage mothers quit high school and go on public assistance?
    (a) 29%
    (b) 50%
    (c) 65%
    (d) 72%

    Answer: B Difficulty: 3 Page: 444

52. According to the text, the *majority* of teens become pregnant
    (a) because they feel a baby will fill an emotional void.
    (b) to fix or keep a relationship.
    (c) because of problems in school.
    (d) because of misunderstandings about reproduction and contraception.

    Answer: D Difficulty: 2 Page: 444

53. Young teens who are sexually active are less likely to use contraception because
    (a) of lack of information.
    (b) they feel it "isn't cool" to use contraception.
    (c) they are not allowed to purchase contraceptives.
    (d) they cannot afford condoms.

    Answer: A Difficulty: 2 Page: 446

54. Among sex educators, how many inform students about how to obtain contraception?
    (a) 85%
    (b) less 50%
    (c) 62%
    (d) 10%

    Answer: B Difficulty: 3 Page: 446

55. Which of the following countries has the highest teenage pregnancy rate?
    (a) the United States
    (b) England
    (c) Japan
    (d) Canada

    Answer: A Difficulty: 1 Page: 448

MATCHING

Match the event occurring in puberty with the appropriate term.

(a) Anovulatory

(b) Secondary Sex Characteristics

(c) Nocturnal Emissions

(d) Gynecomastia

(e) Critical Fat Hypothesis

(f) Menarche

(g) Primary Sex Characteristics

56. Pubic and axillary hair growth, breast development, and beard growth

    Answer: b

57. The beginning of menstruation

    Answer: f

58. Menstrual cycles in which ovulation does not occur

    Answer: a

59. The idea that girls must reach a certain body weight to trigger puberty

    Answer: e

60. Growth of the uterus, ovulation, and sperm production

    Answer: g

61. Ejaculation occurring during sleep

    Answer: c

62. Enlargement of the breasts in boys

    Answer: d

TRUE/FALSE

63. Baby boys show behaviors that resemble orgasm by as early as 5 months.

    Answer: True

64. Preadolescents tend to socialize in large, mixed-gender groups.

    Answer: False

65. Today only a few states mandate or recommend sex education programs.

    Answer: False

66. During puberty, girls generally grow taller before boys do.

    Answer: True

67. Teens with higher educational goals are less likely to engage in intercourse than less academically oriented teens.

    Answer: True

68. White American teenagers are more likely than African American or Hispanic American teens to have an abortion.

    Answer: True

69. Children whose parents are divorced or separated are more likely to engage in premarital intercourse.

    Answer: True

70. Most teenage pregnancies result from the belief that a baby will fill an emotional void.

    Answer: False

71. Contraception is most likely to be used by teenagers who have intercourse with multiple partners.

    Answer: False

72. The vast majority of sex educators recommend abstinence as the best way to prevent pregnancy and the transmission of HIV.

    Answer: True

73. Stimulation of the genitals in infancy may produce sensations of pleasure.

    Answer: True

74. The Kwoma of New Guinea encourage boys to touch their genitals to get familiar with their bodies.

    Answer: False

75. There is evidence that sex education encourages sexual activity among children and adolescents.

    Answer: False

76. Young people today start dating and "going steady" earlier than in past generations.

    Answer: True

77. European American and Latino American males are more likely to have engaged in cunnilingus than African American males.

    Answer: True

78. Teens who feel that they can talk to their parents are more likely to engage in coitus than those who describe communication with their parents as poor.

    Answer: False

79. The rate of birth for teenagers increased drastically through the 1990s.

    Answer: False

ESSAY

80. Describe the childhood sexual practices of three cultures other than the United States.

    Answer:

81. Explain how parents should react to childhood masturbation.

    Answer:

82. Summarize the six suggestions of Calderone and Johnson when talking with children about sex.

    Answer:

83. Compare and contrast the physical changes experienced by boys and girls as they go through puberty.

    Answer:

84. Discuss how premarital intercourse, use of contraception, and the resolution of unwanted pregnancies differs between White American, African American, and Hispanic American teenagers.

    Answer:

85. Discuss the incidence, medical consequences, and social consequences of teenage pregnancy in the United States.

    Answer:

86. Identify the factors associated with both contraceptive use and lack of contraceptive use among teenagers.

    Answer:

Chapter 14: Sexuality in Adulthood

MULTIPLE CHOICE

1. Between 1970 and 1999, the proportion of single men and women between the ages of 20 and 24
   (a) increased.
   (b) decreased.
   (c) remained the same.
   (d) increased for men but not for women.

   Answer: B Difficulty: 2 Page: 454

2. Recent years have seen a sharp increase in the number of
   (a) early marriages.
   (b) single young people.
   (c) polygamous marriages.
   (d) none of the above.

   Answer: B Difficulty: 1 Page: 454

3. "Singlehood," not marriage, is now the most common lifestyle among people in their
   (a) early 30s.
   (b) late 20s.
   (c) early 20s.
   (d) none of the above.

   Answer: C Difficulty: 2 Page: 454

4. Which behavior pattern best defines "serial monogamy?"
   (a) engaging in multiple sexual relationships at the same time
   (b) involvement in one exclusive relationship after another
   (c) having several sexual partners but one primary committed relationship
   (d) having one committed partner for life but not marrying or living together

   Answer: B Difficulty: 2 Page: 456

5. Celibacy is
   (a) having multiple sexual partners.
   (b) living alone.
   (c) the same as serial monogamy.
   (d) refraining from sexual intercourse.

   Answer: D Difficulty: 1 Page: 456

6. Reasons people remain celibate include the following except
   (a) religious reasons.
   (b) temporary accommodations to other pursuits.
   (c) confusion about sexual orientation.
   (d) viewing sex outside of marriage as immoral.

   Answer: C Difficulty: 2 Page: 456

7. Which statement is true about cohabitation in the United States?
   (a) Cohabitation is more prevalent among the highly educated.
   (b) Cohabitation is more prevalent among the less educated and less affluent.
   (c) Cohabitation is highest among White couples.
   (d) None of the above.

   Answer: B Difficulty: 1 Page: 456

8. Reasons for cohabitation are
   (a) economic.
   (b) unwilling to make a marital commitment.
   (c) not wanting to be tied down.
   (d) all of the above.

   Answer: D Difficulty: 2 Page: 456

9. Couples who live together and then later marry
   (a) run a greater risk of divorce than couples who did not live together before marriage.
   (b) are more likely to be married for twenty-five years or more.
   (c) are twice as likely to engage in extramarital affairs.
   (d) are more committed to the values traditionally associated with marriage.

   Answer: A Difficulty: 2 Page: 457

10. In a patriarchal system
    (a) men and women are treated equally.
    (b) men rule but women can own property.
    (c) men dominate.
    (d) men dominate but goods are passed down through the female line.

    Answer: C Difficulty: 1 Page: 459

11. In ancient Hebrew days a man's wife was considered his property. She was called a
    (a) chattel.
    (b) mistress.
    (c) paramour.
    (d) wench.

    Answer: A Difficulty: 1 Page: 459

12. The notion of love as a basis for marriage became widespread in the
    (a) fourteenth century.
    (b) sixteenth century.
    (c) seventeenth century.
    (d) nineteenth century.

    Answer: D Difficulty: 2 Page: 460

13. Regardless of a couples age, sexual frequency _____ with years of marriage.
    (a) increases
    (b) stays the same
    (c) decreases
    (d) fluctuates

    Answer: C Difficulty: 1 Page: 461

14. According to the text, what are the two goals of most contemporary marriages?
    (a) financial security and psychological security
    (b) sexual fulfillment and financial security
    (c) the desire for companionship and intimacy
    (d) the desire to have children and intimacy

    Answer: C Difficulty: 3 Page: 461

15. A Gallop poll conducted in 2000 suggested what about happiness?
    (a) Marriage and happiness are positively correlated.
    (b) Marriage and happiness are negatively correlated.
    (c) Single people report greater happiness because of sexual freedom.
    (d) Married people report greater happiness because of sexual frequency.

    Answer: A Difficulty: 2 Page: 461

16. The two major types of marriage are
    (a) monogamy and polygamy.
    (b) matrimony and cohabitation.
    (c) polygamy and matrimony.
    (d) monogamy and cohabitation.

    Answer: A Difficulty: 1 Page: 462

17. In polygynous societies, a man is permitted to have more than one wife if
    (a) he can financially support them.
    (b) he desires more sexual partners.
    (c) he has high status within the culture.
    (d) there are many available women.

    Answer: A Difficulty: 2 Page: 462

18. In polygynous societies, how many men have more than one wife?
    (a) about 75%
    (b) less than 50%
    (c) about 60%
    (d) about 80%

    Answer: B Difficulty: 3 Page: 462

19. Suzan married Bob because he is of the same race, has a similar education, and he participates at Suzan's church. This is an example of
    (a) simogamy.
    (b) homogamy.
    (c) ontogamy.
    (d) polygamy.

    Answer: B Difficulty: 2 Page: 463

20. According to the U.S. Bureau of the Census, interracial marriages account for
    (a) 33% of all United States marriages.
    (b) 23% of all United States marriages.
    (c) 14% of all United States marriages.
    (d) 1% of all United States marriages.

    Answer: D Difficulty: 2 Page: 464

21. When it comes to picking a mate, which statement is true?
    (a) Women are more likely to believe in love at first sight while men are more practical.
    (b) Men tend to be romantics while women are pragmatists.
    (c) Men are likely to value financial security while women value romance.
    (d) Men are likely to believe they can form loving relationships with many individuals while women believe that love conquers all.

    Answer: B Difficulty: 2 Page: 464

22. In examining patterns of marital sexuality across cultures, which of the following behaviors is valued in almost all cultures?
    (a) restriction of sex to married couples
    (b) privacy for sexual relations
    (c) male dominance and female submission
    (d) sex as a recreational activity

    Answer: B Difficulty: 2 Page: 464

23. Which researcher stated that "men need not feel bound to wait for a woman to achieve orgasm?"
    (a) William Masters
    (b) Margaret Sanger
    (c) Alfred Kinsey
    (d) Morton Hunt

    Answer: C Difficulty: 2 Page: 464

24. Married women in Kinsey's sample reported an average length of foreplay of
    (a) 1-2 minutes.
    (b) 5 minutes.
    (c) 9 minutes.
    (d) 12 minutes.

    Answer: D Difficulty: 3 Page: 465

25. In Kinsey's studies, which factor was associated with an increase in the length of foreplay from 5 to 15 minutes?
    (a) number of years the couple had been married
    (b) feelings of affection
    (c) age
    (d) college education

    Answer: D Difficulty: 2 Page: 465

26. According to the NHSLS study, married couples reported that they engaged in sexual relations an *average* of
    (a) 7 times a month.
    (b) 12 times a month.
    (c) 3 times a month.
    (d) 4 times a month.

    Answer: A Difficulty: 2 Page: 466

27. In Kinsey's day, which coital position did 70% of the males use exclusively?
    (a) male-superior
    (b) female-superior
    (c) lateral-entry
    (d) rear-entry

    Answer: A Difficulty: 2 Page: 466

28. In Kinsey's day, which coital position was used the least by couples?
    (a) male-superior
    (b) female-superior
    (c) lateral-entry
    (d) rear-entry

    Answer: D Difficulty: 2 Page: 466

29. Kinsey estimated that most men achieved orgasm within
    (a) 10 seconds after penetration.
    (b) 2 minutes after penetration.
    (c) 10 minutes after penetration.
    (d) 5 minutes after penetration.

    Answer: B Difficulty: 1 Page: 466

30. According to the NHSLS study "duration of the last sexual event" which is true?
    (a) No couple reported having sex for over an hour.
    (b) About half of the couples said sex for them was less than 15 minutes.
    (c) 75% of the couples reported that sex was 15 minutes to an hour.
    (d) 25% of the couples reported having sex over an hour.

    Answer: C Difficulty: 3 Page: 466

31. After 15 years of marriage, how many women in Kinsey's studies had not experienced orgasm?
    (a) 1%
    (b) 8%
    (c) 12%
    (d) 21%

    Answer: C Difficulty: 2 Page: 466

32. Both the early Kinsey studies and the NHSLS study reported that during sexual relations, men achieve orgasm
    (a) 90% of the time.
    (b) 100% of the time.
    (c) 85% of the time.
    (d) 80% of the time.

    Answer: A Difficulty: 2 Page: 466

33. An NHSLS study found that women in their ____ were more likely to reach orgasm consistently than other women.
    (a) 20s
    (b) 30s
    (c) 40s
    (d) 50s

    Answer: C Difficulty: 3 Page: 466

34. The ability to achieve orgasm has been strongly linked to
    (a) emotional closeness within the relationship.
    (b) knowledge of sexual pleasuring techniques.
    (c) racial and ethnic differences.
    (d) traditional male and female roles within a marriage.

    Answer: A Difficulty: 1 Page: 467

35. Why do people engage in extramarital affairs?
    (a) for variety
    (b) as a way to express hostility towards a spouse
    (c) desire for personal growth
    (d) all of the above

    Answer: D Difficulty: 1 Page: 468

36. In terms of extramarital affairs among women, the sexual motive is often less important than the need for
(a) proof that one is still attractive.
(b) emotional closeness.
(c) retaliating against a partner.
(d) personal growth.

Answer: B Difficulty: 2 Page: 468

37. When comparing the motives of men and women who engage in extramarital affairs, men are more likely to cite a need for
(a) emotional closeness.
(b) personal growth.
(c) sexual excitement.
(d) higher self-esteem.

Answer: C Difficulty: 1 Page: 468

38. Margarie has been seeing a man for about eight months every Friday afternoon. Her husband knows nothing about the affair and Margarie has no intention of telling him. Her affair is typical of
(a) consensual adultery.
(b) mate swapping.
(c) swinging.
(d) conventional adultery.

Answer: D Difficulty: 1 Page: 469

39. In surveys conducted by the National Opinion Research center, about how many men admitted to marital infidelity?
(a) 10%
(b) 15%
(c) 20%
(d) 35%

Answer: C Difficulty: 3 Page: 469

40. In cross-cultural studies, about 54% of preliterate societies permit men to have extramarital affairs. How many permit women to have extramarital affairs?
(a) less than 1%
(b) 11%
(c) 16%
(d) 32%

Answer: B Difficulty: 2 Page: 469

41. What does the research suggest regarding loyalty to one's spouse?
(a) Married people are likely to be faithful.
(b) High percentages of both males and females report that they're faithful.
(c) Roughly half of men have affairs though they are unreported.
(d) The incidence of extramarital sex is probably over-reported.

Answer: B Difficulty: 2 Page: 470

42. Which of the following is true of the software Spector's "stealth mode"?
(a) It logs only connections to pornographic sites.
(b) An icon on the monitor indicates when the software is working.
(c) It can be found by clicking the system directory.
(d) Only the person who installed it knows it's recording.

Answer: D Difficulty: 3 Page: 470

43. Spector was originally designed to be used by
    (a) employers.
    (b) parents.
    (c) private investigators.
    (d) untrusting spouses.

    Answer: B Difficulty: 1 Page: 470

44. In which culture can a man offer visitors the opportunity to sleep with his wife as a gesture of hospitality?
    (a) the Aleut of Alaska
    (b) the Native American Comanches
    (c) the people of the Marshall Islands in the Pacific
    (d) the Fijians of Oceania

    Answer: A Difficulty: 1 Page: 471

45. In which culture is a woman allowed to have sexual relations with her sister's husband?
    (a) the Aleut of Alaska
    (b) the Native American Comanches
    (c) the people of the Marshall Islands in the Pacific
    (d) the Fijians of Oceania

    Answer: C Difficulty: 1 Page: 471

46. Each year in the United States, how many women are victims of violence by partners?
    (a) 1 out of every 3
    (b) 1 out of every 5
    (c) 1 out of every 8
    (d) 1 out of every 12

    Answer: C Difficulty: 2 Page: 472

47. Which statement is true regarding the incidence of violence between men and women?
    (a) Men are generally the initiators of violence between partners.
    (b) In about half of domestic violence cases, both partners are guilty of physical abuse.
    (c) Women rarely initiate violence but will defend themselves.
    (d) Men are more likely to be killed by current or former partners.

    Answer: B Difficulty: 2 Page: 473

48. Which of the following is *heavily* connected with battering?
    (a) alcohol and other drugs
    (b) infidelity
    (c) financial problems
    (d) socialization

    Answer: A Difficulty: 1 Page: 473

49. Feminist theorists look upon domestic violence as a product of
    (a) sexual dissonance.
    (b) the power relationships that exist between men and women in our society.
    (c) men having all the freedom.
    (d) men's inability to cope with the feminist movement.

    Answer: B Difficulty: 1 Page: 473

50. Feminist theorists argue that our society
    (a) supports domestic violence by appearing to condone it.
    (b) has no influence on domestic violence.
    (c) is neutral toward domestic violence.
    (d) gives support to men but not women when it comes to domestic violence.

    Answer: A Difficulty: 1 Page: 473

51. According to the text, how many marriages in the United States end in divorce?
    (a) 50%
    (b) 60%
    (c) 45%
    (d) 40%

    Answer: A Difficulty: 3 Page: 474

52. People today hold ____ expectations of marriage than their parents.
    (a) higher
    (b) lower
    (c) different
    (d) similar

    Answer: C Difficulty: 1 Page: 474

53. Today, the most common reasons given for divorce are
    (a) lack of communication and understanding.
    (b) lack of communication and economic strain.
    (c) infidelity and arguments over parenting.
    (d) lack of sexual satisfaction and financial strain.

    Answer: A Difficulty: 1 Page: 474

54. In the *Time/CNN poll of 1997*, what did respondents cite as the number one reason for the increased divorce rate in the United States?
    (a) Society has become more accepting of divorce.
    (b) It is easier to get a divorce than it used to be.
    (c) Marriage is not taken seriously by couples.
    (d) There have been changes in the earning power of men and women.

    Answer: C Difficulty: 2 Page: 474

55. Which is not a type of marriage?
    (a) open
    (b) group
    (c) fragmented
    (d) polygamous

    Answer: C Difficulty: 1 Page: 476

56. Researchers find that sexual daydreaming, sex drive, and sexual activity tend
    (a) to increase with age.
    (b) to decrease with age.
    (c) not to change with age.
    (d) to increase for women and decrease for men.

    Answer: B Difficulty: 1 Page: 477

57. Which of the following is not a symptom of menopause?
    (a) Vaginal walls lose much elasticity.
    (b) Tonsils swell.
    (c) The labia majora lose much of their fatty deposits.
    (d) The vagina produces less lubrication.

    Answer: B Difficulty: 2 Page: 477

58. After menopause, decline in the production of estrogen can lead to
    (a) loss of energy.
    (b) a lack of sexual desire.
    (c) thinning of the vaginal walls.
    (d) increased vaginal lubrication.

    Answer: C Difficulty: 1 Page: 477

59. Clara is approaching the age of 65. While she and her husband have remained sexually active, Clara has begun to avoid stimulation to orgasm. What might be causing Clara to avoid orgasm?
    (a) She is ashamed of her physical appearance as she ages.
    (b) Her orgasms are less intense and therefore not pleasurable.
    (c) Her orgasms may be causing painful uterine contractions.
    (d) Her clitoris is significantly less responsive to oral or manual stimulation.

    Answer: C Difficulty: 1 Page: 478

60. Many of the physical changes in aging women can be slowed or prevented with
    (a) testosterone replacement therapy.
    (b) estrogen replacement therapy.
    (c) progesterone replacement therapy.
    (d) follicle stimulating hormone replacement therapy.

    Answer: B Difficulty: 2 Page: 478

61. Which of the following is *not* an age-related physical change for men?
    (a) loss of the ability to father children
    (b) lengthening of the refractory period
    (c) the need for direct stimulation of the penis to achieve erection
    (d) delayed ejaculation

    Answer: A Difficulty: 2 Page: 478

62. Which is *true* regarding sexual responses in older men?
    (a) Nocturnal emissions disappear.
    (b) It takes less time to become erect but the refractory period increases significantly.
    (c) Older men produce less ejaculate.
    (d) Orgasmic contractions remain strong but are spaced further apart.

    Answer: C Difficulty: 1 Page: 478

63. What is true about men over the age of 50 compared to younger men?
    (a) They are likely to take longer to achieve erection.
    (b) Their erection subsides faster after an orgasm.
    (c) They produce less ejaculate than younger men.
    (d) All of the above.

    Answer: D Difficulty: 1 Page: 478

64. What is not a change in sexual arousal for aging women?
    (a) reduced myotonia
    (b) desire for sexual relations
    (c) reduced elasticity of the vaginal walls
    (d) smaller increases in breast size during sexual arousal

    Answer: B Difficulty: 2 Page: 478

65. Which is not a factor that plays a role in the decrease of sexual activity in one's life?
    (a) age
    (b) physical problems
    (c) boredom
    (d) cultural attitudes toward sex among the aging

    Answer: A Difficulty: 1 Page: 478

66. Which of the following is *not* one of the five factors Nosek and colleagues mention as important to sexual wellness?
    (a) knowledge about sexuality
    (b) keeping sex in perspective by adopting a healthy sense of humor
    (c) coping with barriers to sexuality
    (d) maintaining the best possible general and sexual health

    Answer: B Difficulty: 2 Page: 481

67. With aging, the frequency of masturbation
    (a) decreases for men and increases for women.
    (b) decreases for men and women.
    (c) increases for both.
    (d) increases for men and decreases for women.

    Answer: B Difficulty: 2 Page: 480

68. Which of the following is not a source of sexual satisfaction?
    (a) tenderness
    (b) cuddling
    (c) caressing
    (d) none of the above

    Answer: D Difficulty: 1 Page: 480

69. In terms of sexual responsiveness and performance, cerebral palsy
    (a) will limit coital positions.
    (b) causes infertility.
    (c) decreases sexual interest and desire.
    (d) impairs the ability to achieve orgasm.

    Answer: A Difficulty: 1 Page: 481

70. What do Margaret Nosek and her colleagues consider to be a factor for sexual wellness, even among the disabled?
    (a) positive sexual self-concept
    (b) knowledge about sexuality
    (c) ability to cope with barriers to sexuality
    (d) all of the above

    Answer: D Difficulty: 1 Page: 481

71. Barbara has cerebral palsy. She may be limited to
    (a) certain types of sexual activities and coital positions.
    (b) using only a diaphragm for contraception.
    (c) non-coital intimacy.
    (d) having infrequent sexual activity.

    Answer: A Difficulty: 1 Page: 481

72. Alexander is a paraplegic who injured his spine in a skiing accident. The nerves affected were just above the lumbar region. In terms of sexual response, Alexander
    (a) will never be able to achieve an erection.
    (b) is still capable of achieving psychogenic and reflexive erections.
    (c) will only be able to achieve psychogenic erections.
    (d) will only be able to achieve reflexive erections.

    Answer: D Difficulty: 2 Page: 481

73. One of the greatest impediments to sexual fulfillment among people with disabilities is
    (a) the severity of their disability.
    (b) lack of sexual knowledge.
    (c) finding a loving and supportive partner.
    (d) the inability to experience vaginal or penile sensations.

    Answer: C Difficulty: 2 Page: 482

74. If you are the victim of a spinal cord injury, what are the chances that you will receive counseling to help with sexual adjustment?
    (a) about 90%
    (b) about 20%
    (c) about 40%
    (d) about 50%

    Answer: B Difficulty: 3 Page: 482

75. When studying men with spinal cord injuries, researchers note that
    (a) only a few continue to ejaculate naturally.
    (b) about 75% are able to achieve erection.
    (c) only 50% still produce semen.
    (d) 25% have received a penile implant.

    Answer: B Difficulty: 3 Page: 482

76. Most women with spinal cord injuries can
    (a) engage in intercourse, become pregnant, and deliver vaginally.
    (b) engage in intercourse and become pregnant, but cannot deliver vaginally.
    (c) engage in intercourse, but cannot become pregnant.
    (d) engage in intercourse, but only in rare cases become pregnant.

    Answer: A Difficulty: 3 Page: 482

77. Which of the following is *not* a stereotype associated with the mentally disabled?
    (a) They are excessively sexual.
    (b) They are asexual.
    (c) They cannot control their sex drive.
    (d) They are more open in expressing sexual feelings.

    Answer: D Difficulty: 2 Page: 483

78. Caretakers of the mentally disabled generally
    (a) offer comprehensive sex education programs.
    (b) discourage retarded people from learning about sexuality.
    (c) view their clients as capable of learning about sexuality.
    (d) encourage their clients to establish committed sexual relationships.

    Answer: B Difficulty: 2 Page: 483

79. One of the greatest impediments to sexual fufillment among people with disabilities is
    (a) using the right contraception.
    (b) learning the best coital positions for their condition.
    (c) finding the right medications to compensate for their disability.
    (d) finding a loving and supportive partner.

    Answer: D Difficulty: 2 Page: 484

MATCHING

For each of the following definitions, match the definition to the appropriate term.

(a) Polyandry

(b) Mating Gradient

(c) Conventional Adultery

(d) Open Marriage

(e) Group Marriage

(f) Polygyny

(g) Homogamy

(h) Comarital Sex

80. Three or more people share an intimate relationship but are not legally married

    Answer: e

81. A form of consensual adultery in which both partners openly share sexual experiences
    with other people

    Answer: h

82. An extramarital affair conducted in secret

    Answer: c

83. The stereotype that an economically established older man takes an attractive, younger
    woman for his wife

    Answer: b

84. A type of marriage in which a man is allowed to have more than one wife

    Answer: f

85. A marriage where partners have the opportunity to
    develop emotionally intimate relationships with others

    Answer: d

86. The concept of marrying persons like ourselves

    Answer: g

87. A type of marriage in which a woman can have more than one husband

    Answer: a

TRUE/FALSE

88. Singlehood is now the most common lifestyle among people in their early 20s.

    Answer: True

89. Cohabitators are more likely to attend church regularly.

    Answer: False

90. Since 1980, the greatest increase in adults living together has been in the age 35 and above category.

    Answer: True

91. About 40% of couples living together eventually marry.

    Answer: True

92. Polyandry is the most prevalent form of polygamy among the world's preliterate cultures.

    Answer: False

93. In mate selection, women are more likely than men to believe in "love at first sight."

    Answer: False

94. Divorced people have higher rates of suicide than married people.

    Answer: True

95. About 40% of children whose parents divorced have problems with anxiety, academic underachievement, and decreased self-worth.

    Answer: True

96. Remarriages are even more likely than first marriages to end in divorce.

    Answer: True

97. The sexual revolution did not seem to change attitudes toward extramarital sex.

    Answer: True

98. In cultures in which extramarital sex is permitted, wives are typically allowed greater sexual freedom than the husbands.

    Answer: False

99. Swinging — also called "mate-swapping" or comarital sex — is a form of consensual adultery in which both partners openly share sexual experiences with other people.

    Answer: True

100. Following orgasm, erection subsides more rapidly for older men than it does younger man.

    Answer: True

101. Coil frequency is synonymous with sexual satisfaction only among healthy adults that stay fit.

    Answer: False

102. People who are paralyzed due to spinal cord injuries usually can't become sexually aroused and engage in coitus.

    Answer: False

ESSAY

103. Identify and explain some of the reasons why more people are remaining single.

    Answer:

104. Describe the events involved in Japan's December 24th celebration and the social implications of this "holiday."

    Answer:

105. Outline the history of how marriage has been perceived by beginning with the ancient Hebrews and progressing to modern Western culture.

    Answer:

106. Compare and contrast the views and values associated with the "traditional marriage" and the "modern marriage."

    Answer:

107. Identify at least four factors that may precipitate violence in a relationship.

    Answer:

108. Discuss the impact of divorce on children and the types of problems identified in children of divorced parents.

    Answer:

109. Identify and discuss three physical changes in men and three physical changes in women that are the result of aging. How might each of these changes affect sexual activity?

    Answer:

110. Using two disabilities identified in your text, discuss the challenges disabled individuals face in developing healthy sexual relationships.

    Answer:

Chapter 15: Sexual Dysfunctions

MULTIPLE CHOICE

1. Derek and Terry have sexual dysfunctions. That is, they have difficulties
   (a) in becoming sexually aroused or reaching orgasm.
   (b) discussing their sex life.
   (c) attaining certain sexual positions.
   (d) all of the above.

   Answer: A Difficulty: 1 Page: 488

2. In the NHSLS study, women were more likely to suffer from all of the following *except*
   (a) painful sex.
   (b) anxiety about performance.
   (c) lack of interest in sex.
   (d) lack of pleasure during sex.

   Answer: B Difficulty: 2 Page: 488

3. Vaginismus is classified as a(n)
   (a) sexual arousal disorder.
   (b) orgasmic disorder.
   (c) sexual pain disorder.
   (d) sexual desire disorder.

   Answer: C Difficulty: 1 Page: 490

4. Which group of disorders involve a lack of sexual interest and/or aversion to genital sexual activity?
   (a) orgasmic disorders
   (b) sexual desire disorders
   (c) sexual arousal disorders
   (d) sexual pain disorders

   Answer: B Difficulty: 2 Page: 490

5. Which is not a sexual dysfunction?
   (a) orgasmic disorder
   (b) sexual pain disorder
   (c) sexual absence disorder
   (d) sexual arousal disorder

   Answer: C Difficulty: 2 Page: 490

6. Sally and Joe sometimes experience painful intercourse. They suffer from
   (a) dyspareunia.
   (b) vaginismus.
   (c) anhedonism.
   (d) none of the above.

   Answer: A Difficulty: 2 Page: 490

7. Seth has never been able to achieve or maintain an erection during sexual relations with a partner but can do so with masturbation. Seth's dysfunction would be categorized as
   (a) lifelong and situational.
   (b) acquired and situational.
   (c) lifelong and generalized.
   (d) acquired and generalized.

   Answer: A Difficulty: 2 Page: 490

8. Yoline was raped two years ago. Since that time, she cannot engage in sexual relations with her husband or any other potential partner. Yoline's dysfunction would be categorized as
   (a) lifelong and situational.
   (b) situational and generalized.
   (c) acquired and situational.
   (d) acquired and generalized.

   Answer: D Difficulty: 3 Page: 490

9. People who have little or no interest in sex are said to have
   (a) sexual aversion disorder.
   (b) hypoactive sexual desire disorder.
   (c) a sexual disorder.
   (d) impotence or frigidity.

   Answer: B Difficulty: 2 Page: 490

10. The sexual dysfunction most commonly diagnosed is
    (a) sexual pain disorder.
    (b) sexual absence disorder.
    (c) orgasmic disorder.
    (d) hypoactive sexual desire.

    Answer: D Difficulty: 2 Page: 490

11. Jerry and Nancy have a lack of desire for intercourse. They could be experiencing
    (a) hormonal deficiencies.
    (b) depression.
    (c) marital dissatisfaction.
    (d) all of the above.

    Answer: D Difficulty: 1 Page: 490

12. Which statement is *true* regarding low interest in sex?
    (a) Women with inhibited sexual desire usually have low levels of testosterone.
    (b) Temporal lobe epilepsy may diminish sexual desire.
    (c) Anxiety is generally not associated with inhibited desire.
    (d) Women with a sexual desire disorder tend to be older than men with the disorder.

    Answer: B Difficulty: 3 Page: 490

13. Hypogonadism is treated with
    (a) estrogen.
    (b) testosterone.
    (c) aspirin.
    (d) Viagra.

    Answer: B Difficulty: 3 Page: 490

14. The *most* common psychological cause of sexual desire disorder is
    (a) depression.
    (b) anxiety.
    (c) a history of sexual assault.
    (d) hypertension.

    Answer: B Difficulty: 1 Page: 491

15. Sexual aversion disorder describes a person with
    (a) little or no interest in sex.
    (b) a phobia of genitalia.
    (c) same sex desires.
    (d) a phobia of masturbation.

    Answer: A Difficulty: 2 Page: 491

16. In women, a prominent cause of sexual aversion disorder is
    (a) having a partner with a sexual aversion disorder.
    (b) a history of inhibited sexual desire.
    (c) depression.
    (d) a history of sexual trauma.

    Answer: D Difficulty: 2 Page: 491

17. A lack of the subjective feelings of sexual pleasure or excitement that normally accompany sexual arousal is characteristic of
    (a) sexual arousal disorder.
    (b) sexual aversion disorder.
    (c) hypoactive sexual desire disorder.
    (d) male erectile disorder.

    Answer: A Difficulty: 3 Page: 491

18. In men, sexual arousal disorder is referred to as
    (a) sexual aversion.
    (b) erectile dysfunction.
    (c) premature ejaculation.
    (d) hypogonadism.

    Answer: B Difficulty: 2 Page: 491

19. In men between 40 and 70, the incidence of intermittent erectile dysfunction is about
    (a) 5%.
    (b) 25%.
    (c) 50%.
    (d) 60%.

    Answer: C Difficulty: 3 Page: 492

20. Primary erectile disorder is erectile dysfunction that is
    (a) acquired.
    (b) situational.
    (c) intermittent.
    (d) lifelong.

    Answer: D Difficulty: 2 Page: 492

21. Performance anxiety is a prominent cause of
    (a) dyspareunia.
    (b) secondary depression.
    (c) erectile disorder.
    (d) arousal disorder.

    Answer: C Difficulty: 2 Page: 492

22. Marcus is able to achieve an erection by either masturbation or manual stimulation by his partner. He has no difficulty ejaculating when he masturbates, but he cannot ejaculate during intercourse. Marcus would likely be diagnosed with
    (a) premature ejaculation.
    (b) sexual arousal disorder.
    (c) orgasmic disorder.
    (d) sexual aversion.

    Answer: C Difficulty: 3 Page: 493

23. Male orgasmic disorder is
    (a) generally lifelong.
    (b) often limited to masturbation.
    (c) frequently limited to coitus.
    (d) common in older men.

    Answer: C Difficulty: 1 Page: 494

24. Male orgasmic disorder may be caused by
    (a) physical problems.
    (b) side effects of certain drugs.
    (c) various psychological factors.
    (d) all of the above.

    Answer: D Difficulty: 1 Page: 494

25. Deanna has never experienced an orgasm during intercourse but can achieve orgasm through masturbation. She is concerned that she has an orgasmic disorder. What should Deanna know?
    (a) She probably holds some deep-seated resentment toward her partner that needs to be resolved.
    (b) She is correct and probably does suffer from female orgasmic disorder.
    (c) Many women cannot achieve orgasm through coitus and require direct stimulation of the clitoris.
    (d) She probably suffers from guilt and sees sex as something shameful.

    Answer: C Difficulty: 3 Page: 494

26. The most commonly reported male sexual dysfunction in the NHSLS study was
    (a) premature ejaculation.
    (b) delayed ejaculation.
    (c) intermittent erectile disorder.
    (d) sexual desire disorder.

    Answer: A Difficulty: 2 Page: 494

27. Dyspareunia is
    (a) constriction of the vaginal opening.
    (b) painful contraction of the pelvic muscles.
    (c) painful orgasm.
    (d) painful coitus.

    Answer: D Difficulty: 1 Page: 495

28. The most common cause of coital pain in women is
    (a) vaginal infection.
    (b) lack of lubrication.
    (c) pelvic inflammatory disease.
    (d) penile contact with the cervix.

    Answer: B Difficulty: 2 Page: 495

29. Vaginismus is the
    (a) voluntary contraction of vaginal muscles that prevents penetration.
    (b) experience of pain during intercourse because of pelvic inflammatory disease.
    (c) experience of pain during intercourse because of deep penile penetration.
    (d) involuntary contraction of the pelvic muscles near the vaginal opening, which prevents penetration.

    Answer: D Difficulty: 1 Page: 496

30. The inhabitants of Inis Beag avoid having sex before a sporting activity or strenuous work because
    (a) it's taboo.
    (b) it drains their strength.
    (c) it's against their religion.
    (d) none of the above.

    Answer: B Difficulty: 1 Page: 496

31. Mangaian boys at the age of 13 are
    (a) taught sexual techniques by their elders.
    (b) sent on a pilgrimage to increase sexual stamina.
    (c) given a bride.
    (d) instructed to wait until marriage to have sex.

    Answer: A Difficulty: 2 Page: 496

32. Physical factors, such as fatigue and lowered testosterone levels, can
    (a) improve erectile functioning.
    (b) increase male sex drive.
    (c) dampen sexual desire and reduce responsiveness.
    (d) reduce the effects of priapism.

    Answer: C Difficulty: 2 Page: 498

33. In erectile disorder, it is now believed that organic (physical) factors are involved in
    (a) about 80% of cases.
    (b) about 60% of cases.
    (c) about 50% of cases.
    (d) about 25% of cases.

    Answer: A Difficulty: 3 Page: 498

34. Eric Rimm in his study found erectile function connected with
    (a) drinking an excessive amount of alcohol.
    (b) physical inactivity.
    (c) a large waist.
    (d) all of the above.

    Answer: D Difficulty: 1 Page: 498

35. High cholesterol levels in men can
    (a) impede the flow of blood to the penis.
    (b) affect semen count.
    (c) affect semen motility.
    (d) improve erectile functioning.

    Answer: A Difficulty: 1 Page: 499

36. Joey has high cholesterol. He visits his doctor to get advice. What would his doctor tell him?
    (a) Have one or two alcoholic drinks a day
    (b) Exercise
    (c) Lose weight
    (d) All of the above

    Answer: D Difficulty: 1 Page: 499

37. Many cases of erectile disorder involve failure of the body to produce enough
    (a) testosterone.
    (b) follicle stimulating hormone.
    (c) nitric oxide.
    (d) inhibin.

    Answer: C Difficulty: 2 Page: 499

38. Miguel has difficulty achieving erection. To determine if his dysfunction is physical or psychological, his physician will probably suggest
    (a) blood tests to determine his testosterone levels.
    (b) that he complete a number of psychological tests for anxiety and depression.
    (c) sleep studies to look at nocturnal erections.
    (d) an anti-anxiety medication.

    Answer: C Difficulty: 3 Page: 499

39. Narcotics can contribute to erectile disorders by
    (a) inflaming the arteries in the penis.
    (b) decreasing testosterone production.
    (c) decreasing the production of luteinizing hormone.
    (d) damaging the nerves that control erection.

    Answer: B Difficulty: 3 Page: 499

40. The United States myth that "sex before an athletic event saps strength" is analogous to the East Indian disorder known as
    (a) Dhat syndrome.
    (b) anorgasmia.
    (c) Koro syndrome.
    (d) dyspareunia.

    Answer: A Difficulty: 1 Page: 501

41. People with Koro syndrome
    (a) fear their genitals are shrinking and retracting into their body.
    (b) fear intercourse.
    (c) fear emotional rejection from the opposite sex.
    (d) fear that sexual contact will infect them.

    Answer: A Difficulty: 1 Page: 501

42. The best sex therapy techniques are of little benefit to couples
    (a) with unresolved conflicts.
    (b) with organic sexual dysfunctions.
    (c) with very different levels of sexual desire.
    (d) that lack sexual knowledge.

    Answer: A Difficulty: 1 Page: 502

43. According to Helen Singer Kaplan, immediate causes must interact with remote causes to produce a sexual dysfunction. Which of the following is a remote cause?
    (a) performance anxiety
    (b) lack of effective communication
    (c) poor sexual technique
    (d) unresolved guilt about sex

    Answer: D Difficulty: 3 Page: 502

44. Which statement best supports the views of Kaplan for treating sexual dysfunctions?
    (a) Treatment is most successful with psychoanalytic techniques.
    (b) Treatment should combine behavioral therapy for immediate causes and insight-oriented techniques for remote causes.
    (c) Remote causes respond best to behavioral therapy.
    (d) Treatment should combine insight-oriented techniques for immediate causes and behavioral therapy for remote causes.

    Answer: B Difficulty: 3 Page: 503

45. In recent studies of premature ejaculation, researchers speculate that premature ejaculation may result from
    (a) an inability to recognize one's level of arousal.
    (b) an inability to develop strategies to delay ejaculation.
    (c) a higher level of sensitivity to sexual stimulation.
    (d) an inability to divert one's attention away from sexual activity.

    Answer: C Difficulty: 2 Page: 503

46. According to Kinsey's surveys, there wasn't any treatment for sexual dysfunctions until after
    (a) 1930s and 40s.
    (b) 1900.
    (c) 1970.
    (d) none of the above.

    Answer: A Difficulty: 2 Page: 504

47. Performance anxiety can set the stage for a vicious cycle in which a sexual failure
    (a) increases anxiety.
    (b) evokes hostility toward one's partner.
    (c) leads to hypoactive sexual desire.
    (d) causes erectile dysfunction.

    Answer: A Difficulty: 1 Page: 504

48. Taken alone, behavioral sex therapy techniques aim to
    (a) modify dysfunctional behavior as directly as possible.
    (b) uncover irrational beliefs that result in performance anxiety.
    (c) uncover unconscious conflicts that interfere with healthy sexual functioning.
    (d) change self-defeating beliefs and attitudes.

    Answer: A Difficulty: 2 Page: 504

49. Who pioneered the use of the direct behavioral approach to treat sexual dysfunctions?
    (a) Sigmund Freud
    (b) Masters and Johnson
    (c) Alfred Kinsey
    (d) Helen Singer Kaplan

    Answer: B Difficulty: 1 Page: 504

50. As part of their sex therapy program, Bill and Melissa practice a series of touching exercises that involve caressing and stroking body areas other than the genitals. These exercises are called
    (a) reciprocal massage.
    (b) erotic fantasies.
    (c) the stop-start technique.
    (d) sensate focus.

    Answer: D Difficulty: 2 Page: 505

51. Today, *most* sex therapists have abandoned Masters and Johnson's use of
    (a) two therapists.
    (b) couples' therapy.
    (c) intensive residential treatment.
    (d) sensate focus.

    Answer: C Difficulty: 1 Page: 505

52. The psychosexual therapy approach was developed by
    (a) Sigmund Freud.
    (b) Albert Ellis.
    (c) Helen Singer Kaplan.
    (d) Alfred Kinsey.

    Answer: C Difficulty: 1 Page: 505

53. In treating hypoactive sexual desire disorder, some therapists prescribe
    (a) self-stimulation exercises and erotic fantasy.
    (b) the start-stop technique.
    (c) the squeeze technique.
    (d) vaginal dilators.

    Answer: A Difficulty: 2 Page: 505

54. A *very* rare cause of hypoactive sexual desire disorder in men is
    (a) childhood sexual abuse or trauma.
    (b) testosterone deficiency.
    (c) a gay sexual orientation.
    (d) depression.

    Answer: B Difficulty: 2 Page: 507

55. According to Eric B. Rimm, what is strongly associated with better erectile functioning?
    (a) physical activity
    (b) vitamin B intake
    (c) additional unsaturated fats
    (d) none of the above

    Answer: A Difficulty: 1 Page: 507

56. Which is not a treatment of sexual aversion disorder?
    (a) biological treatments such as the use of medications to reduce anxiety
    (b) psychological treatments designed to help the individual overcome the underlying sexual phobia
    (c) sensate focus exercises
    (d) none of the above

    Answer: D Difficulty: 1 Page: 508

57. Of the following, which is *not* likely to be a recommended treatment for sexual desire
   disorder?
   (a) arousing fantasies
   (b) the squeeze technique
   (c) masturbation
   (d) sensate focus

   Answer: B Difficulty: 1 Page: 508

58. Sexual arousal disorders involve difficulties with
   (a) vasocongestion.
   (b) sexual interest or drive.
   (c) any sexual sensations.
   (d) sexual orientation.

   Answer: A Difficulty: 2 Page: 508

59. In treating sexual arousal disorders, one of the most important remedies is
   (a) concentration.
   (b) learning to use erotic fantasy.
   (c) learning new sexual techniques.
   (d) learning how to relax.

   Answer: D Difficulty: 2 Page: 509

60. In treating performance anxiety, a woman is taught to help her partner by
   (a) using the lateral coital position.
   (b) using the squeeze technique.
   (c) teasing him to erection and then letting the erection subside.
   (d) using the stop-start technique.

   Answer: C Difficulty: 2 Page: 509

61. Male sexual arousal disorder is also known as
   (a) erectile disorder.
   (b) penile dysfunction.
   (c) prostate disorder.
   (d) insufficient response disorder.

   Answer: A Difficulty: 1 Page: 509

62. In treating erectile dysfunction, *Alprostadil* is
   (a) a drug that increases the level of nitric oxide in the penis.
   (b) an injection that relaxes the muscles surrounding blood vessels in the penis.
   (c) an inflatable type of penile implant.
   (d) a testosterone patch.

   Answer: B Difficulty: 3 Page: 510

63. There are two main types of surgery in treating sexual arousal disorder. They are
   (a) vascular surgery, and the installation of penile implants.
   (b) prostate surgery, and the installation of penile implants.
   (c) installation of penile implants, and Alprostadil surgery.
   (d) installation of penile implants, and penile projection surgery.

   Answer: A Difficulty: 2 Page: 510

64. In treating sexual arousal disorders, *Apomorphine (Spontane)* works by
    (a) stimulating the brain area that triggers erection.
    (b) relaxing the muscles that surround the small blood vessels in the penis.
    (c) increasing the level of testosterone in the blood.
    (d) dilating the blood vessels in the penis to increase blood flow.

    Answer: A Difficulty: 2 Page: 512

65. In a study investigating the reliability of *Viagra*, how many men reported that attempts to engage in intercourse were successful?
    (a) 94%
    (b) 82%
    (c) 69%
    (d) 54%

    Answer: C Difficulty: 3 Page: 513

66. A vacuum constriction device can help a man maintain an erection for about
    (a) 10 minutes.
    (b) 1 hour.
    (c) 2 hours.
    (d) 30 minutes.

    Answer: D Difficulty: 3 Page: 514

67. Which of the following is *not* true of women who experience an orgasmic disorder?
    (a) Because they do not experience feelings of sexual arousal, they generally are unable to lubricate.
    (b) They may be anorgasmic because of deep-seated feelings of guilt regarding sexual activity.
    (c) They may have a partner who ejaculates prematurely.
    (d) A number of anorgasmic women are not concerned about their inability to orgasm and report feeling satisfied with their sex lives.

    Answer: A Difficulty: 3 Page: 514

68. In treating orgasmic disorder in women, once intercourse is introduced, it is recommended that the couple use the
    (a) lateral-entry position.
    (b) female-superior position.
    (c) male-superior position.
    (d) rear-entry position.

    Answer: B Difficulty: 1 Page: 515

69. How many adult women say they have lost interest in sex or have difficulty becoming sexually aroused?
    (a) 15%
    (b) 28%
    (c) 39%
    (d) 50%

    Answer: D Difficulty: 3 Page: 519

70. In premature ejaculation, the squeeze technique involves
    (a) firmly squeezing the frenulum and coronal ridge just as a partner is about to ejaculate.
    (b) firmly squeezing the entire shaft of the penis just before ejaculation.
    (c) gently squeezing the glans of the penis just before ejaculation.
    (d) firmly pressing with the thumb and two fingers at the base of the penis just as a partner is about to ejaculate.

    Answer: A Difficulty: 2 Page: 519

71. In treating premature ejaculation, once intercourse is initiated, it is recommended that the couple use the
    (a) lateral-entry position.
    (b) rear-entry position.
    (c) female-superior position.
    (d) male-superior position.

    Answer: C Difficulty: 3 Page: 520

72. If a woman or a man experiences recurrent pain during or after intercourse, he or she may suffer from
    (a) sexual desire disorder.
    (b) dyspareunia.
    (c) vaginismus.
    (d) hypoactive sexual desire disorder.

    Answer: B Difficulty: 1 Page: 520

73. Antidepressant drugs may be useful in treating premature ejaculation by increasing the action of
    (a) testosterone.
    (b) serotonin.
    (c) norepenephrine.
    (d) inhibin.

    Answer: B Difficulty: 2 Page: 520

74. Which of the following is a drug used to treat both obsessive-compulsive disorder and premature ejaculation?
    (a) fluoxetine
    (b) lithium
    (c) sertraline
    (d) clomipramine

    Answer: D Difficulty: 1 Page: 520

75. Plastic vaginal dilators are used in the treatment of
    (a) female sexual arousal disorder.
    (b) female orgasmic disorder.
    (c) vaginismus.
    (d) dyspareunia.

    Answer: C Difficulty: 2 Page: 520

76. Rhonda and her husband have been married for six months but have not been able to have intercourse because Rhonda has involuntary contractions of the muscles in the outer vagina. The first step in treating Rhonda will involve
    (a) her husband helping her to insert a vaginal dilator.
    (b) intensive psychoanalytic therapy.
    (c) having Rhonda insert vaginal dilators.
    (d) asking her to practice Kegel exercises.

    Answer: C Difficulty: 3 Page: 520

77. Since the addition of biological treatments for erectile dysfunction, the rate of treatment success has
    (a) reached about 30%.
    (b) reached nearly 50%.
    (c) stayed about the same.
    (d) reached the great majority of those seeking treatment.

    Answer: D Difficulty: 3 Page: 521

78. In which of the following disorders have treatment results been generally poor?
    (a) male orgasmic disorder
    (b) vaginismus
    (c) premature ejaculation
    (d) female orgasmic disorder

    Answer: A Difficulty: 2 Page: 521

79. In treatment of anorgasmic women, one study found results indicating that
    (a) only 50% were eventually able to achieve orgasm through masturbation.
    (b) about 85% were eventually able to reach orgasm through manual stimulation by their partner.
    (c) about 75% were eventually able to reach orgasm through intercourse.
    (d) more than half of the women could only achieve orgasm through masturbation but only if their partner was not present.

    Answer: B Difficulty: 3 Page: 522

80. In order to legally use the title, "sex therapist," most states
    (a) require that the individual be a licensed psychologist.
    (b) require certification by AASECT.
    (c) require that an individual be a licensed psychologist with specialized certification in sex therapy.
    (d) have no requirements.

    Answer: D Difficulty: 2 Page: 522

81. One professional organization that does certify sex therapists is the
    (a) Masters and Johnson's Institute of Sex Research.
    (b) Kinsey and Associates Sex Training Institute.
    (c) American Association of Sex Educators, Counselors, and Therapists.
    (d) National Institute of Certified Sex Therapists.

    Answer: C Difficulty: 1 Page: 523

82. Sexual contact between a sex therapist and a client is
    (a) unethical and exploitive.
    (b) recommended for some dysfunctions but certainly not all.
    (c) legal if the therapist is a licensed sex surrogate.
    (d) legal only if the client gives written consent.

    Answer: A Difficulty: 2 Page: 523

Chapter 15: Sexual Dysfunctions

MATCHING

For each of the following individuals, match their symptoms with the correct sexual dysfunction.

(a) Vaginismus

(b) Generalized Erectile Dysfunction

(c) Male Orgasmic Disorder

(d) Dyspareunia

(e) Sexual Aversion Disorder

(f) Hypoactive Sexual Desire Disorder

(g) Situational Erectile Dysfunction

(h) Premature Ejaculation

83. Donna has little difficulty with sexual arousal but cannot tolerate sexual intercourse because it causes her pain.

    Answer: d

84. Darrin finds that he can achieve an erection and ejaculate when he masturbates but he cannot achieve an erection when he has intercourse with his girlfriend.

    Answer: g

85. Han Li has been secretly seeing another woman. Recently he has had difficulty achieving and maintaining an erection with both his girlfriend and his wife and during masturbation.

    Answer: b

86. Allie is totally frustrated with her husband. While he can masturbate to ejaculation, he cannot ejaculate when he has intercourse with her.

    Answer: c

87. Michelle and Joe have yet to consummate their marriage. After three months of trying to have intercourse, they decide to seek help. It appears that despite an adequate erection, the couple cannot get his penis inside her vagina.

    Answer: a

88. Beth is frustrated by her husband's lack of consideration when they make love. Despite her attempts to talk to her lover, he seems to ejaculate immediately upon entering her vagina.

    Answer: h

89. Clarke finds the idea of sexual activity messy and annoying. He has never attempted a sexual relationship.

    Answer: e

90. With sexual stimulation, Cathy lubricates adequately and has a satisfactory experience. She does not, however, initiate sexual activity and generally only engages in sexual activity if her partner "pushes it."

    Answer: f

TRUE/FALSE

91. In terms of sexual dysfunctions, women are more likely than men to report being anxious about their performance.

    Answer: False

92. Only women can suffer from painful intercourse.

    Answer: False

93. Hypogonadism may cause low sexual interest and erectile difficulties in men.

    Answer: True

94. Some researchers consider sexual aversion disorder to be a sexual phobia.

    Answer: True

95. Diabetes mellitus can lead to diminished sexual excitement in women.

    Answer: True

96. Male orgasmic disorder is relatively common and affects about 10% of men.

    Answer: False

97. Statistically, White Americans have consistently higher rates of sexual dysfunctions than African Americans.

    Answer: False

98. Fear of losing control or letting go is a common emotional factor in the orgasmic disorders.

    Answer: True

99. Nerve damage resulting from prostate surgery may impair erectile response.

    Answer: True

100. Regular use of cocaine can cause erectile disorder.

    Answer: True

101. Psychosocial factors are never connected with sexual dysfunctions.

    Answer: False

102. People with Dhat syndrome believe that semen mixes with urine and is excreted by urinating.

    Answer: True

103. Sensate focus exercises may be used to lessen generalized anxiety about sexual contact.

    Answer: True

104. There are no medical solutions for male erectile disorder.

    Answer: False

105. Vasomax promises to have fewer side effects than Viagra.

    Answer: True

ESSAY

106. Compare and contrast hypoactive sexual desire disorder with sexual aversion disorder in terms of the clinical symptoms and potential causes.

    Answer:

107. Given what you have learned about orgasmic disorders, draw conclusions as to why orgasmic disorder is so much more prevalent in women than in men.

     Answer:

108. Using the Inis Beag and Mangian cultures as case studies, discuss the difficulty in diagnosing sexual dysfunctions from a cross-cultural point of view.

     Answer:

109. Discuss three major psychological factors that can lead to sexual dysfunctions.

     Answer:

110. Given a client with premature ejaculation, explain the techniques and process that will be used to treat him.

     Answer:

111. Given a client with vaginismus, explain the techniques and procedures that will be used to treat her.

     Answer:

112. List three biological approaches to treating erectile disorder and explain how each works.

     Answer:

113. Evaluate the ethical and social concerns involved in the use of *Viagra* to restore sexual functioning.

     Answer:

114. Describe the treatments that have proved effective in treating sexual dysfunctions. Identify the dysfunctions for which these techniques have proved successful and the dysfunctions for which these techniques appear to have little if any benefit.

     Answer:

Chapter 16: Sexually Transmitted Infections

1. In the AIDS study, how many of the 16,000 college students had HIV in their blood?
   (a) 30
   (b) 120
   (c) 300
   (d) 1200

   Answer: A Difficulty: 3 Page: 528

2. How many Americans over the age of 12 are estimated to be infected with the *human papilloma virus*?
   (a) 3%
   (b) 10%
   (c) 20%
   (d) 30%

   Answer: C Difficulty: 3 Page: 528

3. A study at Rutgers University found HPV infections in
   (a) 60% of its female students.
   (b) 45% of its male students.
   (c) 35% of its entire student population.
   (d) 35% of its female students.

   Answer: A Difficulty: 2 Page: 528

4. How many Americans are estimated to be infected with STIs other than HIV?
   (a) 1 million
   (b) 28 million
   (c) 56 million
   (d) 89 million

   Answer: C Difficulty: 3 Page: 529

5. How many people in the world are estimated by the World Health Organization to get some form of curable STI each year?
   (a) 112 million
   (b) 67 million
   (c) 856 million
   (d) 333 million

   Answer: D Difficulty: 3 Page: 529

6. Which country has the highest rate of STIs in the industrial world?
   (a) China
   (b) Sweden
   (c) the United States
   (d) France

   Answer: C Difficulty: 1 Page: 529

7. Two-thirds of the STIs reported each year in the United States occur in people
   (a) between the ages of 40 and 55.
   (b) between the ages of 35 and 40.
   (c) between the ages of 25 and 35.
   (d) under the age of 25.

   Answer: D Difficulty: 2 Page: 529

8. Which of the following is *not* a bacterial STI?
   (a) syphilis
   (b) trichomoniasis
   (c) chlamydia
   (d) gonorrhea

   Answer: B Difficulty: 1 Page: 529

9. Gonorrhea is also known as
   (a) the clap.
   (b) the faucet.
   (c) piles.
   (d) scurvy.

   Answer: A Difficulty: 1 Page: 532

10. Gonorrhea is caused by
    (a) a virus.
    (b) the *treponema pallidum* bacterium.
    (c) ciprofloaxin.
    (d) none of the above.

    Answer: D Difficulty: 2 Page: 532

11. Gonococcus bacteria like a
    (a) clean environment.
    (b) dry, cold environment.
    (c) warm, moist environment.
    (d) warm, dry environment.

    Answer: C Difficulty: 2 Page: 532

12. The organism that causes gonorrhea can survive outside the body for about
    (a) 1 minute.
    (b) 30 minutes.
    (c) 1 hour.
    (d) 2 hours.

    Answer: A Difficulty: 2 Page: 532

13. Pharyngeal gonorrhea is characterized by
    (a) a yellow-green pus at the tip of the penis.
    (b) a persistent sore throat and throat infection.
    (c) swelling and inflammation of the cervix.
    (d) eye problems that could lead to blindness.

    Answer: B Difficulty: 3 Page: 532

14. What is gonorrhea of the eyes in a new born called?
    (a) ophthalmia neonatorum
    (b) optoliptic gonococcus
    (c) ophthalimia ciprofloaxin
    (d) optoliptic neonatorum

    Answer: A Difficulty: 3 Page: 532

15. What is the chance that a woman will contract gonorrhea after one exposure?
    (a) 10%
    (b) 25%
    (c) 40%
    (d) 50%

    Answer: D Difficulty: 3 Page: 532

16. For men, what are the symptoms of a gonorrheal infection?
    (a) a clear discharge that appears about 7 days after infection
    (b) a clear discharge within 2-3 days which changes to yellow-green within a day
    (c) flu-like symptoms that occur about 14 days after infection
    (d) the appearance of a soft sore on the glans of the penis and pain with urination

    Answer: B Difficulty: 2 Page: 536

17. Where is the primary site of the gonorrhea infection in women?
    (a) uterus
    (b) cervix
    (c) kidneys
    (d) vulva

    Answer: B Difficulty: 2 Page: 536

18. For women with a gonorrheal infection, how many are asymptomatic during the early stages of the disease?
    (a) 25%
    (b) 80%
    (c) 65%
    (d) 50%

    Answer: B Difficulty: 3 Page: 536

19. When a gonorrheal infection enters the later stages, men and women both run the risk of developing
    (a) heart disease.
    (b) dementia.
    (c) infertility.
    (d) kidney infections.

    Answer: C Difficulty: 1 Page: 536

20. Because of resistant strains, the recommended antibiotic for treating gonorrhea is
    (a) ceftriaxone.
    (b) penicillin.
    (c) doxycycline.
    (d) erythromycin.

    Answer: A Difficulty: 2 Page: 536

21. The organism that causes syphilis is
    (a) *Ureaplasma urealyticum.*
    (b) *Trichmonas vaginalis.*
    (c) *Treponema pallidum.*
    (d) *S. sarcoptes.*

    Answer: C Difficulty: 2 Page: 536

22. In the United States, there was a dramatic resurgence of syphilis in the
    (a) 1960s.
    (b) 1970s.
    (c) 1980s.
    (d) 1990s.

    Answer: C Difficulty: 3 Page: 537

23. Syphilis can be transmitted in all of the following ways *except*
    (a) contact with open lesions of an infected person.
    (b) from mother to fetus.
    (c) touching a chancre.
    (d) touching objects an infected person has had contact with.

    Answer: D Difficulty: 1 Page: 537

24. A pregnant women infected with the syphilis organism must be treated
    (a) with antiviral drugs before the sixth week of pregnancy.
    (b) with antibiotics before the fourth month of pregnancy.
    (c) with antiviral drugs but not until the second trimester.
    (d) with antibiotics but not until the second trimester.

    Answer: B Difficulty: 2 Page: 538

25. Glen woke up this morning with a skin rash consisting of painless, red bumps over most of his body. He is running a slight temperature. At first he thought it was simply the flu, but then he remembered that he had seen a spot similar to those on his body but larger on his penis several months earlier. Glen's symptoms would be characteristic of
    (a) secondary stage syphilis.
    (b) primary stage syphilis.
    (c) latency stage syphilis.
    (d) tertiary stage syphilis.

    Answer: A Difficulty: 2 Page: 538

26. The appearance of a painless soft sore that ulcerates, scabs, and disappears may indicate that an individual has
    (a) herpes.
    (b) genital warts.
    (c) syphilis.
    (d) gonorrhea.

    Answer: C Difficulty: 1 Page: 538

27. In a syphilis infection, a chancre usually heals in
    (a) 3-5 days.
    (b) 7-10 days.
    (c) 10-14 days.
    (d) 14-28 days.

    Answer: C Difficulty: 3 Page: 538

28. Which statement is *true* about latent stage syphilis?
    (a) The latent stage is marked by infections of the central nervous system.
    (b) A person can be in the latent stage from 1 to 40 years.
    (c) In the latent stage, a mother cannot pass the syphilis organism to her unborn child.
    (d) In the latent stage, a person may experience many flu-like symptoms.

    Answer: B Difficulty: 3 Page: 538

29. Neurosyphilis can cause
    (a) general paresis.
    (b) liver damage.
    (c) sexual dysfunction.
    (d) extreme malaise.

    Answer: A Difficulty: 2 Page: 539

30. General paresis is
    (a) a dementia caused by the syphilis organism.
    (b) a fatal heart infection caused by untreated gonorrhea.
    (c) an infection of the epididymus caused by chlamydia.
    (d) a form of pelvic inflammatory disease caused by the chlamydia organism.

    Answer: A Difficulty: 1 Page: 539

31. In the VDRL test
    (a) urine is examined for the presence of *T. pallidum.*
    (b) the cervix or penis is swabbed and the pus examined for gonorrhea.
    (c) blood is drawn to determine if an individual has antibodies for *T. pallidum.*
    (d) cervical cells are examined for the presence of HSV.

    Answer: C Difficulty: 2 Page: 539

32. What is true about chlamydia?
    (a) Chlamydia infections are caused by the Chlamydia trachomatis bacterium.
    (b) Chlamydia is an STI.
    (c) Chlamydia is more common than gonorrhea and syphilis.
    (d) All of the above.

    Answer: D Difficulty: 1 Page: 539

33. Which is not an infection caused by chlamydia?
    (a) nongonococcal urethritis
    (b) calymmatobacterium granulomatous
    (c) cervicitis
    (d) endometritis

    Answer: B Difficulty: 3 Page: 539

34. *Chlamydia trachomatis* can infect all of the following except
    (a) the cervix.
    (b) the urogenital tract.
    (c) the eyes.
    (d) open cuts or sores.

    Answer: D Difficulty: 2 Page: 539

35. If infants contract chlamydia in the birth process, they run the risk of
    (a) eye infections and urogenital tract infections.
    (b) kidney infections and pneumonia.
    (c) limb defects and sterility as adults.
    (d) pneumonia and eye infections.

    Answer: B Difficulty: 2 Page: 539

36. Which is not true of nongonococcal urethritis?
    (a) It is an inflammation of the urethra.
    (b) It refers to a form of urethritis that is not caused by the gonococcal bacterium.
    (c) It may give rise to a yellow-green discharge from the penis during urination.
    (d) It was formerly called nonspecific urethritis.

    Answer: C Difficulty: 3 Page: 539

37. Of the women who contract chlamydia, approximately how many have no symptoms?
    (a) 70%
    (b) 60%
    (c) 50%
    (d) 40%

    Answer: A Difficulty: 3 Page: 540

38. About half of the more than 1 million annual cases of PID are attributed to
    (a) gonorrhea.
    (b) chlamydia.
    (c) the herpes virus.
    (d) the human papilloma virus.

    Answer: B Difficulty: 2 Page: 540

39. Which is not a type of bacterial STI?
    (a) chancroid
    (b) shigellosis
    (c) melatoma
    (d) granuloma inguinale

    Answer: C Difficulty: 3 Page: 541

40. What is a symptom of chancroid?
    (a) cold sores inside the mouth
    (b) a rash around the genitals
    (c) small bumps or pimples on the genitals
    (d) none of the above

    Answer: C Difficulty: 2 Page: 541

41. In nearly half of the cases of gonorrhea, individuals were also infected with
    (a) herpes.
    (b) chlamydia.
    (c) hepatitis B.
    (d) HIV.

    Answer: B Difficulty: 2 Page: 540

42. Marcia has just learned from her gynecologist that she has a chlamydia infection. He advises her to immediately begin antibiotic therapy. Marcia learns that without treatment, she runs an increased risk of
    (a) cervical cancer.
    (b) uterine cancer.
    (c) kidney damage.
    (d) infertility.

    Answer: D Difficulty: 3 Page: 540

43. What is not a symptom of shigellosis?
    (a) diarrhea
    (b) lesions
    (c) inflammation of the large intestine
    (d) fever

    Answer: B Difficulty: 2 Page: 541

44. Shigellosis can be contracted as a sexually transmitted infection through
    (a) cunnilingus.
    (b) fellatio.
    (c) oral-anal sex.
    (d) anal sex.

    Answer: C Difficulty: 2 Page: 541

45. Which is true about granuloma inguinale?
    (a) It is more common in tropical regions.
    (b) It is caused by the bacterium calymmatobacterium granulomatous.
    (c) Its primary symptoms are painless red bumps or sores in the groin area.
    (d) all of the above

    Answer: D Difficulty: 2 Page: 541

46. Which two STIs can cause elephantiasis if left untreated?
    (a) granuloma inguinale and lymphogranuloma venereum
    (b) shigellosis and gardnerella
    (c) lymphogranuloma venereum and chancroid
    (d) chancroid and shigellosis

    Answer: A Difficulty: 2 Page: 541

47. The most common symptom for women with vaginitis is
    (a) genital irritation.
    (b) itching and burning during urination.
    (c) inflammation.
    (d) odorous discharge.

    Answer: D Difficulty: 1 Page: 542

48. Bacterial vaginosis is most often caused by
    (a) Candida Albicans.
    (b) Gardnerella vaginalis.
    (c) Trichomoniasis vaginalis.
    (d) Molluscum contagiosum.

    Answer: B Difficulty: 2 Page: 542

49. Which is not another term for candidiasis?
    (a) vaginosis
    (b) moniliasis
    (c) thrush
    (d) yeast infection

    Answer: A Difficulty: 3 Page: 542

50. Erica is seeing her gynecologist because she is experiencing itching, burning, and inflammation of the labia. In addition, she has noticed a white, thick, curdlike discharge. Erica's symptoms are characteristic of
    (a) a gardnerella infection.
    (b) a trichomonal infection.
    (c) a candida infection.
    (d) a gonorrheal infection.

    Answer: C Difficulty: 2 Page: 543

51. Which of the following would *not* reduce the possibility of a yeast infection?
    (a) Douching with a slightly acidic mixture of water and vinegar.
    (b) Wearing cotton underwear and loose fitting clothing.
    (c) Ingesting a pint of yogurt a day.
    (d) Reducing the intake of dairy products, sugars, and artificial sweeteners.

    Answer: A Difficulty: 3 Page: 543

52. How many women will experience at least one yeast infection in their lifetime?
    (a) 15%
    (b) 30%
    (c) 60%
    (d) 75%

    Answer: D Difficulty: 3 Page: 543

53. *Trichomonas vaginalis* is a
    (a) bacteria.
    (b) parasite.
    (c) virus.
    (d) fungus.

    Answer: B Difficulty: 1 Page: 543

54. Kendra complains of burning and itching in the vulva. In addition, she has noticed a foamy yellow-green discharge with a particularly foul smell. Which STI has Kendra contracted?
    (a) gardnerella
    (b) trichomoniasis
    (c) herpes
    (d) chlamydia

    Answer: B Difficulty: 2 Page: 543

55. Of the following STIs, which can be transmitted through discharges on towels, washcloths, bedclothes, and toilet seats?
    (a) candidiasis
    (b) gonorrhea
    (c) syphilis
    (d) trichomonas

    Answer: D Difficulty: 1 Page: 543

56. What are viruses?
    (a) bacteria
    (b) tiny particles of DNA surrounded by a protein coating
    (c) particles linked to antibodies
    (d) STIs

    Answer: B Difficulty: 1 Page: 544

57. Which of the following is *not* a viral sexually transmitted infection?
    (a) genital warts
    (b) genital herpes
    (c) gardnerella
    (d) molluscum contagiosum

    Answer: C Difficulty: 2 Page: 544

58. In the United States, AIDS is currently the leading killer of people between the ages of
    (a) 13 and 21.
    (b) 21 and 25.
    (c) 25 and 44.
    (d) 35 and 50.

    Answer: C Difficulty: 3 Page: 544

59. About how many people worldwide are living with the HIV virus today?
    (a) 34 million
    (b) 12 million
    (c) 58 million
    (d) over 90 million

    Answer: A Difficulty: 2 Page: 544

60. Worldwide, the main route of transmission for HIV is
    (a) heterosexual sex.
    (b) through blood and blood products.
    (c) through shared needles.
    (d) homosexual sex.

    Answer: A Difficulty: 2 Page: 545

61. Which ethnicity claims the highest number of AIDS victims?
    (a) European American
    (b) African American
    (c) Latino American
    (d) American Indian

    Answer: A Difficulty: 2 Page: 545

62. The gp120 spikes on the surface of the HIV allow the virus to
    (a) enter the CD4 cell.
    (b) replicate within the CD4 cell.
    (c) copy the CD4 cell DNA.
    (d) bind to the surface of the CD4 cell.

    Answer: D Difficulty: 2 Page: 545

63. The CD4 cell is considered the ____ of the immune system.
    (a) halfback
    (b) quarterback
    (c) free safety
    (d) running back

    Answer: B Difficulty: 1 Page: 546

64. The immune system
    (a) is the body's natural line of defense.
    (b) promotes inflammation.
    (c) produces white blood cells.
    (d) all of the above.

    Answer: D Difficulty: 1 Page: 545

65. Which is not a pathogen?
    (a) leukocytes
    (b) fungi
    (c) viruses
    (d) worn-out body cells

    Answer: A Difficulty: 1 Page: 546

66. Persons with HIV are most vulnerable to opportunistic infections when the number of CD4 cells falls below
    (a) 200.
    (b) 400.
    (c) 700.
    (d) 1000.

    Answer: A Difficulty: 3 Page: 548

67. Shortly after infection with the HIV virus, individuals will
    (a) have no symptoms.
    (b) begin to have night sweats and chronic diarrhea.
    (c) experience a slow decline in circulating CD4 cells.
    (d) have flu-like symptoms that last for a few weeks, then disappear.

    Answer: D Difficulty: 2 Page: 548

68. About 50% of the people infected with HIV develop AIDS within
    (a) 2 years.
    (b) 5 years.
    (c) 10 years.
    (d) 15 years.

    Answer: C Difficulty: 2 Page: 548

69. Which is not a disease connected with AIDS?
    (a) pneumocystis carinii pneumonia
    (b) transcriptase
    (c) Kaposi's sarcoma
    (d) toxoplasmosis of the brain

    Answer: B Difficulty: 2 Page: 548

70. What percentage of AIDs victims have a wasting syndrome?
    (a) 65%
    (b) 48%
    (c) 32%
    (d) 10%

    Answer: D Difficulty: 3 Page: 548

71. Which of the following sexual practices poses the *greatest* risk for HIV transmission?
    (a) anal intercourse
    (b) fellatio
    (c) cunnilingus
    (d) vaginal intercourse

    Answer: A Difficulty: 2 Page: 549

72. Which is not a bodily fluid that can transmit the HIV virus?
    (a) blood
    (b) breast milk
    (c) vaginal secretions
    (d) sputum

    Answer: D Difficulty: 2 Page: 549

73. In testing for HIV infection, an ELIZA test detects
    (a) the number of CD4 cells circulating in the blood.
    (b) the amount of virus circulating in the blood.
    (c) the amount of virus in semen or vaginal fluids.
    (d) the presence of antibodies to HIV in the blood.

    Answer: D Difficulty: 2 Page: 551

74. What has been the most widely used drug for HIV/AIDS?
    (a) hydrocodone
    (b) andrasolic glucosamine
    (c) zidovudine
    (d) podophyllin

    Answer: C Difficulty: 2 Page: 551

75. AZT and other nucleoside analogues work by
    (a) preventing attachment of the HIV to CD4 cells.
    (b) targeting reverse transcriptase and inhibiting replication.
    (c) dismantling the virus prior to attachment.
    (d) directly killing the virus and mounting an immune response.

    Answer: B Difficulty: 2 Page: 551

76. Which of the following is *true* regarding herpes infections?
    (a) Oral herpes cannot be spread to the genitals.
    (b) *Herpes Simplex-Type 2* cannot be contracted except through intercourse.
    (c) *Herpes Simplex-Type 1* is genital herpes.
    (d) *Herpes Simplex-Type 1* can be transferred to the genitals.

    Answer: D Difficulty: 3 Page: 555

77. Which is not a way to get herpes?
    (a) sharing a towel
    (b) kissing
    (c) drinking from the same glass
    (d) none of the above

    Answer: D Difficulty: 1 Page: 555

78. In regard to transmission of the herpes virus, which statement is *false*?
    (a) Genital herpes can only be spread to others during an outbreak of blisters.
    (b) The most common means of spreading HSV-1 is through shared drinking glasses.
    (c) The herpes viruses can survive for several hours on toilet seats or other objects.
    (d) One potentially serious complication of herpes is ocular herpes.

    Answer: A Difficulty: 2 Page: 555

79. Pregnant women with genital herpes
    (a) can deliver vaginally if they are treated with Acyclovir for three days before labor begins.
    (b) will be advised to have a caesarean section if they have active lesions or prodromal symptoms at the time of delivery.
    (c) often deliver vaginally because herpes poses little risk to newborns.
    (d) must take Acyclovir throughout their pregnancies to prevent outbreaks.

    Answer: B Difficulty: 2 Page: 556

80. Which is not a way to promote the outbreak of herpes?
    (a) lack of vitamin C
    (b) stress
    (c) fatigue
    (d) exposure to the sun

    Answer: A Difficulty: 2 Page: 557

81. In terms of symptoms, what differentiates primary syphilis from a herpes infection?
    (a) The sores seen in a syphilis infection are painful while those seen in a herpes infection are painless.
    (b) Syphilis produces a soft, painless sore, while herpes lesions are clusters of blisters that are extremely painful.
    (c) Syphilis produces a distinct vaginal or penile discharge that is cloudy and foul smelling but herpes does not produce any vaginal or penile discharge.
    (d) Syphilis can be contracted through sexual contact or contact with towels or other objects but herpes can only be contracted through sexual contact.

    Answer: B Difficulty: 2 Page: 557

82. What is hepatitis?
    (a) inflammation of the liver
    (b) inflammation of the large intestines
    (c) inflammation of the small intestines
    (d) inflammation of the pituitary gland

    Answer: A Difficulty: 1 Page: 558

83. Which is not a symptom of people with acute hepatitis?
    (a) jaundice
    (b) nausea
    (c) loss of appetite
    (d) loss of feeling

    Answer: D Difficulty: 2 Page: 559

84. Which type of hepatitis is associated with contaminated food but can also be transmitted through oral-anal contact?
    (a) *hepatitis D*
    (b) *hepatitis B*
    (c) *hepatitis A*
    (d) *hepatitis C*

    Answer: C Difficulty: 1 Page: 558

85. Which is *true* regarding transmission of hepatitis?
    (a) Hepatitis A can be transmitted through vaginal intercourse, fellatio, or cunnilingus.
    (b) Hepatitis C is transmitted through contact with infected fecal matter.
    (c) Hepatitis D can be transmitted by contact with contaminated saliva.
    (d) Hepatitis B can be transmitted sexually, or through contaminated blood, menstrual blood, nasal secretions, or personal items like toothbrushes.

    Answer: D Difficulty: 2 Page: 559

86. The world's most common sexually transmitted infection is
    (a) HPV.
    (b) chlamydia.
    (c) gonnorrhea.
    (d) HSV.

    Answer: A Difficulty: 2 Page: 559

87. In the United States, how many college women are believed to be infected with HPV?
    (a) 10%
    (b) 28%
    (c) 50%
    (d) 60%

Answer: C Difficulty: 3 Page: 559

88. HPV has been associated with an increased risk of
    (a) cervical and penile cancer.
    (b) pelvic inflammatory disease and infertility.
    (c) ovarian and prostate cancer.
    (d) pelvic inflammatory disease and testicular cancer.

Answer: A Difficulty: 2 Page: 559

89. Genital warts
    (a) are similar to common plantar warts.
    (b) are hard and yellow-gray in color.
    (c) take on cauliflower shapes in moist areas.
    (d) all of the above.

Answer: D Difficulty: 1 Page: 559

90. Molluscum contagiosum is caused by a
    (a) herpes virus.
    (b) papilloma virus.
    (c) pox virus.
    (d) protozoa.

Answer: C Difficulty: 2 Page: 560

91. Which is not true about pediculosis?
    (a) It is also called "crabs."
    (b) It causes itching.
    (c) It can be transmitted only through intercourse.
    (d) It can be treated with a prescription medication, a 1% solution of lindane.

Answer: C Difficulty: 2 Page: 560

92. Joe is suffering from intense itching in the pubic region. He notices that there are tiny red lines on his groin and a few areas that look like welts. What has Joe contracted?
    (a) trichomoniasis
    (b) scabies
    (c) molluscum contagiosum
    (d) pubic lice

Answer: B Difficulty: 2 Page: 561

93. What is a parasitic infestation caused by tiny mites that may be transmitted through sexual contact?
    (a) scabies
    (b) herpes
    (c) crabs
    (d) hepatitis

Answer: A Difficulty: 1 Page: 561

94. Which of the following is good advice to ensure that you have the best chance of determining if your partner has an STI?
(a) Keep the lights on and look at your partner's genitals.
(b) Ask them.
(c) Wash your genitals before and after sex.
(d) Use only mutual masturbation pleasuring techniques.

Answer: A   Difficulty: 2   Page: 563

TRUE/FALSE

95. Gonorrhea can only be transmitted through vaginal or anal intercourse, not oral-genital sexual activity.

Answer: False

96. In men, untreated gonorrhea can lead to epididymitis.

Answer: False

97. Nongonococcal urethritis leads to a yellow-green penile discharge and a burning sensation when urinating.

Answer: True

98. A chancroid is caused by the virus *Hemophilus ducreyi*.

Answer: False

99. The use of antibiotics and/or birth control pills can cause candidiasis.

Answer: True

100. Trichomoniasis is caused by a one-celled protozoa.

Answer: True

101. If a woman or a man has trichomoniasis, both are treated with Flagyl.

Answer: True

102. In the United States, 40% of HIV cases are the result of female-male sexual contact.

Answer: True

103. *Pneumocystis carinii pneumonia* is a complication that can develop if a newborn contracts chlamydia in the birth canal.

Answer: False

104. In HIV transmission, female-to-male transmission through vaginal intercourse is twice as likely as male-to-female transmission.

Answer: False

105. STIs are only transmitted through sexual means, such as vaginal or anal intercourse or oral sex.

Answer: False

106. Overall, STIs are believed to account for 15% to 30% of cases of infertility among women.

Answer: True

107. There is evidence that gonorrhea can be picked up from public toilet seats.

Answer: False

108. Men have a greater chance of getting gonorrhea than women.

    Answer: False

109. Medical treatment is unnecessary if the symptoms of an STI disappear by themselves.

    Answer: True

110. Antibiotics other than penicillin are highly effective in eradicating chlamydia infections.

    Answer: True

MATCHING

For each of the following, match the symptoms or description of the STI with the correct organism.

(a) *Neisseria gonorrhoeae*

(b) *Human papilloma virus*

(c) *Herpes Simplex-Type-2*

(d) *Pthirus pubis*

(e) *Hepatitis B*

(f) *Treponema pallidum*

(g) *Trichomonas vaginalis*

(h) *Candida albicans*

(i) *Shigella*

111. The appearance of painless growths resembling cauliflowers inside the vagina or urethra or on the outer genitals.

    Answer: b

112. In women, this organism produces a foamy, yellow-green, foul smelling discharge.

    Answer: g

113. Painful clusters of bumps that become blisters or sores that fill with pus and break.

    Answer: c

114. Produces mild flu-like symptoms or more severe symptoms including fever, abdominal pain, and jaundice.

    Answer: e

115. In the initial stage, a hard, round, painless sore appears at the site of infection.

    Answer: f

116. In women, this organism produces itching and a white, cottage cheese-like discharge.

    Answer: h

117. Intense itching in the pubic area or other hairy regions of the body.

    Answer: d

118. In men, a thick yellow-green discharge appears within 2-3 days of infection.

Answer: a

119. A food-borne disease that can be transmitted sexually through oral-fecal contact.

Answer: i

ESSAY

120. Outline the four stages of syphilis infection by discussing the symptoms associated with each stage.

Answer:

121. Explain why chlamydia is called the "silent STD," and the complications associated with untreated chlamydia infections.

Answer:

122. Explain how women can develop vaginitis. Discuss at least three steps women can take to lessen the chances of developing vaginitis.

Answer:

123. Describe how HIV enters the host cell, replicates, and eventually kills its victims.

Answer:

124. Discuss each of the ways HIV can be contracted and each of the ways it cannot be contracted.

Answer:

125. Compare nucleoside analogues with protease inhibitors. Describe how each drug attacks the HIV virus and how they are currently used.

Answer:

126. From a world-view, discuss the significance of the AIDS crisis and its potential impact as we enter the new millennium.

Answer:

127. Discuss the different types of herpes, how each is transmitted, and how each is treated.

Answer:

128. Differentiate between Hepatitis A, B, C, and D in terms of transmission, symptoms, and health consequences.

Answer:

129. Explain all the steps you should take to get rid of a pubic lice or scabies infestation.

Answer:

130. Discuss the four factors researchers have associated with risky sexual behavior among young people.

Answer:

131. List ten steps you can take to protect yourself from contracting a sexually transmitted infection.

Answer:

Chapter 17: Atypical Sexual Variations

MULTIPLE CHOICE

1. The statistical approach to normality defines "normal" sexual behavior as behavior that
   (a) the majority engages in.
   (b) is valued within a particular culture.
   (c) co-occurs with a mental illness.
   (d) is sadistic.

   Answer: A Difficulty: 2 Page: 573

2. Before 1973, a gay male or lesbian sexual orientation was
   (a) seen as a form of normal sexual experimentation.
   (b) labeled as a mental disorder.
   (c) called gender dysphoria.
   (d) called gender identity disorder.

   Answer: B Difficulty: 2 Page: 574

3. Atypical patterns of sexual arousal or behavior that become problematic are called
   (a) sexual dysfunctions.
   (b) paraphilias.
   (c) sexual disorders.
   (d) normal deviations.

   Answer: B Difficulty: 1 Page: 574

4. Paraphilias may represent a type of
   (a) depression.
   (b) gender disorder.
   (c) gender dysphoria.
   (d) sexual compulsion.

   Answer: D Difficulty: 2 Page: 574

5. Which of the following individuals could be diagnosed with a paraphilia?
   (a) John: who exposes himself to women, feels compelled to do so, and feels distressed by his behavior.
   (b) Damon: who was arrested for distributing child pornography and sometimes watches videotapes of young children engaged in sexual acts.
   (c) Traci: who frequently fantasizes about using pain or humiliation with her sex partner.
   (d) Julio: who likes his wife to wear garter belts, stockings, and high-heeled shoes when they have sex.

   Answer: A Difficulty: 3 Page: 574

6. People with paraphilias usually feel that their urges are
   (a) insistent.
   (b) demanding.
   (c) compulsory.
   (d) all of the above.

   Answer: D Difficulty: 1 Page: 574

7. A person with a paraphilia typically
   (a) has difficulty sleeping during episodes.
   (b) acts in response to stress.
   (c) replays the paraphilic act in sexual fantasies to stimulate arousal during masturbation.
   (d) suppresses memories of his paraphilic behavior.

   Answer: C Difficulty: 2 Page: 574

8. Which factor tends to separate a paraphilia from a normal variant in sexual behavior?
   (a) the frequency of the behavior
   (b) the type of behavior
   (c) feeling helpless to resist the behavior
   (d) occasionally fantasizing about the behavior

   Answer: C Difficulty: 2 Page: 574

9. Of the following paraphilias, which does not occur almost exclusively in men?
   (a) masochism
   (b) transvestitism
   (c) fetishism
   (d) pedophilia

   Answer: A Difficulty: 1 Page: 575

10. Laura is sexually aroused by men's briefs. What type of paraphilia does she have?
    (a) pedophilia
    (b) fetishism
    (c) partialism
    (d) exhibitionism

    Answer: B Difficulty: 1 Page: 575

11. In pedophilia, _____ become the objects of sexual arousal.
    (a) articles of clothing
    (b) children
    (c) certain body parts
    (d) sex toys

    Answer: B Difficulty: 2 Page: 575

12. In which disorder does an individual become sexually aroused through the use of inanimate objects?
    (a) voyeurism
    (b) exhibitionism
    (c) frotteurism
    (d) fetishism

    Answer: D Difficulty: 1 Page: 575

13. Partialism is a fetish where an individual becomes aroused by
    (a) leather.
    (b) dead bodies.
    (c) non-human animals.
    (d) particular body parts.

    Answer: D Difficulty: 1 Page: 575

14. Finding objects associated with the other gender sexually alluring only when wearing them is a type of paraphilia known as
    (a) exhibitionism.
    (b) transvestism.
    (c) necrophilia.
    (d) frotteurism.

    Answer: B Difficulty: 2 Page: 575

15. What is the typical "profile" of a transvestite?
    (a) They are generally single, transsexual males.
    (b) They are generally married, heterosexual males.
    (c) They are generally single, homosexual males.
    (d) They are homosexual males who suffer from gender dysphoria.

    Answer: B Difficulty: 2 Page: 576

16. Who of the following has practiced transvestism?
    (a) Napolean
    (b) King Henry III of France
    (c) Prince Arthur of Belgium
    (d) King Edward II of England

    Answer: B Difficulty: 1 Page: 576

17. Transvestism is often confused with
    (a) fetishism.
    (b) transsexualism.
    (c) partialism.
    (d) fetishism.

    Answer: B Difficulty: 2 Page: 576

18. Which of the following is *true* regarding family relationships and transvestism?
    (a) Transvestites are more likely than other people to be the youngest child in the family.
    (b) Transvestites report having distant relationships with their mothers.
    (c) Transvestites may have been humiliated as children for dressing in clothing traditionally associated with the opposite sex.
    (d) Transvestites are more likely to come from families with a gay sibling.

    Answer: C Difficulty: 3 Page: 576

19. For sixteen years, Enrico has donned a dress, wig, and make-up to impersonate Barbara Streisand at a local club. Enrico's behavior
    (a) is typical of most transvestites.
    (b) is considered deviant.
    (c) does not indicate that he is a transvestite.
    (d) is typical of exhibitionists.

    Answer: C Difficulty: 2 Page: 577

20. Most transvestites
    (a) keep their behavior very private.
    (b) have antisocial personality disorders.
    (c) enjoy enticing men into a potential sexual encounter.
    (d) wear articles of female clothing when having sex with their wives.

    Answer: A Difficulty: 3 Page: 577

21. Persistent urges to expose one's genitals to unsuspecting people for sexual arousal is typical of
    (a) voyeurism.
    (b) scatalogia.
    (c) exhibitionism.
    (d) hypoxyphilia.

    Answer: C Difficulty: 1 Page: 578

22. Exhibitionists are almost always
    (a) males.
    (b) transvestites.
    (c) masochists.
    (d) voyeurs.

    Answer: A Difficulty: 2 Page: 578

23. Of arrests involving sexual offenses, how many involve exhibitionism?
    (a) about 50%
    (b) about 30%
    (c) about 20%
    (d) about 10%

    Answer: B Difficulty: 2 Page: 578

24. Geer and his colleagues see exhibitionism as
    (a) a projection of childhood issues.
    (b) an indirect means of expressing hostility toward women.
    (c) a means to release sexual frustration.
    (d) a symptom of loneliness.

    Answer: B Difficulty: 2 Page: 578

25. In a study of college women in the United States, how many reported they had been the victim of a "flasher?"
    (a) 50%
    (b) 30%
    (c) 20%
    (d) 10%

    Answer: B Difficulty: 3 Page: 578

26. The typical exhibitionist is
    (a) older, single, and sexually immature.
    (b) older, happily married, and sexually over-expressive.
    (c) young, unhappily married, and sexually repressed.
    (d) young, single, and sexually immature.

    Answer: C Difficulty: 3 Page: 578

27. Exhibitionistic behavior usually begins
    (a) after age 40.
    (b) between the ages of 20 and 30.
    (c) between the ages of 16 and 20.
    (d) between age 13 and 16.

    Answer: D Difficulty: 2 Page: 578

28. Exhibitionism
    (a) inevitably leads to pedophilia.
    (b) frequently leads to urges to rape or harm.
    (c) may be an expression of hostility towards women.
    (d) stems from an inflated sense of masculinity.

    Answer: C Difficulty: 2 Page: 578

29. Which of the following is *not* a typical characteristic of exhibitionists?
    (a) Many exhibitionists report having poor relationships with their fathers.
    (b) Exhibitionists take elaborate precautions to avoid arrest.
    (c) Exhibitionists have difficulty establishing intimate relationships with women.
    (d) Exhibitionists suffer from feelings of inadequacy or inferiority.

    Answer: B Difficulty: 2 Page: 579

30. The factor that separates exhibitionism from other forms of exposure is
    (a) the sexual arousal associated with exposing.
    (b) the need to have an audience.
    (c) the need to sexually excite or entice others.
    (d) the need to shock or surprise a stranger.

    Answer: D Difficulty: 2 Page: 579

31. What would be the *best* way to respond if you are the victim of a flasher?
    (a) Show no reaction and walk away.
    (b) Tell the flasher that he needs psychological help.
    (c) Insult the flasher to get him to stop future behavior.
    (d) Stop and directly confront the flasher in an angry tone of voice.

    Answer: A Difficulty: 2 Page: 579

32. According to the text, the typical obscene phone caller is
    (a) a male who has difficulty forming intimate relationships with women.
    (b) a socially inadequate male.
    (c) a heterosexual.
    (d) all of the above.

    Answer: D Difficulty: 1 Page: 580

33. Obscene phone calling is a paraphilia called telephone
    (a) exhibitionism.
    (b) scatologia.
    (c) frotteurism.
    (d) necrophilia.

    Answer: B Difficulty: 1 Page: 580

34. In contrast to male obscene callers, women callers are usually motivated by
    (a) the desire for sexual arousal.
    (b) the desire to humiliate their victim.
    (c) rage.
    (d) the desire to shock their victim.

    Answer: C Difficulty: 2 Page: 580

35. Mohammed seeks opportunities to watch women undress by walking through his neighborhood at night and peering through bedroom windows. Mohammed's behavior is characteristic of
    (a) fetishism.
    (b) voyeurism.
    (c) exhibitionism.
    (d) scatologia.

    Answer: B Difficulty: 1 Page: 581

36. Bobby likes to watch his neighbors have sex through their bedroom window. This type of behavior is called
    (a) frotteurism.
    (b) exhibitionism.
    (c) voyeurism.
    (d) fetishism.

    Answer: C Difficulty: 2 Page: 581

37. Voyeurism typically begins
    (a) in preadolescence.
    (b) in late adolescence.
    (c) in early adulthood.
    (d) after the age of 45.

    Answer: A Difficulty: 3 Page: 581

38. What is true about voyeurs?
    (a) They often put themselves in risky situations.
    (b) They are typically shy people.
    (c) They are usually exhibitionists.
    (d) They sometimes use violence for stimulation.

    Answer: A Difficulty: 2 Page: 581

39. Which of the following individuals would fit the definition of a voyeur?
    (a) Anita: who secretly rents pornographic films and masturbates while watching them.
    (b) Michael: who frequently asks his wife to dress up, put erotic music on the stereo, strip, and then masturbate while he watches.
    (c) Marcus: who frequents the strip clubs several times a week either alone or with his male friends.
    (d) Tom: who has installed a telescope so he can watch the couple in the apartment building across the street when they have sex.

    Answer: D Difficulty: 2 Page: 581

40. Which is true for *both* exhibitionists and voyeurs?
    (a) Both need an element of risk to heighten their sexual arousal.
    (b) Both tend to be older, single men who lack opportunities to engage in sex.
    (c) In both cases, most go on to commit more serious sexual offenses.
    (d) In both cases, individuals will frequent places where it is legal to watch or to expose oneself.

    Answer: A Difficulty: 2 Page: 581

41. Compared to other types of offenders, voyeurs tend to be
    (a) married.
    (b) male or female.
    (c) homosexual.
    (d) single.

    Answer: D Difficulty: 3 Page: 581

42. People who become sexually aroused through the experience of pain or humiliation are sexual
    (a) sadists.
    (b) necrophiliacs.
    (c) frotteurists.
    (d) masochists.

    Answer: D Difficulty: 1 Page: 582

43. The only paraphilia that is found with some degree of frequency in females is
    (a) necrophilia.
    (b) masochism.
    (c) exhibitionism.
    (d) fetishism.

Answer: B Difficulty: 1 Page: 583

44. What is not true about sexual masochists?
    (a) Some cannot be sexually aroused unless they are bound, flogged, or humiliated.
    (b) The majority of sexual masochists are female.
    (c) Some masochists enjoy bondage.
    (d) The name masochist was derived from an Austrian storyteller.

Answer: B Difficulty: 2 Page: 583

45. The practice of being restrained in masochistic behavior is called?
    (a) flogged
    (b) bondage
    (c) crowning
    (d) shacking

Answer: B Difficulty: 1 Page: 583

46. Which is not a source of pleasure for a masochist?
    (a) blindfolding
    (b) being cut
    (c) spanking
    (d) humiliation

Answer: B Difficulty: 1 Page: 584

47. People who become sexually aroused by inflicting pain or humiliation on others are known as
    (a) frotteurists.
    (b) sadists.
    (c) masochists.
    (d) exhibitionists.

Answer: B Difficulty: 1 Page: 584

48. Baumister (1988) proposed that sexual masochism might provide temporary relief from
    (a) being seen as a sexual object.
    (b) both painful and pleasant sexual sensations.
    (c) repressed anger.
    (d) the responsibilities of independent selfhood.

Answer: D Difficulty: 2 Page: 584

49. Bradley uses neckties to build an elaborate contraption. While he masturbates, he leans into a harness that puts pressure on the vessels in his neck. As he approaches orgasm, he increases the pressure to cut off oxygen to the brain. Bradley's activity is typical of
    (a) hypoxyphilia.
    (b) frotteurism.
    (c) necrophilia.
    (d) coprophilia.

Answer: A Difficulty: 2 Page: 584

50. Who is "sadism" named after?
    (a) Marquis de Sade
    (b) Charles Sadim
    (c) William Sade
    (d) Forrest Stanley

    Answer: A Difficulty: 1 Page: 584

51. Which is true of sadomasochism?
    (a) It involves mutual gratification.
    (b) Its nature is more violent and extreme than masochism.
    (c) It involves three or more partners.
    (d) It is used to describe masochists who enjoy being strangled.

    Answer: A Difficulty: 2 Page: 585

52. Mutually gratifying, but painful sexual interactions between consenting partners is called
    (a) masochism.
    (b) sadomasochism.
    (c) sadofrotteurism.
    (d) voyeurism.

    Answer: B Difficulty: 1 Page: 585

53. Which is not true about sadomasochism?
    (a) Sadomasochists are usually men.
    (b) Sadomasochists also enjoy psychological pain such as humiliation.
    (c) The causes of sadomasochism are unclear.
    (d) Sadomasochist only like to receive pain.

    Answer: D Difficulty: 2 Page: 585

54. Toucherism is a form of
    (a) exhibitionism.
    (b) frotteurism.
    (c) voyeurism.
    (d) fetishism.

    Answer: B Difficulty: 1 Page: 586

55. In Dr. Cooper's survey what percentage of men reported they had used computers at work for some sexual pursuit?
    (a) 20%
    (b) 39%
    (c) 52%
    (d) 75%

    Answer: A Difficulty: 3 Page: 588

56. The erotic appeal of sadomasochistic activities seems to be *most* connected to
    (a) humiliation.
    (b) pain.
    (c) control or being controlled.
    (d) childhood abuse.

    Answer: C Difficulty: 2 Page: 586

57. Frotteurism involves urges to
    (a) expose one's genitals to strangers.
    (b) rub against or touch a nonconsenting person.
    (c) augment sexual arousal by cutting off oxygen supplies to the brain.
    (d) use enemas to heighten arousal.

    Answer: B Difficulty: 2 Page: 586

58. All of the individuals who engage in mashing are
    (a) males who fear rejection from women.
    (b) happily married males.
    (c) single males or females.
    (d) homosexual males who are still closeted.

    Answer: A Difficulty: 3 Page: 586

59. In the Kinsey studies, how prevalent was zoophilia?
    (a) About 20% of both men and women reported having had sexual contact with animals.
    (b) About 20% of males but only 1% of females reported having had sexual contact with animals.
    (c) About 8% of men and 3-4% of women reported having had sexual contact with an animal.
    (d) Only 1-2% of men and women reported having had some sexual contact with an animal.

    Answer: C Difficulty: 3 Page: 587

60. Compared to only a few city boys, how many adolescent farm boys had achieved orgasm through sexual contact with farm animals?
    (a) 5%
    (b) 8%
    (c) 11%
    (d) 17%

    Answer: D Difficulty: 3 Page: 587

61. Which of the following paraphilias involves the urge to have sex with dead bodies?
    (a) urophilia
    (b) klismaphilia
    (c) coprophilia
    (d) necrophilia

    Answer: D Difficulty: 2 Page: 587

62. William needs anal stimulation through enemas to achieve sexual arousal and gratification. William's paraphilia is called
    (a) coprophilia.
    (b) klismaphilia.
    (c) frotteurism.
    (d) urophilia.

    Answer: B Difficulty: 1 Page: 587

63. If urine becomes eroticized by experiences in which erections occurred while clothed in a wet diaper, an adult might develop a paraphilia called
    (a) klismaphilia.
    (b) urophilia.
    (c) satyriasis.
    (d) coprophilia.

    Answer: B Difficulty: 1 Page: 589

64. Classical psychoanalytic theory suggests that paraphilias are psychological defenses against
    (a) unresolved castration anxiety.
    (b) hurtful past relationships.
    (c) having a "small" penis.
    (d) an overprotective mother.

    Answer: A Difficulty: 2 Page: 591

65. As a small boy, Jonathan would hide in his mother's closet and stroke his genitals. As an adolescent, Jonathan developed a shoe fetish that continues into his adult sexual relations. Which theory offers the best explanation for Jonathan's fetish?
    (a) psychoanalytic theory
    (b) observational learning theory
    (c) behavioral conditioning theory
    (d) social learning theory

    Answer: C Difficulty: 2 Page: 591

66. In the development of masochism, one explanation suggests that children may develop an association between masturbation and
    (a) affection.
    (b) parental punishment.
    (c) peer rejection.
    (d) angry feelings.

    Answer: B Difficulty: 2 Page: 591

67. Psychoanalytic theory suggests that masochism in the male
    (a) results from fixation at the oral stage.
    (b) may be the turning inward of aggressive impulses toward threatening fathers.
    (c) has a direct correlation with dominant controlling mothers.
    (d) reflects a passive and repressed personality.

    Answer: B Difficulty: 2 Page: 591

68. Martin Weinberg suggests that the sadomasochistic lifestyle may reflect
    (a) the power relationships that exist within society at large.
    (b) an early learned association between masturbation and punishment.
    (c) a childhood with cold and indifferent parenting.
    (d) predisposing factors such as difficulty forming intimate relationships.

    Answer: A Difficulty: 2 Page: 592

69. Who proposed an explanation of the development of paraphilias in terms of the gradual acquisition of sexual arousal to an unusual object or activity through its incorporation in masturbatory fantasies?
    (a) Mcguire
    (b) Breslow
    (c) Freud
    (d) Coles

    Answer: B Difficulty: 3 Page: 592

70. A brain pattern that determines the type of stimuli and activities that are sexually arousing is called a
    (a) sexual script.
    (b) gender schema.
    (c) lovemap.
    (d) fetish.

    Answer: C Difficulty: 1 Page: 594

71. Research suggests that voyeurs and exhibitionists are often
    (a) overprotected as children.
    (b) below average in intelligence.
    (c) victims of childhood sexual abuse.
    (d) personality disordered.

    Answer: C Difficulty: 2 Page: 594

72. Which of the following is *true* regarding treatment for paraphilias?
    (a) Most people with paraphilias are distressed by their behavior and seek help.
    (b) Most people with paraphilias seek treatment only after they come into conflict with the law.
    (c) Most people with paraphilias are motivated to change their behavior.
    (d) Most people with paraphilias take responsibility for their behavior.

    Answer: B Difficulty: 3 Page: 594

73. In treating paraphilias, the *most* difficult issue is
    (a) getting family members or spouses involved in treatment.
    (b) alleviating a client's guilt and shame.
    (c) breaking through the client's belief that he is powerless to control his behavior.
    (d) setting therapeutic goals.

    Answer: C Difficulty: 2 Page: 595

74. Dr. Jimand believes that his client's exhibitionistic behavior stems from unconscious conflicts he has with his father and perceived fear of punishment for sexual thoughts. Dr. Jimand is treating his client from a
    (a) psychoanalytical perspective.
    (b) behavioral perspective.
    (c) social learning theory perspective.
    (d) biological perspective.

    Answer: A Difficulty: 2 Page: 595

75. Which is not a technique used in behavior therapy?
    (a) sexual arousal technique
    (b) covert sensitization
    (c) aversion therapy
    (d) desensitization

    Answer: A Difficulty: 1 Page: 595

76. A behavior therapy that attempts to break the link between the sexual stimulus and the sexual arousal is called
    (a) aversion therapy.
    (b) systematic desensitization.
    (c) covert sensitization.
    (d) modeling.

    Answer: B Difficulty: 1 Page: 595

77. Pairing undesirable sexual behavior with negative stimuli, such as mild electric shocks, is a treatment technique called
    (a) systematic desensitization.
    (b) orgasmic reconditioning.
    (c) chemical castration.
    (d) aversion therapy.

    Answer: D Difficulty: 2 Page: 595

78. Which is a variation of aversion therapy in which paraphilic fantasies are paired with an aversive stimulus in a client's imagination?
    (a) covert sensitization
    (b) desensitization
    (c) sexual arousal technique
    (d) modeling

    Answer: A Difficulty: 2 Page: 595

79. Which is not true about social skills training?
    (a) It focuses on helping the individual improve his or her ability to relate to the other gender.
    (b) The client may role play.
    (c) Attention is focused on letting the client express deeper emotions during sexual urges.
    (d) The therapist might first model a desired behavior.

    Answer: C Difficulty: 3 Page: 596

80. Nic is being treated for his paraphilia by first imagining the paraphilic object to become sexually aroused. Next, just before orgasm, he is instructed to switch from the paraphilic imagery to culturally appropriate imagery. The technique being used is called
    (a) social skills training.
    (b) aversion therapy.
    (c) orgasmic reconditioning.
    (d) systematic desensitization.

    Answer: C Difficulty: 3 Page: 596

81. The use of Prozac to treat paraphilias is based on the theory that paraphilias may be a
    (a) type of obsessive-compulsive disorder.
    (b) form of depression.
    (c) variant of post-traumatic stress disorder.
    (d) sexual addiction.

    Answer: A Difficulty: 2 Page: 596

82. In some men, the intensity of their sex drive and urge to act on their impulses can be lowered through the use of
    (a) estrogen patches.
    (b) Depo-Provera.
    (c) testosterone injections.
    (d) inhibin injections.

    Answer: B Difficulty: 2 Page: 597

MATCHING

For each of the following descriptions of an atypical sexual pattern, match the pattern with the correct term.

(a) Exhibitionism

(b) Frotteurism

(c) Necrophilia

(d) Masochism

(e) Klismaphilia

(f) Sadism

(g) Fetishism

(h) Voyeurism

83. Sexual gratification is achieved through sexual behavior with corpses.

    Answer: c

84. Sexual gratification is achieved through masturbation in the presence of an inanimate object.

    Answer: g

85. Sexual gratification is achieved through the infliction of pain or humiliation on another person.

    Answer: f

86. Sexual gratification is achieved through exposing one's genitals to unsuspecting persons.

    Answer: a

87. Sexual gratification is achieved by rubbing against unsuspecting persons.

    Answer: b

88. Sexual gratification is achieved through pain inflicted on oneself by oneself or another person.

    Answer: d

89. Sexual gratification is achieved through the use of enemas.

    Answer: e

90. Sexual gratification is achieved by watching unsuspecting individuals as they undress or engage in sex.

    Answer: h

TRUE/FALSE

91. Cross-dressing to achieve sexual arousal is generally a harmless and victimless paraphilia.

    Answer: True

92. Some brutal rapes involve sexual sadism.

    Answer: True

93. True transvestism has only been described among homosexual males.

    Answer: False

94. In exhibitionism, the urge to expose almost always follows an incident in which the exhibitionist felt that his masculinity was insulted.

    Answer: True

95. For nearly half of exhibitionists, their behavior progresses to more serious crimes of sexual aggression.

    Answer: False

96. Voyeurs are careful and rarely put themselves in a position where they face the prospect of getting caught.

    Answer: False

97. In the new millennium, exhibitionists and voyeurs may find a haven in the videoconferencing capacities of the Internet.

    Answer: True

98. The appeal of wanting to feel pain during sexual activity may be linked to the release of endorphins.

    Answer: True

99. In true hypersexuality, individuals are driven to engage in sexual activity to reassure themselves that they are sexually desirable.

    Answer: True

100. Exhibitionists have significantly lower levels of the testosterone most closely linked to sex drive.

    Answer: False

101. In the psychoanalytic view, the "primal scene" is an experience in which a child identifies with his father during childhood observations of parental intercourse.

    Answer: True

102. In chemical castration, the vas deferens are removed.

    Answer: False

103. In U.S. culture, sexual practices such as oral sex and masturbation were once considered deviant or abnormal.

    Answer: True

104. King Henry III of France insisted on being considered a woman and addressed as "Her Majesty."

    Answer: True

105. The survey of 504 transvestite men showed that 200 of them had kept their transvestism a secret.

    Answer: False

106. Pain is always administered in some form during a sadomasochistic encounter.

    Answer: False

107. The psychiatric diagnosis of paraphilia requires that the person has acted on the urges or is distinctly distressed by them.

    Answer: True

108. Fetishism comes from the Latin word *Fetisera* meaning "magic charm."

    Answer: False

109. Some men cross-dress for reasons other than sexual arousal and are considered transvestites.

    Answer: False

110. Most transvestites are married and engage in sexual activity with their wives.

    Answer: True

111. Like exhibitionists, obscene phone callers seek to become sexually aroused by shocking their victims.

    Answer: True

112. People who enjoy watching their mates undress are considered voyeurs.

    Answer: False

113. Some sexual masochists cannot become sexually aroused unless they are bound flogged, or humiliated by their sex partners.

    Answer: True

ESSAY

114. Discuss the difficulties involved in defining normal versus abnormal sexual behavior.

    Answer:

115. List four different paraphilias. Describe the characteristic behaviors associated with each paraphilia and theories as to how each paraphilia develops.

    Answer:

116. Apply Patrick Carne's four-step model of sexual addiction to voyeurism.

    Answer:

117. Discuss the factors that differentiate hypersexuality from a normally healthy, but high sex drive.

    Answer:

118. Explain how exhibitionism and masochism develop from the psychoanalytic point of view.

    Answer:

119. Using the conditioning model of learning, explain how a male might develop a fetish for women's shoes.

    Answer:

120. It has been proposed that voyeurism, exhibitionism, and frotteurism may be *courtship disorders*. Explain what this means.

    Answer:

121. Describe Weinberg's sociological model of sadomasochism.

    Answer:

122. Cite four issues of concern in treating paraphilic behavior.

    Answer:

123. Compare and contrast systematic desensitization, aversion therapy, covert sensitization, and orgasmic reconditioning in treating a fetish.

    Answer:

Chapter 18:   Sexual Coercion

MULTIPLE CHOICE

1. Which form of rape is defined as sexual intercourse with a non-consenting person by the use of force or the threat of force?
   (a) forcible rape
   (b) statutory rape
   (c) date rape
   (d) none of the above

   Answer: A Difficulty: 1 Page: 602

2. Throughout much of ancient history, victims of rape were
   (a) put to death with the rapist.
   (b) forced to marry the rapist.
   (c) banished from the community.
   (d) sent to live in monasteries.

   Answer: A Difficulty: 2 Page: 603

3. Statutory rape refers to
   (a) sexual intercourse with a person who is below the age of consent, even if the person cooperates.
   (b) sexual intercourse with a non-consenting person by the use of force or the threat of force.
   (c) date rape.
   (d) none of the above.

   Answer: A Difficulty: 1 Page: 603

4. Which is a form of sexual assault?
   (a) statutory rape
   (b) date rape
   (c) any kind of rape
   (d) forcible rape

   Answer: D Difficulty: 1 Page: 603

5. Legally, what is the difference between rape and sexual assault?
   (a) Rape does not involve violence. Sexual assault involves violence.
   (b) Rape is penetration of the vagina by any object. Sexual assault does not involve vaginal penetration.
   (c) Rape is forced sexual intercourse. Sexual assault can be any sexual act not involving intercourse.
   (d) Rape is forced sexual intercourse. Sexual assault involves coercion, not force.

   Answer: C Difficulty: 2 Page: 604

6. According to the United States National Crime Victimization Survey in 1995, a woman was reported to be raped about every
   (a) 60 seconds.
   (b) 30 minutes.
   (c) 10 minutes.
   (d) 3 minutes.

   Answer: D Difficulty: 3 Page: 604

7. In the United States, evidence suggests that between
   (a) 5% and 10% of women will be raped at some point in their lifetime.
   (b) 14% and 25% of women will be raped at some point in their lifetime.
   (c) 26% and 31% of women will be raped at some point in their lifetime.
   (d) 32% and 44% of women will be raped at some point in their lifetime.

   Answer: B Difficulty: 2 Page: 604

8. One of the central myths about rape in our culture is that most rapes are perpetrated
   (a) by acquaintances.
   (b) by husbands against their wives.
   (c) by strangers.
   (d) on dates.

   Answer: C Difficulty: 1 Page: 605

9. In stranger rape, it is typical for rapists to
   (a) choose a victim and then carefully plan the rape.
   (b) choose a victim impulsively and immediately commit the rape.
   (c) invite a woman on a date and then force sex.
   (d) target prepubescent children.

   Answer: A Difficulty: 2 Page: 605

10. In general, women are more likely to be raped by
    (a) men they know.
    (b) strangers.
    (c) criminals.
    (d) none of the above.

    Answer: A Difficulty: 1 Page: 605

11. In a national college survey, of the women who had been raped, how many actually believed they were raped?
    (a) 56%
    (b) 45%
    (c) 37%
    (d) 27%

    Answer: D Difficulty: 3 Page: 605

12. Date rape is a form of
    (a) acquaintance rape.
    (b) stranger rape.
    (c) sexual assault.
    (d) forcible rape.

    Answer: A Difficulty: 1 Page: 605

13. Acquaintance rapes are frequently not reported, but when they are, they are often treated as
    (a) violent assaults.
    (b) misunderstandings or lovers' quarrels.
    (c) the woman's fault.
    (d) a consequence of too much alcohol.

    Answer: B Difficulty: 1 Page: 605

14. Which of the following is *true* regarding date rape?
    (a) Most date rapes are committed within the first three dates with the rapist.
    (b) Most date rapes take place at parties.
    (c) Most date rapes involve the use of alcohol by the couple.
    (d) In most date rapes, the male purposefully sets out to get the female drunk.

Answer: C Difficulty: 2 Page: 605

15. Determining whether a sexual act is rape boils down to the issue of
    (a) consent.
    (b) intoxication.
    (c) past sexual history.
    (d) length of dating.

Answer: A Difficulty: 1 Page: 607

16. Which statement is *true* regarding male rape?
    (a) Most men who rape other men are homosexual.
    (b) The only motive cited for male rape is retaliation.
    (c) Males are generally attacked by a single assailant.
    (d) Most male rapes occur in prisons.

Answer: D Difficulty: 2 Page: 608

17. The *major* motive behind gang rape is
    (a) anger.
    (b) power.
    (c) solidarity.
    (d) competition.

Answer: B Difficulty: 1 Page: 606

18. What did the Koss college survey indicate?
    (a) It showed that sexual assaults involving a group of assailants tend to be more vicious than individual assaults.
    (b) It proved sexual assaults were informal all of the time.
    (c) It showed a very large percentage of statutory rape.
    (d) It showed that men's motivation to rape is rarely sexual.

Answer: A Difficulty: 2 Page: 607

19. Men who rape other men are rarely motivated by
    (a) revenge.
    (b) domination.
    (c) the need for sex.
    (d) sadism.

Answer: C Difficulty: 1 Page: 608

20. Male rape victims
    (a) are often attacked by multiple assailants.
    (b) are generally held captive for shorter periods of time than female victims.
    (c) suffer fewer physical injuries than female victims.
    (d) are more willing to report the rape than female victims.

Answer: A Difficulty: 2 Page: 608

21. A committee of the United States Congress estimated that
    (a) 1 out of every 2 women is a victim of marital rape.
    (b) 1 out of every 4 women is a victim of marital rape.
    (c) 1 out of every 5 women is a victim of marital rape.
    (d) 1 out of every 7 women is a victim of marital rape.

    Answer: D Difficulty: 3 Page: 608

22. Barbara is a victim of marital rape. She doesn't report the incident to anyone. What is the most significant reason she keeps it a secret?
    (a) No one will believe her.
    (b) She is ashamed.
    (c) She is afraid it will make her husband not like her.
    (d) She doesn't want to lose her reputation.

    Answer: A Difficulty: 2 Page: 608

23. As Margarette's husband began to drink more, he became more sexually aggressive. In the last three months, he has forced sex on Margarette three times. If she is typical of most victims of marital rape, Margarette is likely to
    (a) seek counseling.
    (b) get the police involved.
    (c) stay silent and stay with her husband.
    (d) secretly run away.

    Answer: C Difficulty: 2 Page: 608

24. Rape by women generally involves
    (a) aiding men who are attacking another woman.
    (b) a prepubescent male.
    (c) force with a weapon.
    (d) more than one woman.

    Answer: A Difficulty: 1 Page: 608

25. Which of the following is *not* one of the myths about rape mentioned in the text?
    (a) "women say no when they mean yes"
    (b) "rapists are crazed by sexual desire"
    (c) "women make up rapes to retaliate against men"
    (d) "women like a man who is forceful and pushy"

    Answer: C Difficulty: 2 Page: 609

26. College men who held "traditional" views of gender roles were
    (a) less likely to accept violence against women.
    (b) more likely to blame rape survivors.
    (c) less likely to become aroused by depictions of rape.
    (d) less likely to have engaged in sexual coercion.

    Answer: B Difficulty: 2 Page: 609

27. The idea that women fantasize about being overpowered by a man is *consistently* reinforced by
    (a) pornography.
    (b) romance novels.
    (c) horror films.
    (d) the advertising industry.

    Answer: B Difficulty: 1 Page: 610

28. In Malamuth's 1981 studies, how many men said they would force sex on a woman if they could "get away with it"?
    (a) 10%
    (b) 16%
    (c) 35%
    (d) 45%

    Answer: C Difficulty: 3 Page: 610

29. Which of the following groups commit a disproportionate number of sexual assaults?
    (a) homosexual men
    (b) undereducated men
    (c) fraternity members
    (d) student athletes

    Answer: D Difficulty: 2 Page: 610

30. Koss and her colleagues found that in their national college sample of nearly 3,000 college men, about _____ admitted to committing or attempting rape.
    (a) 16%
    (b) 7%
    (c) 34%
    (d) 2%

    Answer: B Difficulty: 2 Page: 611

31. In studies looking for commonalities among rapists, evidence suggests that
    (a) most have antisocial personality disorders.
    (b) there is no single type of rapist.
    (c) the majority display narcissistic traits.
    (d) they come from highly dysfunctional families.

    Answer: B Difficulty: 2 Page: 611

32. Based on estimates, how many rapists are eventually caught and convicted?
    (a) about 4%
    (b) about 10%
    (c) about 15%
    (d) about 18%

    Answer: A Difficulty: 2 Page: 611

33. What percentage of the 3,000 college men that Koss and her colleagues interviewed admitted to committing or attempting rape?
    (a) under 10%
    (b) 30%
    (c) 45%
    (d) over 50%

    Answer: A Difficulty: 2 Page: 611

34. As a child, Hans was verbally and physically abused by an exceptionally cruel mother. When he rapes, he does not plan his attack, but likes to degrade his victims through anal rape because of the force it requires. Hans best represents the
    (a) sadistic rapist.
    (b) power rapist.
    (c) anger rapist.
    (d) desire rapist.

    Answer: C Difficulty: 3 Page: 612

35. In which type of rape is the rapist motivated by the need to control and dominate in order to combat deep-seated feelings of insecurity?
    (a) sadistic rape
    (b) desire rape
    (c) power rape
    (d) anger rape

    Answer: C Difficulty: 2 Page: 612

36. Sadistic rapists
    (a) often carefully plan their assaults.
    (b) use a "con" or pretext to approach their targets, such as asking for directions.
    (c) bind their victims and subject them to humiliating experiences and threats.
    (d) all of the above.

    Answer: D Difficulty: 1 Page: 612

37. Among rape survivors, how many will experience emotional problems that linger a year or longer after the rape?
    (a) 10%
    (b) 20%
    (c) 25%
    (d) 40%

    Answer: C Difficulty: 3 Page: 613

38. In one study of rape victims, concerns about contracting AIDS were reported by
    (a) 15% of the victims.
    (b) 20% of the victims.
    (c) 25% of the victims.
    (d) 50% of the victims.

    Answer: C Difficulty: 2 Page: 614

39. Among rape victims, the most commonly reported emotion was
    (a) anger.
    (b) fear.
    (c) anxiety.
    (d) guilt.

    Answer: A Difficulty: 1 Page: 613

40. Of sexual assault survivors in a Los Angeles survey, how many reported the assault to the police?
    (a) 1 in 3
    (b) 1 in 10
    (c) 1 in 6
    (d) 1 in 5

    Answer: B Difficulty: 3 Page: 614

41. Which is not true about posttraumatic stress disorder (PTSD)?
    (a) PTSD is the leading cause of depression.
    (b) PTSD is brought on by exposure to a traumatic event.
    (c) People with PTSD may have flashbacks to the traumatic experience.
    (d) PTSD may persist for years.

    Answer: A Difficulty: 2 Page: 614

42. A key component of the treatment process for rape survivors is to help the survivor
    (a) mobilize support.
    (b) remember the details of the event.
    (c) forgive the rapist.
    (d) report the rape to police.

    Answer: A Difficulty: 2 Page: 616

43. Treatment of rape survivors typically involves two stages. What are these two stages?
    (a) crisis intervention and psychotherapy
    (b) medication and peer counseling
    (c) rehabilitation and counseling
    (d) learning and advising

    Answer: A Difficulty: 1 Page: 616

44. In terms of rape prevention, which of the following is *not* an appropriate prevention measure?
    (a) Keep doorways and entries well lit.
    (b) Don't walk by yourself after dark.
    (c) List yourself on your mailbox by first initials only.
    (d) If you are attacked, shout "Rape!" as loudly as you can.

    Answer: D Difficulty: 1 Page: 617

45. Yonnie has recently broken up with her boyfriend who was quite angry over her rejection of him. Last evening, he showed up at her door asking if they could at least "talk" about the breakup. What is the best advice for Yonnie?
    (a) Call the police.
    (b) Let him in, but agree to a time limit.
    (c) Do not let him in.
    (d) Step outside to talk to him.

    Answer: C Difficulty: 3 Page: 618

46. Research has shown that if attacked, pleading, begging, or attempting to reason with a rapist
    (a) is an effective strategy for preventing rape.
    (b) can be dangerous and increase the risk of injury.
    (c) will not stop the rape but will lessen the chance of serious injury.
    (d) will buy enough time for a passerby to intervene or call the police.

    Answer: B Difficulty: 2 Page: 619

47. In a randomized national telephone survey, how many women reported having been sexually abused prior to age 19?
    (a) 4%
    (b) 15%
    (c) 10%
    (d) 21%

    Answer: B Difficulty: 3 Page: 620

48. In a randomized national telephone survey, how many men reported having been sexually abused prior to age 19?
    (a) 5%
    (b) 15%
    (c) 7%
    (d) 10%

    Answer: D Difficulty: 3 Page: 620

49. Which of the following is *not* a form of child sexual abuse?
    (a) Masturbation or fondling of the genitals in children of similar ages.
    (b) Intimate kissing between an adult and a child under the age of consent.
    (c) Masturbating while a child under the age of consent watches.
    (d) An adult fondling the genitals of a child who gives willing consent.

    Answer: A Difficulty: 2 Page: 621

50. In the vast majority of sexual abuse cases, the abuse occurs between a child and
    (a) a stranger who lures them into a car.
    (b) a parent.
    (c) relatives, family friends, or neighbors.
    (d) a stranger who lures them into his/her apartment or house.

    Answer: C Difficulty: 1 Page: 621

51. In a Boston community survey, how many parents whose children had been sexually abused by a family member notified the police?
    (a) 80%
    (b) 0%
    (c) 50%
    (d) 15%

    Answer: B Difficulty: 3 Page: 621

52. In contrast to adult sexual assault, child sexual abuse
    (a) involves more force.
    (b) always involves penetration.
    (c) generally involves the use of restraints.
    (d) rarely involves the use of force.

    Answer: D Difficulty: 2 Page: 621

53. The most common type of child sexual abuse is
    (a) oral sex.
    (b) vaginal penetration.
    (c) genital fondling.
    (d) exhibitionism.

    Answer: C Difficulty: 1 Page: 622

54. Sexual abuse of children by women may be underreported because women
    (a) are allowed a freer range of physical contact with children.
    (b) do not leave any physical evidence of abuse.
    (c) are treated more lightly by the justice system.
    (d) are more careful to cover up their abuse.

    Answer: A Difficulty: 2 Page: 622

55. Which of the following is *not* a factor that motivates a woman to sexually abuse children?
    (a) a history of dependence on abusive males
    (b) inadequate sex lives with their husbands
    (c) unmet emotional needs and low self-esteem
    (d) unresolved feelings of anger, powerlessness, or jealousy

    Answer: B Difficulty: 2 Page: 622

56. Which of the following is *true* regarding pedophilia?
    (a) Most pedophiles are so distressed by their urges that they never act on them.
    (b) Most pedophiles target a single victim for long-term sexual abuse.
    (c) All pedophiles are sexual molesters.
    (d) Most pedophiles are responsible for large numbers of sexual assaults on children.

    Answer: D Difficulty: 3 Page: 623

57. The factor that *best* distinguishes a pedophile from a child molester is
    (a) the number of victims.
    (b) the age of the victims.
    (c) persistent or recurrent attraction to children.
    (d) lack of other sexual outlets.

    Answer: C Difficulty: 2 Page: 623

58. In one college survey, how many students admitted to having been sexually attracted to small children?
    (a) 21%
    (b) 16%
    (c) 10%
    (d) 3%

    Answer: A Difficulty: 3 Page: 623

59. Research generally supports the stereotype of the pedophile as
    (a) controlling and resorting to children in times of stress.
    (b) weak, passive, and socially inept.
    (c) manipulative, aggressive, and socially skilled.
    (d) passive but socially skilled.

    Answer: B Difficulty: 2 Page: 623

60. Consanguineous means
    (a) sexually frustrated.
    (b) related by blood.
    (c) oppressed, as in oppressed attitudes toward the opposite sex.
    (d) very masculine.

    Answer: B Difficulty: 1 Page: 624

61. According to *cooperation theory*, incest taboos were established to
    (a) ensure the creation of larger, cooperative communities.
    (b) reduce the rate of genetic diseases.
    (c) reduce genetic variation in the gene pool.
    (d) reduce sexual competition within families, thus keeping families intact.

    Answer: A Difficulty: 2 Page: 624

62. The most common type of incest is
    (a) father-daughter incest.
    (b) brother-sister incest.
    (c) stepfather-stepdaughter incest.
    (d) mother-son incest.

    Answer: B Difficulty: 3 Page: 624

63. Many fathers who commit incest with daughters see their daughters as
    (a) sexual objects.
    (b) wanting and willing to have sex.
    (c) a surrogate wife.
    (d) in love with them.

    Answer: C Difficulty: 2 Page: 624

64. Children who are sexually abused may suffer from
    (a) a litany of short- and long-term psychological complaints.
    (b) genital injuries.
    (c) psychosomatic problems.
    (d) all of the above.

    Answer: A Difficulty: 2 Page: 626

65. Rehabilitation of sexual offenders
    (a) is offered to few offenders and is always unsuccessful.
    (b) has been somewhat successful with victim empathy training.
    (c) is offered to all offenders, but 90% will repeat their crimes upon release.
    (d) has been so unsuccessful that surgical castration is the only viable option.

    Answer: B Difficulty: 3 Page: 630

66. Approximately ____ of cases of sexual abuse of children go unreported.
    (a) 75%
    (b) 10%
    (c) 35%
    (d) almost 100%

    Answer: A Difficulty: 2 Page: 626

67. Which of the following is not a way to prevent sexual harassment?
    (a) convey a professional attitude
    (b) discourage harassing behavior
    (c) avoid being alone with a harasser
    (d) none of the above

    Answer: D Difficulty: 2 Page: 634

68. Which of the following is *not* an example of sexual harassment?
    (a) asking a co-worker out on a date
    (b) leering at a co-worker's body
    (c) hanging nude pictures in your locker
    (d) telling sexual jokes

    Answer: A Difficulty: 2 Page: 630

69. Sexual harassment generally involves all of the following *except*
    (a) abuse of power.
    (b) sexual desire.
    (c) social control.
    (d) hostility towards women.

    Answer: B Difficulty: 1 Page: 631

70. Two of the most common settings in which sexual harassment takes place are the workplace and
    (a) physician's offices.
    (b) psychologist's offices.
    (c) colleges or universities.
    (d) high schools.

    Answer: C Difficulty: 2 Page: 631

71. Which of the following is *true* about sexual harassment in the workplace?
    (a) Employees cannot sue their employers for sexual harassment unless they can prove psychological harm.
    (b) An employee cannot charge an employer with sexual harassment unless he/she was demoted or deprived of a promotion for failure to comply with sexual requests.
    (c) Employers cannot be held responsible or sued for sexual harassment if the employee did not first file a complaint within the company.
    (d) Sexual harassment can include any behavior of a sexual nature that creates a hostile, intimidating, or offensive environment.

    Answer: D Difficulty: 2 Page: 632

72. Overall, how many students are estimated to have been the victims of sexual harassment on the job or in college?
    (a) 50-60%
    (b) 60-70%
    (c) 25-30%
    (d) 10-20%

    Answer: C Difficulty: 3 Page: 633

73. In high schools in the United States, how many students reported that they are grabbed, groped, or sexually taunted in the hallways of the schools?
    (a) about 40% of the girls and 5% of the boys
    (b) about 70% of the girls and 40% of the boys
    (c) about 50% of the girls and 10% of the boys
    (d) about 20% of the girls and 10% of the boys

    Answer: B Difficulty: 3 Page: 633

74. As a first step in stopping sexual harassment, it is important that you
    (a) keep accurate records of the dates and times that harassment occurred.
    (b) avoid being alone with the harasser.
    (c) tell the harasser firmly to stop the behavior.
    (d) seek legal advice.

    Answer: C Difficulty: 1 Page: 634

MATCHING

Match the following descriptions of the coercive behavior with the correct term.

(a) Sadistic rape

(b) Marital rape

(c) Date rape

(d) Statutory rape

(e) Anger rape

(f) Power rape

75. Intercourse with a person below the age of consent.

    Answer: d

76. Rape where sexual gratification is secondary and the primary motive is the desire to control and dominate.

    Answer: f

77. Rape that occurs because the rapist believes that resistance indicates coyness and that women really mean "yes" when they say "no."

    Answer: c

78. Rape that is motivated by the belief that husbands are supposed to "rule" their wives.

    Answer: b

79. Rape that involves a ritualized, savage attack where a victim is humiliated, degraded, and sometimes, tortured.

    Answer: a

80. Rape that is unplanned and motivated by anger and resentment towards women.

    Answer: e

TRUE/FALSE

81. In both the Babylonian and Hebrew cultures, a wife who was raped was charged with adultery.

    Answer: True

82. In the United States, a woman is raped about every 6 minutes.

    Answer: False

83. Most women are raped by men they have never met.

    Answer: False

84. Most reported date rapes were committed by men whom the women had known for nearly a year.

    Answer: True

85. In gang rape, followers serve to fortify the courage of the instigator.

    Answer: True

86. A number of researchers have found that men who hold more liberal views of gender roles are more likely to rape.

Answer: False

87. In one study, men who held traditional views of gender roles were more aroused by depictions of rape.

Answer: True

88. Rape-prone societies are characterized by equality between the sexes in terms of power and contributions to the society.

Answer: False

89. The number of reported rapes in the United States is 13 times greater than that in Great Britain and more than 20 times greater than that in Japan.

Answer: True

90. Rape survivors have a higher risk of developing anxiety disorders and depression, and of abusing alcohol or other substances.

Answer: True

91. Men who commit date rape may believe that acceptance of a date indicates that a girl is willing to have sex.

Answer: True

92. Charges of date rape often come down to a case of his word against hers.

Answer: True

93. In child sexual abuse, physical force is seldom used because the abuser has already established trust with the child.

Answer: True

94. Pedophiles generally turn to children when they are drinking, stressed, or rejected by their wives.

Answer: False

95. Most women fail to report sexual assaults to police.

Answer: True

96. Marriages in incestuous families tend to be characterized by an uneven power relationship between the spouses.

Answer: True

97. Adolescent girls who were sexually abused tend to avoid sexual activity with their peers.

Answer: False

98. Sexual jokes, suggestive comments, and sexual innuendos are forms of sexual harassment.

Answer: True

99. In the United States a women is raped at least every 5 minutes.

Answer: True

100. The prevalence of rape is 20 times greater in Japan than in the U.S.

Answer: False

101. Most women are raped by men they know, not by strangers.

    Answer: True

102. Most men who rape other men are homosexual.

    Answer: False

103. Malamuth found that 35% of the college men in his sample said they would force a women into sex if they knew they could get away with it.

    Answer: True

104. Most rapists are mentally ill, even diagnosed with certain psychological disorders.

    Answer: False

ESSAY

105. Discuss the types of attitudes within a culture or an individual that might foster or reinforce rape behavior.

    Answer:

106. Differentiate between anger rape, power rape, and sadistic rape.

    Answer:

107. List and discuss six attitudes or behaviors that seem to characterize sexually aggressive men in general.

    Answer:

108. Describe rape trauma syndrome and both the short- and long-term effects of rape on rape survivors.

    Answer:

109. List five suggestions to consider if you are the victim of a rape.

    Answer:

110. List twelve suggestions that may help prevent rape.

    Answer:

111. Compare and contrast the characteristics of the typical pedophile with those of a child molester.

    Answer:

112. Discuss the family factors that appear to contribute to incest.

    Answer:

113. Discuss the elements that are important in a strong school-based sex-abuse prevention program.

    Answer:

114. Discuss six of the nine suggestions that may be helpful if you are dealing with sexual harassment in the workplace or any other setting.

    Answer:

Chapter 19: Commercial Sex

MULTIPLE CHOICE

1. Prostitution is illegal everywhere in the United States except in
   (a) New York City.
   (b) the San Francisco Bay area.
   (c) some rural counties of Nevada.
   (d) some southern counties of Texas.

   Answer: C Difficulty: 1 Page: 640

2. In the business of prostitution, Johns refer to
   (a) pimps.
   (b) customers.
   (c) web advertisers.
   (d) billy-goats.

   Answer: B Difficulty: 1 Page: 640

3. Prostitution can only be traced as far back as
   (a) Victorian England.
   (b) ancient Greece.
   (c) ancient Mesopotamia.
   (d) the Middle Ages.

   Answer: C Difficulty: 2 Page: 640

4. Throughout recorded history, the major motive for prostitution has been
   (a) economic.
   (b) sexual pleasure.
   (c) the procurement of drugs.
   (d) unusual sexual acts.

   Answer: A Difficulty: 1 Page: 640

5. In Kinsey's studies, how many White males reported visiting a prostitute at least once?
   (a) 10%
   (b) 25%
   (c) 50%
   (d) 65%

   Answer: D Difficulty: 3 Page: 641

6. In Kinsey's sample, visits to prostitutes were higher among
   (a) men over age 50.
   (b) non-college-educated men.
   (c) men under age 20.
   (d) married men over age 25.

   Answer: B Difficulty: 3 Page: 641

7. Where in Amsterdam is prostitution legal?
   (a) commercial districts
   (b) red light districts
   (c) tourists locations
   (d) it is not actually legal—only socially accepted

   Answer: B Difficulty: 1 Page: 643

8. What type of prostitution earns the lowest income?
   (a) call girls
   (b) streetwalkers
   (c) escort service
   (d) massage parlors

   Answer: B Difficulty: 1 Page: 644

9. Which countries have largely replaced Thailand and the Philippines in trafficking women?
   (a) Bolivia, the United States, and Honduras
   (b) Mexico and China
   (c) Russia, Ukraine, and Belarus
   (d) England and Argentina

   Answer: C Difficulty: 2 Page: 644

10. Economic problems in the former Soviet Union have opened a profitable market to
    (a) the criminal gangs that have risen since the fall of communism.
    (b) poor communities.
    (c) the black market.
    (d) lower ethical standards.

    Answer: A Difficulty: 2 Page: 644

11. Rates of prostitution are particularly high in countries
    (a) that have liberal sexual attitudes.
    (b) that have strong comprehensive sex education programs.
    (c) that are economically stressed.
    (d) where traditional gender roles are valued.

    Answer: C Difficulty: 2 Page: 644

12. In Israel prostitution is ____ and brothels are _____.
    (a) legal; illegal
    (b) illegal; legal
    (c) legal; legal
    (d) illegal; illegal

    Answer: A Difficulty: 2 Page: 644

13. In the hierarchy of prostitution, the bottom rung of the ladder goes to
    (a) escorts.
    (b) streetwalkers.
    (c) brothel workers.
    (d) massage parlor workers.

    Answer: B Difficulty: 1 Page: 644

14. Streetwalkers tend to come from
    (a) poverty and unhappy childhoods.
    (b) religious parents.
    (c) small towns.
    (d) educated backgrounds.

    Answer: A Difficulty: 1 Page: 644

15. Approximately how many streetwalkers are survivors of rape, sexual abuse, or incest?
    (a) 30%
    (b) 50%
    (c) 70%
    (d) 80%

    Answer: D Difficulty: 3 Page: 644

16. What percentage of the Philadelphia sample of streetwalkers reported achieving orgasm with clients?
    (a) 10%
    (b) 30%
    (c) 60%
    (d) 90%

    Answer: C Difficulty: 2 Page: 644

17. Pimps provide a streetwalker with
    (a) a car.
    (b) a secret identity.
    (c) a passport.
    (d) none of the above.

    Answer: C Difficulty: 2 Page: 645

18. While pimps may provide protection, bail, and sometimes room and board, their typical cut from a streetwalker's earnings is
    (a) 90%.
    (b) 50%.
    (c) 35%.
    (d) 20%.

    Answer: A Difficulty: 3 Page: 645

19. Which is not a place of prostitution?
    (a) joy house
    (b) bordello
    (c) tea group
    (d) cat wagon

    Answer: C Difficulty: 2 Page: 646

20. Some prostitutes die young from
    (a) drug abuse.
    (b) disease.
    (c) suicide.
    (d) all of the above.

    Answer: D Difficulty: 1 Page: 646

21. Today the brothel has largely been replaced by
    (a) cat houses.
    (b) streetwalkers.
    (c) massage parlors.
    (d) bar prostitutes.

    Answer: C Difficulty: 2 Page: 646

22. Prostitutes who work for escort services typically come from
    (a) backgrounds involving physical or sexual abuse.
    (b) lower-class families with little education.
    (c) middle-class backgrounds and are well-educated.
    (d) upper-class families but are not well-educated.

    Answer: C Difficulty: 2 Page: 647

23. The highest status on the social ladder of prostitution goes to
    (a) call girls.
    (b) hotel prostitutes.
    (c) bar prostitutes.
    (d) brothel workers.

    Answer: A Difficulty: 1 Page: 647

24. Call girls are not only expected to provide sex but also
    (a) charming and gracious company.
    (b) soothing massage.
    (c) business connections.
    (d) all of the above.

    Answer: A Difficulty: 1 Page: 647

25. Which type of prostitute is generally well-educated, provides conversation and companionship, and generally accompanies her client on "dates"?
    (a) streetwalker
    (b) call girl
    (c) hotel prostitute
    (d) brothel prostitute

    Answer: B Difficulty: 2 Page: 647

26. Which type of prostitute generally works on her own?
    (a) streetwalkers
    (b) brothel workers
    (c) escorts
    (d) call girls

    Answer: D Difficulty: 1 Page: 647

27. In their interviews with prostitutes, Farley and her colleagues (1998) found that nearly two-thirds could be diagnosed with
    (a) a sexual addiction.
    (b) posttraumatic stress disorder.
    (c) narcissistic personality disorder.
    (d) antisocial personality disorder.

    Answer: B Difficulty: 2 Page: 648

28. Melissa Farley and her colleagues reported two-thirds of the prostitutes they interviewed had
    (a) abusive fathers.
    (b) grown up with a lot of siblings.
    (c) very creative personalities.
    (d) posttraumatic stress disorder.

    Answer: D Difficulty: 1 Page: 648

29. In the United States and Canada, many initiates into prostitution are
    (a) teenage runaways.
    (b) drug dealers.
    (c) college dropouts.
    (d) young single mothers.

    Answer: A Difficulty: 2 Page: 649

30. Of the male teenage runaways in a New York City study, how many used condoms consistently?
    (a) 30%
    (b) 21%
    (c) 12%
    (d) 8%

    Answer: D Difficulty: 3 Page: 649

31. Because of the sex trade recession in Romania, prostitutes offer to
    (a) do degrading sex acts.
    (b) clean and cook.
    (c) run errands.
    (d) none of the above.

    Answer: B Difficulty: 2 Page: 650

32. "Habitual" Johns use prostitutes
    (a) as their major or exclusive sexual outlet.
    (b) because they desire novelty or sexual variety.
    (c) to meet specific fetishes.
    (d) as an outlet for their transvestism.

    Answer: A Difficulty: 2 Page: 651

33. Men who are compulsive users of prostitution suffer from a(n)
    (a) paraphilia.
    (b) whore-madonna complex.
    (c) biological disorder.
    (d) Oedipus complex.

    Answer: B Difficulty: 1 Page: 651

34. Which of the following is not a motive for using prostitution?
    (a) sex for eroticism and variety
    (b) sex without commitment
    (c) sex without negotiation
    (d) none of the above

    Answer: D Difficulty: 1 Page: 651

35. Which of the following is *not* a reason cited in the text for utilizing a prostitute?
    (a) You can have sex without negotiation.
    (b) You can test your sexual identity.
    (c) You can obtain sexual variety.
    (d) You can have sex with no commitment.

    Answer: B Difficulty: 2 Page: 651

36. Which of the following is *not* a typical client of prostitutes?
    (a) men who travel frequently on business or are from out of town
    (b) men who are lonely
    (c) men who want to humiliate their wives or retaliate against them
    (d) men who have no other sexual outlets

    Answer: D Difficulty: 2 Page: 652

37. In what country is it legal to have sex with children who are older than 12?
    (a) Mexico
    (b) India
    (c) Japan
    (d) France

    Answer: C Difficulty: 1 Page: 652

38. Many Japanese men are obsessed with
    (a) women in bikinis.
    (b) school girls in uniform.
    (c) European American women.
    (d) large-breasted women.

    Answer: B Difficulty: 1 Page: 652

39. Most male prostitutes service
    (a) older, wealthy women.
    (b) gay men.
    (c) young, bored housewives.
    (d) middle-aged wealthy, married women.

    Answer: B Difficulty: 1 Page: 652

40. The average age of a hustler is
    (a) 14.
    (b) 26.
    (c) 21.
    (d) 18.

    Answer: D Difficulty: 3 Page: 652

41. The majority of male prostitutes describe themselves as
    (a) heterosexual.
    (b) gay.
    (c) bisexual.
    (d) being unclear about their sexual orientation.

    Answer: B Difficulty: 2 Page: 653

42. Fellatio is
    (a) oral sex.
    (b) anal sex.
    (c) male/male sex.
    (d) cunnilingus.

    Answer: A Difficulty: 3 Page: 653

43. August is a "kept boy." In the culture of male prostitution, what does this mean?
    (a) He has an older male client who serves in a parental role and keeps him economically secure.
    (b) He works through an agency or escort service that serves wealthy clients.
    (c) He is a prison inmate who is used for sex and rewarded with protection from other inmates.
    (d) He is a streetwalker who frequents districts where men search for homosexual sex.

    Answer: A Difficulty: 2 Page: 653

44. In the 1960s what percentage of prostitutes surveyed by Gebhard had contracted syphilis and gonorrhea?
    (a) 65%
    (b) 10%
    (c) 90%
    (d) 35%

    Answer: A Difficulty: 2 Page: 654

45. One study found that the rate of HIV infection for gay male prostitutes was
    (a) 50%.
    (b) 60%.
    (c) 30%.
    (d) 40%.

    Answer: A Difficulty: 3 Page: 654

46. What percentage of the 20 street prostitutes of Camden, New Jersey, reported using condoms with their clients?
    (a) 30%
    (b) 10%
    (c) 50%
    (d) 75%

    Answer: A Difficulty: 3 Page: 654

47. In the 1980s, how many of the prostitutes in the United States tested positive for HIV?
    (a) 4%
    (b) 12%
    (c) 32%
    (d) 21%

    Answer: B Difficulty: 3 Page: 654

48. Which of the following is *not* a reason that feminists oppose pornography?
    (a) Pornography portrays women as sexual masochists.
    (b) Pornography portrays women as sexually insatiable.
    (c) Pornography portrays women in degrading roles.
    (d) Pornography portrays women as sexually aggressive.

    Answer: D Difficulty: 1 Page: 655

49. In defining pornography as "writing, pictures, etc., intended to arouse desire," the most problematic word is
    (a) desire.
    (b) intended.
    (c) arouse.
    (d) writing.

    Answer: B Difficulty: 1 Page: 655

50. The word *prurient* means to
    (a) excite lust.
    (b) seek artistic expression.
    (c) be sexually explicit.
    (d) be obscene.

    Answer: A Difficulty: 2 Page: 655

51. Legislative bodies usually write laws about ____ rather than pornography.
    (a) obscenity
    (b) prostitution
    (c) language
    (d) homosexuality

Answer: A Difficulty: 2 Page: 656

52. Erotica is generally defined as
    (a) any literary or visual depiction that is obscene.
    (b) any literary or visual depiction that is sexually explicit.
    (c) any sexually explicit material that is artistically produced or motivated.
    (d) any literary or visual depiction intended to arouse sexual desire.

Answer: C Difficulty: 1 Page: 656

53. In 1873, the anti-obscenity bill passed by the United States Congress was called the
    (a) Roth Act.
    (b) Comstock Act.
    (c) Miller Act.
    (d) Stanley Act.

Answer: B Difficulty: 1 Page: 657

54. In *Roth v. United States*, the U.S. Supreme Court ruled that portrayal of sexual activity was
    (a) illegal.
    (b) legal as long as it was not offensive.
    (c) protected by the First Amendment.
    (d) protected by the Fifth Amendment.

Answer: C Difficulty: 2 Page: 657

55. The quote, "the proper inquiry is not whether an ordinary member of any given community would find serious literary, artistic, or political values in allegedly obscene material, but whether a reasonable person would find value in the material..." is taken from
    (a) *Pope v. Illinois*.
    (b) *Miller v. United States*.
    (c) *Roth v. United States*.
    (d) *Stanley v. Georgia*.

Answer: A Difficulty: 3 Page: 657

56. In *Stanley v. Georgia*, the United States Supreme Court ruled that
    (a) the possession of child pornography is illegal.
    (b) sexual material is obscene if it lacks any serious literary or artistic value.
    (c) communities could determine what is obscene based on community standards.
    (d) the possession of obscene material in one's home is not illegal.

Answer: D Difficulty: 2 Page: 657

57. In the NHSLS study, how many men had purchased an X-rated video in the past year?
    (a) 16%
    (b) 62%
    (c) 50%
    (d) 23%

Answer: D Difficulty: 3 Page: 659

58. In the NHSLS study, how many women had purchased an X-rated video in the past year?
    (a) 2%
    (b) 11%
    (c) 18%
    (d) 6%

    Answer: B Difficulty: 2 Page: 659

59. Which statement is *true* regarding male or female reactions to pornography?
    (a) Men, but very few women, are physiologically aroused by pornography.
    (b) Men tend to rate romantic scenes as more arousing.
    (c) Both women and men are physiologically aroused by pornography.
    (d) Women are more accepting of pornography that is very sexually explicit.

    Answer: C Difficulty: 2 Page: 659

60. What is a blacklist?
    (a) a list of pornographic sites on the internet
    (b) a list of compiled data about pornographic web sites
    (c) a list of effective browsers for pornographic web sites
    (d) a list of companies advertising on pornographic web sites

    Answer: A Difficulty: 1 Page: 660

61. Clicksafe uses something called _____ to identify tip-off words and photos of naked ladies.
    (a) NPRX
    (b) fuzzy logic
    (c) sex-wizard
    (d) yahoo

    Answer: B Difficulty: 2 Page: 660

62. The 1960s Commission on Obscenity and Pornography found that exposure to pornography
    (a) increased the risk of committing a violent crime against women.
    (b) did not lead to crimes of violence or sexual offenses.
    (c) led to sexual offenses such as exhibitionism and voyeurism.
    (d) increased the risk of committing a rape.

    Answer: B Difficulty: 3 Page: 661

63. When pornographic materials became widely available in Denmark following legalization of pornography in the late 1960s, there was
    (a) no corresponding increase in the incidence of sex crimes.
    (b) little interest in the pornographic market.
    (c) a jump in sex crimes.
    (d) a decrease.

    Answer: A Difficulty: 3 Page: 661

64. Which statement is *true* about pornography, rape, and child molestation?
    (a) Rapists spent a great deal of their time viewing pornography.
    (b) Child molesters had a history of viewing child pornography.
    (c) Compared to non-sex offenders, sex offenders were drawn to pornographic materials.
    (d) Some sex offenders use pornography to become sexually aroused immediately preceding their crime.

    Answer: D Difficulty: 2 Page: 661

65. Research investigating links between pornography and violence or sexual aggression has generally concluded that
    (a) pornography increases sexual aggression in men but not women.
    (b) the use of pornography with violent themes causes men to commit more crimes.
    (c) pornography may stimulate sexual violence in men who are predisposed to commit such crimes.
    (d) there is no correlation between pornography and violence in any subgroups of men studied.

    Answer: C Difficulty: 2 Page: 661

66. In 1986, the Meese Commission claimed to find
    (a) that the incidence of violent pornography was decreasing in the United States.
    (b) no evidence that exposure to pornography led to sexual offenses.
    (c) a causal link between exposure to violent pornography and sexual violence.
    (d) a causal link between violent pornography and non-sexual criminality.

    Answer: C Difficulty: 3 Page: 661

67. Which of the following is *not* a concern cited in response to the Meese Commission findings?
    (a) Critics fought against recommendations that child pornography be made a felony.
    (b) Critics noted that the commission failed to distinguish between violent materials and sexually explicit materials.
    (c) Critics do not agree with the finding that violent pornography is increasing.
    (d) Critics contend that the commission over-generalized laboratory-based findings.

    Answer: A Difficulty: 2 Page: 661

68. A variety of research on exposure of men to violent pornography has concluded that
    (a) exposure to violent pornography does not lead to any attitudinal changes.
    (b) exposure to violent pornography leads men to become more accepting of rape myths.
    (c) exposure to violence, not necessarily pornography, leads men to become more accepting of rape myths.
    (d) exposure to violent pornography actually decreased arousal and softened men's attitudes towards rape victims.

    Answer: C Difficulty: 2 Page: 662

69. In studies, which type of film was connected with the strongest antisocial effects?
    (a) hard-core pornography
    (b) soft-core pornography
    (c) teenage sex films
    (d) "slasher-type" violent films

    Answer: D Difficulty: 2 Page: 662

70. Research evidence suggests that repeated exposure to non-violent pornography
    (a) decreases male aggression towards women.
    (b) loosens traditional sexual and family values.
    (c) increases acceptance of rape myths in both men and women.
    (d) results in more extramarital affairs.

    Answer: B Difficulty: 3 Page: 662

71. Zillman (1989) argues that prolonged exposure to pornography may foster
    (a) dissatisfaction with the physical appearance of one's partner.
    (b) attitudes of disrespect for one's partner.
    (c) acceptance of marital rape.
    (d) greater sexual satisfaction with one's intimate partner.

    Answer: A Difficulty: 2 Page: 664

72. Which of the following is *not* a caution that should be considered when reviewing research on the effects of pornography?
    (a) Most research has utilized college men.
    (b) A large percentage of college men have engaged in attempted rape or coercion.
    (c) All experiments in this area are laboratory-based, not real life situations.
    (d) Well-educated men are generally less likely to have engaged in rape or coercion.

    Answer: D Difficulty: 1 Page: 664

MATCHING

For each of the following decisions regarding pornography, match the decision with the correct title.

(a) *Roth v. United States*

(b) *Stanley v. Georgia*

(c) *The Comstock Act*

(d) *Miller v. California*

(e) *Pope v. Illinois*

73. Passed by Congress in 1873, this general anti-obscenity law also deemed that information about contraception was obscene.

    Answer: c

74. A 1973 case in which the U.S. Supreme Court held that obscenity is based on whether the average person, applying community standards, finds that a work is of prurient interest.

    Answer: d

75. A 1987 case in which the Supreme Court held that a work could not be judged obscene by a community unless a "reasonable" person were to reach the same judgment.

    Answer: e

76. A 1969 case in which the U.S. Supreme Court ruled that the possession of obscene material in the home is not illegal.

    Answer: b

77. A 1957 case in which the U.S. Supreme Court ruled that the portrayal of sexual activity is protected by the 1st Amendment.

    Answer: a

TRUE/FALSE

78. Prostitution is illegal in every state in the United States.

    Answer: False

79. In Victorian England, prostitution was widely regarded as a necessary outlet for men to satisfy their sexual appetites.

    Answer: True

80. In the Kinsey sample, 15-20% of the White males surveyed visited prostitutes on a regular basis.

    Answer: True

81. In Israel, brothel prostitution is legal but street prostitution is not.

    Answer: False

82. Streetwalkers occupy the bottom rung in the hierarchy of prostitutes.

    Answer: True

83. The incidence of posttraumatic stress disorder among prostitutes in the United States, Europe, Africa, and Asia is about 5%.

    Answer: False

84. Of runaway teenage boys in New York City, only 8% reported using condoms consistently.

    Answer: True

85. Some men who are compulsive users of prostitutes suffer from a complex where they see women as either sinners or saints.

    Answer: True

86. In Tokyo, it is popular to pay $150 an hour to act out sexual fantasies with make-believe school girls in make-believe classrooms.

    Answer: True

87. Prostitutes are never physically abused by their pimps.

    Answer: False

88. In Tokyo, the age of consent for sexual activity is age 13.

    Answer: True

89. Compared to female prostitution, male prostitutes generally have longer careers.

    Answer: False

90. Attempts to market visual erotic materials to women have been largely unsuccessful.

    Answer: True

91. Research has shown that exposing men to violent pornography leads men to become more empathic towards rape victims.

    Answer: False

92. Message parlors can be a disguise for prostitution.

    Answer: True

93. Research on the effects of explicit sexual material has linked exposure to nonviolent pornography with undesirable effects.

    Answer: False

94. Only a minority of people in the United States support legislation making sexually explicit materials illegal.

    Answer: True

95. Seventy-five percent of United States citizens favor legislation making violent pornography illegal.

    Answer: True

96. Prostitution is illegal throughout the United States, except for parts of Alaska.

    Answer: False

97. Not all of the massage and escort services advertised in the Yellow Pages are fronts for prostitution.

    Answer: True

98. Call girls are the same as streetwalkers, except they are more fashionable.

    Answer: False

99. 42% of female prostitutes were sexually abused as children.

    Answer: False

100. Typical customers of prostitutes have difficulty forming sexual relationships with other women.

    Answer: False

101. Hustlers typically are not attached to a pimp; they generally make contacts with clients in gay bars and social clubs or by working the streets.

    Answer: True

102. Men who frequent male prostitutes may represent a vector, or conduit, for male-female sexual transmission of HIV.

    Answer: True

103. Laboratory-based studies have shown that men exposed to violent pornography are more likely to become more passive towards females.

    Answer: False

ESSAY

104. Identify and discuss five of the most common motives for engaging in sexual activity with a prostitute.

    Answer:

105. Discuss several socioeconomic, psychological, and cultural factors that may lead to the decision to engage in prostitution as a profession.

    Answer:

106. Distinguish between pornography, obscenity, and erotica. Give examples of each.

    Answer:

107. Discuss the difficulties involved in defining "obscenity" by citing at least two Supreme Court decisions and their outcomes.

    Answer:

108. Evaluate arguments supporting pornography on the Internet and arguments refuting the use of the Internet to make sexually explicit materials readily available to the public.

    Answer:

109. Analyze three research studies on the effects of violent and non-violent pornography.

    Answer:

110. Give four examples of advertisements you recently encountered that use sex to sell. Evaluate these ads in terms of how women and/or men were portrayed or utilized.

    Answer:

Chapter 20: Making Responsible Sexual Decisions

MULTIPLE CHOICE

1. When a decision must be made between alternatives that have both negative and positive features, we experience
   (a) competition.
   (b) conflict.
   (c) pressure.
   (d) frustration.

   Answer: B Difficulty: 1 Page: 668

2. Nikki is considering the pill as a contraceptive method. She determines that the pill is effective and will allow for sexual spontaneity. On the other hand, it is costly and has side effects. In her attempt to make a decision, Nikki will experience
   (a) frustration.
   (b) pressure.
   (c) competition.
   (d) conflict.

   Answer: D Difficulty: 1 Page: 668

3. People in conflict generally
   (a) enjoy the challenge.
   (b) become severely depressed.
   (c) feel damned if they do and damned if they don't.
   (d) see conflict as energizing.

   Answer: C Difficulty: 2 Page: 668

4. Which is not a way to facilitate decision making?
   (a) information gathering
   (b) talking to friends
   (c) weighing pros and cons
   (d) none of the above

   Answer: D Difficulty: 1 Page: 669

5. Our value systems
   (a) provide a framework for judging the acceptability of sexual behavior.
   (b) always determine the outcomes of our sexual decisions.
   (c) strictly determine our behavior.
   (d) allow us to act quickly by knowing the right thing to do.

   Answer: A Difficulty: 2 Page: 669

6. Which is a source of influence on our decision making?
   (a) culture
   (b) parents
   (c) ethical subcultures
   (d) all of the above

   Answer: D Difficulty: 1 Page: 669

7. Basing ethical behavior on a code of laws provided by an external source is called
   (a) asceticism.
   (b) utilitarianism.
   (c) situation ethics.
   (d) legalism.

   Answer: D Difficulty: 2 Page: 669

8. In her Christian religion, Monica has learned that she should be "fruitful and multiply." Based on that learning, she chooses not to use any birth control in her marriage. Monica's decision is based in
   (a) ethical relativism.
   (b) legalism.
   (c) rationalism.
   (d) asceticism.

   Answer: B Difficulty: 3 Page: 670

9. Many religious followers today accept moral codes of their religion as a matter of
   (a) faith and commitment.
   (b) psychology.
   (c) ethical subcultures.
   (d) fundamentals.

   Answer: A Difficulty: 2 Page: 670

10. Today liberal Jews and Christians tend to view Biblical or church teachings as
    (a) an absolute set of rules.
    (b) a general framework for decision-making.
    (c) totally irrelevant to decision-making.
    (d) relevant only in decisions immediately involving church affairs.

    Answer: B Difficulty: 2 Page: 670

11. Fundamental Protestants, conservative Catholics, and orthodox Jews who follow biblical teachings "to the letter" might choose to make decisions from a(n)
    (a) rationalist approach.
    (b) hedonistic approach.
    (c) legalistic approach.
    (d) ascetic approach.

    Answer: C Difficulty: 1 Page: 670

12. Who stated that ethical decision-making should be guided by genuine love for others rather than rigid moral codes?
    (a) Leviticus
    (b) John Stuart Mill
    (c) Joseph Fletcher
    (d) Sheri Oz

    Answer: C Difficulty: 1 Page: 671

13. Which type of ethics involves decision-making based on the context of the particular situation?
    (a) hedonism
    (b) situation ethics
    (c) ethical relativism
    (d) utilitarianism

    Answer: B Difficulty: 1 Page: 671

14. A Roman Catholic woman has been taught that abortion is wrong but she decides to have an abortion because it is her sixth pregnancy and her income is limited. In this situation, she made a decision from a
    (a) legalistic approach.
    (b) ascetic approach.
    (c) hedonistic approach.
    (d) situation ethics approach.

    Answer: D Difficulty: 1 Page: 671

15. A moral situation ethicist acts in a manner that he or she believes will lead to
    (a) pleasure.
    (b) human favor.
    (c) the greater good.
    (d) none of the above.

    Answer: C Difficulty: 1 Page: 671

16. Ethical relativism
    (a) is based on that which brings the greatest good to the greatest number.
    (b) rejects the idea of a single correct moral point of view.
    (c) is based in the pursuit of pleasure above all other considerations.
    (d) is based in self-denial in order to pursue spiritual pursuits.

    Answer: B Difficulty: 2 Page: 671

17. An ethical relativist believes
    (a) that culture defines ethical standards.
    (b) in religious reverence.
    (c) that there is no objective way of justifying one set of moral values over another.
    (d) none of the above.

    Answer: C Difficulty: 2 Page: 671

18. One taking a long-term hedonistic view will attempt to
    (a) make responsible sexual decisions that lead to a lifetime of sexual pleasure.
    (b) apply moral standards to sexual intimacy.
    (c) understand religious context to help in decision-making.
    (d) understand cultural influences on sexual relations.

    Answer: A Difficulty: 1 Page: 671

19. Those who choose celibacy in order to devote themselves to spiritual pursuits are
    applying the ethical principles of
    (a) hedonism.
    (b) cultural relativism.
    (c) situation ethics.
    (d) asceticism.

    Answer: D Difficulty: 1 Page: 671

20. In which type of ethics is moral conduct based on that which will bring about the
    greatest good for the greatest number?
    (a) hedonism
    (b) asceticism
    (c) utilitarianism
    (d) cultural relativism

    Answer: C Difficulty: 1 Page: 671

21. Whenever Abigail has to make a difficult decision, she centers herself and sets her
    emotions aside. To ensure that she makes the correct decisions, she pursues the facts
    and carefully weighs each one before arriving at the logical conclusion. Abigail is
    using
    (a) an ascetic approach.
    (b) a rationalist approach.
    (c) a utilitarian approach.
    (d) a legalist approach.

    Answer: B Difficulty: 2 Page: 671

22. Marvin is in an unhappy marriage but stays because he believes that the greater good of the family and community is served by maintaining the marriage rather than dissolving it. Which approach is Marvin using?
    (a) rationalism
    (b) legalism
    (c) utilitarianism
    (d) cultural relativism

    Answer: C Difficulty: 2 Page: 671

23. Religious celibates, such as Roman Catholic priests and nuns choose _____ in order to devote themselves to spiritual pursuits.
    (a) hedonism
    (b) ascetism
    (c) religion
    (d) ethical relativism

    Answer: B Difficulty: 2 Page: 672

24. Many people in the United States consider clitoridectomy and infibulation inhumane and abhorrent practices. Others believe that we cannot dictate our standards of what constitutes appropriate sexual behavior or practice upon other nations. Those who believe it is not our right to interfere in these practices are operating from an ethical base called
    (a) utilitarianism.
    (b) hedonism.
    (c) cultural relativism.
    (d) legalism.

    Answer: C Difficulty: 1 Page: 672

25. Who is most likely to risk being so driven by the pursuit of sexual pleasure that sex becomes a form of "addiction" that overshadows other aspects of life?
    (a) the hedonist
    (b) the utilitarian
    (c) the ascetic
    (d) the cultural relativist

    Answer: A Difficulty: 2 Page: 672

26. In trying to weigh the pluses and minuses of alternatives, it is useful to use a
    (a) rationalist approach.
    (b) balance sheet.
    (c) legalist approach.
    (d) legal approach.

    Answer: B Difficulty: 1 Page: 673

27. Research has shown that people who use balance sheets
    (a) have fewer regrets about the path not taken.
    (b) experience more conflict in trying to reach a decision.
    (c) are less likely to stick with their decisions.
    (d) feel like they cannot change their minds once a decision is made.

    Answer: A Difficulty: 2 Page: 673

MATCHING

For each of the following descriptions of an ethical principle, match the principle with the correct term.

(a) Utilitarianism

(b) Legalism

(c) Rationalism

(d) Asceticism

(e) Cultural Relativism

(f) Hedonism

28. The belief that decisions should be based on intellect and reasoning rather than emotions or strict obedience to a particular faith.

    Answer: c

29. The belief in self-denial in order to devote oneself to spiritual pursuits.

    Answer: d

30. The belief that moral decisions must be understood in terms of the cultural beliefs that affect decisions.

    Answer: e

31. The belief that moral conduct should be based on that which will bring the greatest good for the greatest number.

    Answer: a

32. Decisions are guided solely by the pursuit of pleasure.

    Answer: f

33. Ethical decisions are based on a code of laws derived from an external source.

    Answer: b

TRUE/FALSE

34. People in conflict are often obsessed with what the right thing to do is.

    Answer: True

35. People in conflict never vacillate—take tentative steps in one direction and then in the other.

    Answer: False

36. *Not* making a decision is, in fact, a decision.

    Answer: True

37. Laws strictly determine people's behavior.

    Answer: False

38. Many early religious laws were designed to promote strict obedience to authority and had little to do with the greater good of the community.

    Answer: False

39. The situationist adheres to strict moral codes and does not violate those codes based on the circumstances of the particular situation.

    Answer: False

40. In ethical relativism, individuals use their own principles and apply them according to their own consciences.

    Answer: True

41. Opponents of ethical relativism believe that allowing people free rein to determine what is right or wrong may bring about social chaos and decay.

    Answer: True

42. In Eastern and Western religions, hedonists seek to transcend physical and worldly desires.

    Answer: False

43. The core ethic of utilitarianism is that moral conduct is based on that which will bring about "the greatest good for the greatest number."

    Answer: True

44. The English philosopher John Stuart Mill proposed an ethical system based on utilitarianism.

    Answer: True

45. The United States' decision to intervene in Kosovo despite the fact that many lives could be lost is an example of utilitarianism.

    Answer: True

46. Balance sheets can be used only for non-ethical decisions.

    Answer: False

47. The hedonist is guided by the pursuit of pleasure, not by whether a particular behavior is morally justified.

    Answer: True

48. Religious teachings may be viewed as a general framework for decision-making rather than a set of absolute rules.

    Answer: True

ESSAY

49. Compare and contrast legalism, situation ethics, and ethical relativism.

    Answer:

50. Compare and contrast hedonism, asceticism, and utilitarianism.

    Answer:

51. Discuss the features of legalism and rationalism that are similar and those that are different.

    Answer:

52. Explain why a "balance sheet" is important in decision-making. Construct an example of this document that illustrates how to use it.

    Answer:

53. Create a moral dilemma and formulate a decision using three of the ethical approaches discussed in this chapter.

    Answer:

NOTES

NOTES

NOTES

NOTES

NOTES

NOTES